INTRODUCTION TO

Vector Analysis

HARRY F. DAVIS

ASSOCIATE PROFESSOR OF MATHEMATICS

UNIVERSITY OF WATERLOO, CANADA

INTRODUCTION TO

Vector Analysis

ALLYN AND BACON, INC., Boston

COLLEGE MATHEMATICS SERIES

IN MEMORIAM

Percy Lowe   *February 6, 1900   August 30, 1959*

John F. Twiss   *February 16, 1895   April 4, 1960*

PREFACE

This is an elementary textbook requiring a minimum of pre-requisites. It can be studied concurrently with a second year of calculus. There is more emphasis on motivation than is usual in books on vector analysis, and considerably more emphasis on the intuitive content of the more difficult ideas. It is designed for classroom use or for self-study. There are more than 400 exercises. Answers are given at the end of the book.

The book is intended for engineering students of average ability as well as honors students in mathematics and physics. For that reason, some proofs are given twice, first in the formal style of physics texts and later more rigorously. My hope is that the reader will acquire a sound understanding of the fundamental ideas and their physical interpretation, and in the process will gain some appreciation for pure mathematics as well. Discussions that are oversimplified are clearly labeled as such. No attempt is made to cover up difficulties, and nothing learned here will have to be un-learned later.

While there is emphasis on physical ideas related to vector concepts, no topic in theoretical physics is treated in detail. Since this is not intended as a reference work, many conventional topics are omitted or treated in a cavalier way. This has made space for inclusion of some relatively modern material.

The last chapter is a review of the fundamental topics from a more advanced viewpoint. This material is not intended to anticipate or duplicate anything the student will learn later in courses on modern algebra, tensor analysis, or physics. It is not a tail-end flourish to give a modern appearance. I have included these topics because they are an essential part of understanding vector analysis, and because I have found that they stimulate many students to take a greater interest in mathematics and theoretical physics.

I wish to thank Professor Solomon Leader of Rutgers University for his criticism, always pertinent and valuable; Mr. Jack Hiscocks for his interest and assistance; Miss Mary Sullivan, who cheerfully typed the manuscript in several revisions; and the editorial staff of Allyn and Bacon for their encouragement and co-operation.

H. F. D.

CONTENTS

5 : Generalizations 221

INTRODUCTION TO

Vector Analysis

O N E

VECTOR ALGEBRA

1.1 : Definitions

The vector concept is closely related to the geometrical idea of a *directed line segment*. Roughly speaking, a vector is a quantity which has direction as well as magnitude. It is represented by an arrow of length equal to its magnitude, pointing in the appropriate direction. Two vectors **A** and **B** are said to be equal, $\mathbf{A} = \mathbf{B}$, if they have the same length and direction.

The definition just given suffers from a lack of precision that will be partially rectified in the following discussion. In a later section, a more sophisticated definition will be given.

Let us consider two points P and Q in space. If P and Q are distinct points, there will exist one and only one line passing through them both. That part of the line between P and Q, including both P and Q as endpoints, is called a *line segment*. A line segment is said to be *directed* when the endpoints are given a definite order. The same line segment determines two directed line segments, one denoted PQ and the other QP (or $-PQ$). If P and Q coincide, PQ is said to be *degenerate*.

The magnitude of a directed line segment is defined to be its length, i.e., the distance between its endpoints. A degenerate line segment has zero magnitude.

Two directed line segments that are both nondegenerate are said to have the *same direction* if they are parallel and have the same directed sense. They are said to be *equal* if they have the same direction and also the same magnitude. Any two directed line segments that are both degenerate are said to be equal.

When this notion of equality is used, a directed line segment is called a *vector*. Thus, in Figure 1, **A** and **B** are considered to be

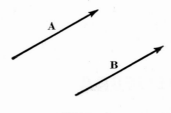

Figure 1

identical vectors, even though, as directed line segments, they occupy different positions in space. Arrows representing equal nondegenerate directed line segments can be made to coincide by moving one of them through space, keeping it always parallel to its initial position.

Any degenerate line segment is said to represent the *zero vector* **0**. The vector **0** has zero magnitude and no defined direction. Since a direction can be ascribed only to nonzero vectors, the statement in the first paragraph is technically incorrect. It ignores the exceptional zero vector.

Many of the quantities of physics are conveniently represented by vectors. As examples we mention force, displacement, velocity, acceleration, and magnetic field intensity. Such quantities are represented graphically by arrows of length proportional to the magnitude of the quantity, and pointing in the appropriate direction.

Sometimes the word *scalar* is used as a synonym for *number*. Those quantities of physics that are characterized by numerical magnitude alone are called scalars or *scalar quantities*. Examples are mass, time, density, distance, temperature, and speed (as read from a speedometer).

Comment on the Exercises

Most sections of this book are followed by exercises. They are not intended as tests of understanding, but as exercises which help to develop understanding. If a section appears difficult, it may be well to read the exercises and use them as *motivation* for studying the section. There are always a few students who feel the exercises should not be attempted before the theoretical material is thoroughly mastered. In the opinion of this author, such an attitude is unwise and leads to inefficient studying.

The section *Answers and Notes* is intended to be used. Only a pedant would claim that looking at the answer first is sinful. However, since all answer books are fallible, you are advised not to spend too much time on any one problem.

Students using this book for self-study are invited to correspond with the author.

1.2 : Addition and Subtraction

The *sum* $\mathbf{A} + \mathbf{B}$ of two vectors may be defined in the following way. Let the vectors be represented by arrows so placed that the terminal point of $\mathbf{A}$ coincides with the initial point of $\mathbf{B}$. Then $\mathbf{A} + \mathbf{B}$ is represented by the arrow extending from the initial point of $\mathbf{A}$ to the terminal point of $\mathbf{B}$ (Fig. 2). It is evident that this

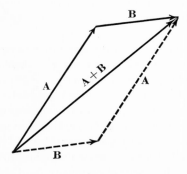

Figure 2

definition of addition is compatible with the definition of equality; that is, if $\mathbf{A} = \mathbf{A}'$ and $\mathbf{B} = \mathbf{B}'$, then $\mathbf{A} + \mathbf{B} = \mathbf{A}' + \mathbf{B}'$. Since opposite sides of a parallelogram are equal in magnitude and have the same direction (Fig. 2), vector addition is commutative, $\mathbf{A} + \mathbf{B} = \mathbf{B} + \mathbf{A}$. It is easy to see that it is also associative,

$$(\mathbf{A} + \mathbf{B}) + \mathbf{C} = \mathbf{A} + (\mathbf{B} + \mathbf{C})$$

so that there is no ambiguity in writing $\mathbf{A} + \mathbf{B} + \mathbf{C}$ without parentheses (Fig. 3).

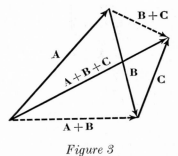

Figure 3

If $\mathbf{B}$ is a vector, $-\mathbf{B}$ is defined to be the vector with the same magnitude as $\mathbf{B}$ but opposite direction (Fig. 4). Subtraction of vectors is defined by adding the negative,

$$\mathbf{A} - \mathbf{B} = \mathbf{A} + (-\mathbf{B})$$

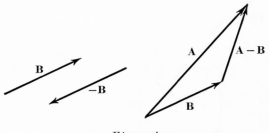

Figure 4

The student who ignores this definition and simply memorizes Figure 4 will inevitably confuse $\mathbf{A} - \mathbf{B}$ with $\mathbf{B} - \mathbf{A}$, which has the opposite direction.

The above definitions apply to the vector **0** if it is represented by a degenerate line segment. We have $0 = -0$, $A - A = 0$, $A + 0 = A$, $0 + A = A$, for every vector **A**.

EXERCISES

1. If **A** and **B** are represented by arrows whose initial points coincide, what arrow represents $A + B$?

2. By drawing a diagram, show that if $A + B = C$, then
$$B = C - A$$

3. Is the following statement correct? If **A**, **B**, **C**, and **D** are non-zero vectors represented by arrows from the origin to the points A, B, C, D, and if $B - A = C - D$, then $ABCD$ is a parallelogram.

4. Let the sides of a regular hexagon be drawn as arrows, with the terminal point of each arrow at the initial point of the next.
    (a) If **A** and **B** are vectors represented by consecutive sides, find the other four vectors in terms of **A** and **B**.
    (b) What is the vector sum of all six vectors?

The following problems refer to Figure 5:

5. Write **C** in terms of **E, D, F**.

6. Write **F** in terms of **C, D, E**.

7. Write **H** in terms of **E, F, D, K**.

8. Write **G** in terms of **C, D, E, K**.

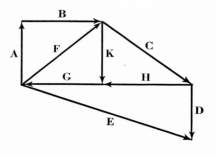

Figure 5

1.3 : Multiplication of Vectors by Numbers

The symbol $|\mathbf{A}|$ denotes the *magnitude* of the vector $\mathbf{A}$. Although it should not be confused with $|s|$, which denotes (as usual) the absolute value of a number s, it does have many properties that are quite similar. For example, $|\mathbf{A}|$ is never negative, and $|\mathbf{A}| = 0$ if and only if $\mathbf{A} = \mathbf{0}$. Since $\mathbf{A}$ and $-\mathbf{A}$ have the same magnitude, we can always write $|\mathbf{A}| = |-\mathbf{A}|$ and $|\mathbf{A} - \mathbf{B}| = |\mathbf{B} - \mathbf{A}|$. The inequality

$$|\mathbf{A} + \mathbf{B}| \leq |\mathbf{A}| + |\mathbf{B}|$$

is the vector expression of the fact that the side of any triangle does not exceed, in length, the sum of the lengths of the other two sides.

If s is a number and $\mathbf{A}$ is a vector, $s\mathbf{A}$ is defined to be the vector having magnitude $|s|$ times that of $\mathbf{A}$ and pointing in the same direction if s is positive or in the opposite direction if s is negative. Any vector $s\mathbf{A}$ is called a *scalar multiple* of $\mathbf{A}$ (Fig. 6).

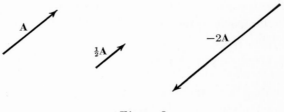

Figure 6

Here are the fundamental properties of the operation of multiplying vectors by numbers:

(1) $$\mathbf{0A} = \mathbf{0}, \quad 1\mathbf{A} = \mathbf{A}, \quad (-1)\mathbf{A} = -\mathbf{A}$$

(2) $$(s + t)\mathbf{A} = s\mathbf{A} + t\mathbf{A}$$

(3) $$s(\mathbf{A} + \mathbf{B}) = s\mathbf{A} + s\mathbf{B}$$

(4) $$s(t\mathbf{A}) = (st)\mathbf{A}$$

EXERCISES

1.　Is it ever possible to have $|\mathbf{A}| < 0$?

2.　If $|\mathbf{A}| = 3$, what is $|4\mathbf{A}|$? $|-2\mathbf{A}|$? What can you say about $|s\mathbf{A}|$ if you know that $-2 \leq s \leq 1$?

3.　If $\mathbf{A}$ is a nonzero vector, and if $s = |\mathbf{A}|^{-1}$, what is $|s\mathbf{A}|$? What is $|-s\mathbf{A}|$?

4.　If $\mathbf{B}$ is a nonzero vector, and $s = |\mathbf{A}|/|\mathbf{B}|$, what can you say about $|s\mathbf{B}|$?

5.　If $|\mathbf{A}| = |\mathbf{B}|$, is it necessarily true that $\mathbf{A} = \mathbf{B}$?

6.　If $\mathbf{A} - \mathbf{B} = 0$, is it necessarily true that $\mathbf{A} = \mathbf{B}$?

7.　You are given a plane in space. How many distinct vectors of unit magnitude are perpendicular to this plane?

8.　If $\mathbf{A}$ is a nonzero vector, how many distinct scalar multiples of $\mathbf{A}$ will have unit magnitude?

9.　Let $\mathbf{A}$ and $\mathbf{B}$ be nonzero vectors represented by arrows with the same initial point to points A and B respectively. Let $\mathbf{C}$ denote the vector represented by an arrow from this same initial point to the midpoint of the line segment AB. Write $\mathbf{C}$ in terms of $\mathbf{A}$ and $\mathbf{B}$.

10.　How many distinct vectors exist, all having unit magnitude, perpendicular to a given line in space?

11.　Prove that $|\mathbf{A} - \mathbf{B}| \geq |\mathbf{A}| - |\mathbf{B}|$.

12.　If $\mathbf{A}$ is a scalar multiple of $\mathbf{B}$, is $\mathbf{B}$ necessarily a scalar multiple of $\mathbf{A}$?

1.4 : Cartesian Coordinates

Let us consider a Cartesian coordinate system in the plane, obtained by introducing two mutually perpendicular axes, labeled x and y, with the same unit of length on both axes (Fig. 7). We assume that the reader is already familiar with this construction, which sets up a one-to-one correspondence between points in the plane and ordered pairs (x,y) of numbers.

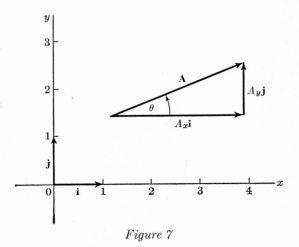

Figure 7

Let **i** denote the unit vector parallel to the x axis, in the positive x direction, and **j** the unit vector in the positive y direction. Every vector in the plane can be written in the form

$$\mathbf{A} = A_x\mathbf{i} + A_y\mathbf{j}$$

for a suitable choice of numbers A_x and A_y. These numbers are called the *components of* **A** in the x direction and y direction respectively.

The magnitude of **A** can be determined from its components by using the Pythagorean theorem:

$$|\mathbf{A}| = \sqrt{A_x^2 + A_y^2}$$

If $P_1(x_1,y_1)$ and $P_2(x_2,y_2)$ are points in the xy plane, the vector represented by the arrow P_1P_2 (initial point P_1, terminal point P_2) is $(x_2 - x_1)\mathbf{i} + (y_2 - y_1)\mathbf{j}$.

✓ EXERCISES

1. What is the x component of **i**?
2. What is the x component of **j**?

3. What is the magnitude of $\mathbf{i} + \mathbf{j}$?

4. What is the magnitude of $3\mathbf{i} - 4\mathbf{j}$?

5. In Figure 7, if $|\mathbf{A}| = 6$ and $\theta = 30°$, determine A_x and A_y.

6. The direction of a nonzero vector in the plane can be described by giving the angle θ it makes with the positive x direction. This angle is conventionally taken to be positive in the counterclockwise sense. Write A_x and A_y in terms of $|\mathbf{A}|$ and this angle θ.

7. Vector $\mathbf{A}$ is represented by an arrow with initial point $(4,2)$ and terminal point $(5,-1)$. Write $\mathbf{A}$ in terms of $\mathbf{i}$ and $\mathbf{j}$.

8. In terms of $\mathbf{i}$ and $\mathbf{j}$, determine
   (a) the unit vector at positive angle $60°$ with the x axis;
   (b) the unit vector with $\theta = -30°$ (θ as in Exercise 6);
   (c) the unit vector having the same direction as $3\mathbf{i} + 4\mathbf{j}$;
   (d) the unit vectors having x components equal to $\frac{1}{2}$;
   (e) the unit vectors perpendicular to the line $x + y = 0$.

9. Determine $|6\mathbf{i} + 8\mathbf{j}|$, $|-3\mathbf{i}|$, $|\mathbf{i} + s\mathbf{j}|$, $|(\cos \theta)\mathbf{i} + (\sin \theta)\mathbf{j}|$.

10. In terms of $\mathbf{i}$ and $\mathbf{j}$, determine the vector represented by the arrow extending from the origin to the midpoint of the line segment joining $(1,4)$ with $(3,8)$.

11. With the axes in conventional position (Fig. 7), directions may be specified in geographical terms. What is the unit vector pointing west? south? northeast?

1.5 : Space Vectors

Throughout most of this book, we shall be concerned with vectors in space. By the introduction of three mutually perpendicular axes, with the same unit of length along all three axes, we obtain the usual Cartesian coordinate system. The conventional orientation of axes is shown in Figure 8. Every vector can be expressed in the form $\mathbf{A} = A_x\mathbf{i} + A_y\mathbf{j} + A_z\mathbf{k}$ where $\mathbf{i}$, $\mathbf{j}$, and $\mathbf{k}$ are unit vectors in the positive x, y, and z directions respectively. The numbers A_x, A_y, and A_z are the components of $\mathbf{A}$ in the x, y, and z directions respectively.

If $P_1(x_1,y_1,z_1)$ and $P_2(x_2,y_2,z_2)$ are points in space, the vector represented by the arrow extending from P_1 to P_2 is

$$(x_2 - x_1)\mathbf{i} + (y_2 - y_1)\mathbf{j} + (z_2 - z_1)\mathbf{k}$$

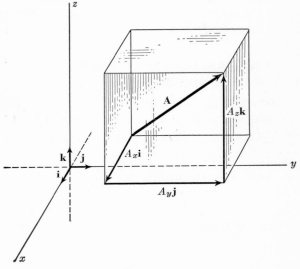

Figure 8

In terms of components, the laws of vector addition and multiplication of vectors by numbers are expressed as follows:

$$\mathbf{A} + \mathbf{B} = (A_x + B_x)\mathbf{i} + (A_y + B_y)\mathbf{j} + (A_z + B_z)\mathbf{k}$$

$$s\mathbf{A} = sA_x\mathbf{i} + sA_y\mathbf{j} + sA_z\mathbf{k}$$

By a double application of the Pythagorean theorem, we obtain

$$|\mathbf{A}| = \sqrt{A_x^2 + A_y^2 + A_z^2}$$

EXERCISES

In the first seven problems below, let $\mathbf{A} = 3\mathbf{i} + 4\mathbf{j}$, $\mathbf{B} = 2\mathbf{i} + 2\mathbf{j} - \mathbf{k}$, and $\mathbf{C} = 3\mathbf{i} - 4\mathbf{k}$.

1.   Find $|\mathbf{A}|$, $|\mathbf{B}|$, and $|\mathbf{C}|$.

2. Find $\mathbf{A} + \mathbf{B}$ and $\mathbf{A} - \mathbf{C}$.

3. Determine $|\mathbf{A} - \mathbf{C}|$.

4. For what values of s is $|s\mathbf{B}| = 1$?

5. Find the unit vector having the same direction as $\mathbf{A}$.

6. Let $\mathbf{A}$ and $\mathbf{C}$ be represented by arrows extending from the origin.
   (a) Find the length of the line segment joining their endpoints.
   (b) This line segment is parallel to one of the coordinate planes. Which one?

7. Let α denote the angle between $\mathbf{A}$ and the positive x direction. Determine $\cos \alpha$.   Generalize.

8. Determine all unit vectors perpendicular to the xz plane.

9. Compute $|\mathbf{i} + \mathbf{j} + \mathbf{k}|$.

10. Find the vector represented by the arrow P_1P_2 where $P_1(3,4,7)$ and $P_2(4,-1,6)$ are points in space.

11. What vector is represented by the arrow OP, if O is the origin and $P(x,y,z)$ is a general point in space?

12. Let $\mathbf{D} = \mathbf{i} + \mathbf{j} + \mathbf{k}$, $\mathbf{E} = \mathbf{i} + \mathbf{j} - \mathbf{k}$, and $\mathbf{F} = \mathbf{i} - \mathbf{j}$.   Determine scalars s, t, and r such that $4\mathbf{i} + 6\mathbf{j} - \mathbf{k} = s\mathbf{D} + t\mathbf{E} + r\mathbf{F}$.

1.6 : Digression

This section can be omitted with no loss of continuity.

A first step in solving a problem in mechanics is to choose a coordinate system.   For instance, if the problem involves a particle sliding down an inclined plane, it may be convenient to take one of the axes, say the x axis, parallel to the plane, and another axis, say the z axis, perpendicular to the plane.   After we have chosen a particular coordinate system, we can speak of the *position vector* of the particle. This is the vector represented by the directed line segment extending from the origin $(0,0,0)$ to the point (x,y,z) where the particle is located, and (in terms of $\mathbf{i}$, $\mathbf{j}$, and $\mathbf{k}$) it is the vector $x\mathbf{i} + y\mathbf{j} + z\mathbf{k}$. (Strictly speaking, we should not say "position vector of a particle" because this might give someone the false impression that it is an intrinsic property of the particle, whereas it depends entirely on the choice of the coordinate system.)

If a particle moves from an initial position (x_1, y_1, z_1) to another position (x_2, y_2, z_2), the displacement of the particle is the vector represented by the directed line segment extending from its initial position to its final position. This vector is $(x_2 - x_1)\mathbf{i} + (y_2 - y_1)\mathbf{j} + (z_2 - z_1)\mathbf{k}$. Notice that if the initial position vector is $\mathbf{R}_1 = x_1\mathbf{i} + y_1\mathbf{j} + z_1\mathbf{k}$ and the final position vector is $\mathbf{R}_2 = x_2\mathbf{i} + y_2\mathbf{j} + z_2\mathbf{k}$, the displacement is $\mathbf{R}_2 - \mathbf{R}_1$. *The displacement of a particle is the final position vector minus the initial position vector.*

In Section 1.1 we stated that displacement is a vector quantity. This seems obvious since it is a physical quantity that can be represented by a directed line segment. Moreover, we defined the addition of vectors so that they add in the same way that displacements "add." Thus (Fig. 2) if a particle undergoes a displacement $\mathbf{A}$, and then another displacement $\mathbf{B}$, it is clear that the resultant displacement is $\mathbf{A} + \mathbf{B}$. That is, $\mathbf{A} + \mathbf{B}$ is the single displacement that produces the same net effect as the two displacements $\mathbf{A}$ and $\mathbf{B}$. From the physicist's viewpoint, this is the reason for defining vector addition this way.

Occasionally it is helpful to think of vectors as representing displacements, even when no physics is involved. For example, consider Exercise 5 of Section 1.2, where we are asked to write $\mathbf{C}$ in terms of $\mathbf{E}$, $\mathbf{D}$, and $\mathbf{F}$. The answer is $\mathbf{C} = -\mathbf{F} + \mathbf{E} - \mathbf{D}$, which is clear since the net result of the three displacements $-\mathbf{F}$, $\mathbf{E}$, and $-\mathbf{D}$ is $\mathbf{C}$, as one can see by looking at Figure 5.

Do not get the mistaken impression that when we represent a displacement by a vector $\mathbf{A}$, the path of the particle has necessarily been straight. The directed line segment representing a displacement extends directly from the initial position to the final position, but the particle itself may have gone by way of the North Pole.

Forces are also vector quantities. This may *seem* obvious since a force is conveniently represented geometrically by a directed line segment. It is *not* so obvious, however. How do we know that forces "add" in the same way as vectors? We shall simply take the word of the physicists that they do, and let the interested reader study the matter elsewhere.

If $\mathbf{F}_1$ and $\mathbf{F}_2$ are forces acting on a particle, their vector sum $\mathbf{F}_1 + \mathbf{F}_2$ is the single force that would produce the same effect, and is sometimes called the *resultant* of the two forces. In elementary physics the resultant of two or more forces is usually found in the following manner: One draws a diagram showing the forces, then systematically marks out each force, replacing it by its components along the coordinate axes. The forces along each axis are summed algebraically, so that one has a single force remaining along each of the coordinate axes. The magnitude of the resultant force **F** can then be found by the Pythagorean theorem, since the axes are perpendicular. This is discussed with examples in F. W. Sears' *Mechanics, Heat, and Sound* (Addison-Wesley, 1950).

This process is equivalent to writing each force in terms of **i**, **j**, and **k**, and adding them in the manner of the preceding section. In working with vectors in space, the use of the unit vectors **i**, **j**, and **k** is especially convenient, since it is hard to draw suitable diagrams.

There is an increasing trend nowadays to avoid the use of **i**, **j**, and **k** altogether, writing (say) [3,2,7] instead of $3\mathbf{i} + 2\mathbf{j} + 7\mathbf{k}$. Many mathematicians prefer this, but it is difficult for some to depart from the **i**,**j**,**k** tradition.

Before concluding this section, we wish to mention that we have not yet given a really satisfactory general definition of *vector*. The definition we have given is based on the notion of a directed line segment. It is unsatisfactory in several ways. First of all, it is not general enough for some purposes in physics. Certain physical quantities can be represented by directed line segments only in a very superficial way. These physical quantities (we will discuss them later) have magnitude and direction, and hence should qualify to be called vector quantities, but when we change from one coordinate system to another, their components do not change in the same way as the components of a directed line segment would change under the same circumstances. In other words, such a physical quantity may be represented by a particular directed line segment only if we do not ever change from one coordinate system to another. When we change coordinates, we must use a different directed line segment. Because of this, some physicists prefer to consider a space vector as simply an ordered triple of numbers (the components), classifying various kinds of vectors according to the way these numbers change when the coordinate system is changed (Section 5.11).

On the other hand, mathematicians find the definition we have given unsatisfying for a number of reasons, not the least of which is that it is very narrow conceptually. Most mathematicians prefer not to define "vector" at all, but to give an axiomatic definition of what is meant by a "vector space." This directs attention to the fundamental properties of vector addition and multiplication by scalars. With respect to this viewpoint, there are objects that can qualify to be called "vectors" not because they have direction and magnitude (these are very specialized notions) but because they are manipulated algebraically in a certain manner.

Both physicists and mathematicians have occasion to deal with "vectors" in spaces that are n-dimensional, where n is greater than 3. Such spaces cannot be visualized, but are important nonetheless (Section 5.2).

The reader is not expected to understand much of this as yet. We will return to these deeper matters in the last chapter.

1.7 : Some Problems in Geometry

To avoid circumlocution, no distinction will henceforth be made, in terminology, between vectors and directed line segments. Thus we will say "the vector **A**" where we mean "the vector represented by the directed line segment **A**."

PROBLEM 1: Show that the line segment joining the midpoints of two sides of a triangle is parallel to the third side, and has length equal to one half the length of the third side.

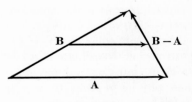

Figure 9

Solution: Let the sides of the triangle be vectors **A**, **B**, and **B** − **A** (Fig. 9). The line segment is

$$-\tfrac{1}{2}\mathbf{B} + \mathbf{A} + \tfrac{1}{2}(\mathbf{B} - \mathbf{A})$$

Clearing parentheses, this is simply $\tfrac{1}{2}\mathbf{A}$, which shows that the segment is parallel to side **A** and has half the magnitude of **A**.

PROBLEM 2:   Line segments are drawn from a vertex of a parallelogram to the midpoints of the opposite sides. Show that they trisect a diagonal.

Solution: This problem is solved by a standard technique, using the obvious fact that if **A** and **B** are nonzero vectors that are not parallel, then $m\mathbf{A} = n\mathbf{B}$ if and only if $m = 0$ and $n = 0$. Write the vector **C** (Fig. 10) in two different ways: It is obvious that

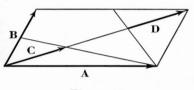

Figure 10

$\mathbf{C} = s(\mathbf{A} + \mathbf{B})$ for some number s, as yet unknown; we want to prove that $s = \frac{1}{3}$. Moreover, $\mathbf{C} = \mathbf{A} + t(\frac{1}{2}\mathbf{B} - \mathbf{A})$, where t is unknown. Setting equal these two expressions for **C** and rearranging terms, we obtain

$$(1 - t - s)\mathbf{A} = \left(s - \frac{t}{2}\right)\mathbf{B}$$

As noted above, this implies $1 - t - s = 0$ and $s - (t/2) = 0$. Solving, we obtain $s = \frac{1}{3}$, as desired.

The reader should complete the solution as an exercise, by showing that $\mathbf{D} = \frac{1}{3}(\mathbf{A} + \mathbf{B})$.

PROBLEM 3:   Let θ denote the angle between two nonzero vectors **A** and **B**. Show that

$$\cos \theta = \frac{A_x B_x + A_y B_y + A_z B_z}{|\mathbf{A}|\ |\mathbf{B}|}$$

Solution: The solution we are about to give is quite ingenious. First we introduce two new vectors having unit magnitude and making the same angle θ: $\mathbf{U} = \mathbf{A}/|\mathbf{A}|$ and $\mathbf{V} = \mathbf{B}/|\mathbf{B}|$. Thus

$$\mathbf{U} = U_x\mathbf{i} + U_y\mathbf{j} + U_z\mathbf{k} = \frac{A_x}{|\mathbf{A}|}\mathbf{i} + \frac{A_y}{|\mathbf{A}|}\mathbf{j} + \frac{A_z}{|\mathbf{A}|}\mathbf{k}$$

$$\mathbf{V} = V_x\mathbf{i} + V_y\mathbf{j} + V_z\mathbf{k} = \frac{B_x}{|\mathbf{B}|}\mathbf{i} + \frac{B_y}{|\mathbf{B}|}\mathbf{j} + \frac{B_z}{|\mathbf{B}|}\mathbf{k}$$

Let **U** and **V** be represented by arrows extending from the origin O to points U and V respectively. Then OUV is an isosceles triangle, and the length of side UV equals the positive square root of

$$|UV|^2 = (U_x - V_x)^2 + (U_y - V_y)^2 + (U_z - V_z)^2$$

Expanding the right side, and using the fact that $U_x^2 + U_y^2 + U_z^2 = 1$, $V_x^2 + V_y^2 + V_z^2 = 1$, we obtain

$$|UV|^2 = 2 - 2(U_xV_x + U_yV_y + U_zV_z)$$

Now let us consider a triangle in the plane with vertices at $(0,0)$, $P(1,0)$, $Q(\cos \theta, \sin \theta)$ (Fig. 11). This triangle is congruent to OUV, and therefore $|UV| = |PQ|$. Hence

$$|UV|^2 = |PQ|^2 = (\cos \theta - 1)^2 + \sin^2 \theta = 2 - 2 \cos \theta$$

Comparing these two expressions for $|UV|^2$, we obtain

$$\cos \theta = U_xV_x + U_yV_y + U_zV_z$$

Now substitute $U_x = A_x/|\mathbf{A}|$, $V_x = B_x/|\mathbf{B}|, \ldots$, and the proof is complete.

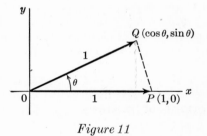

Figure 11

PROBLEM 4: Show that the vectors $\mathbf{A} = 2\mathbf{i} - \mathbf{j} + 5\mathbf{k}$ and $\mathbf{B} = \mathbf{i} + 7\mathbf{j} + \mathbf{k}$ are perpendicular.

Solution: $\qquad \cos \theta = \dfrac{2 - 7 + 5}{\sqrt{30}\ \sqrt{51}} = 0$

hence $\theta = \pm 90°$.

EXERCISES

1. Find the angle between $2\mathbf{i} + \mathbf{j} - 2\mathbf{k}$ and $3\mathbf{i} + 4\mathbf{k}$.

2. Find the angle between $2\mathbf{i} + 3\mathbf{j} + 4\mathbf{k}$ and $2\mathbf{i} + 4\mathbf{j} - 4\mathbf{k}$.

3. Find the angle between the x axis and $\mathbf{i} + \mathbf{j} + \mathbf{k}$.

4. Find the three angles of the triangle with vertices $(2,-1,1)$, $(1,-3,-5)$, $(3,-4,-4)$.

5. Find the angle between the xy plane and $2\mathbf{i} + 2\mathbf{j} - \mathbf{k}$. (Note that $\mathbf{k}$ is perpendicular to the xy plane.)

6. By the *direction cosines* of a vector $\mathbf{A}$ one means the three numbers $\cos \alpha$, $\cos \beta$, and $\cos \gamma$, where α, β, and γ are the angles between $\mathbf{A}$ and the positive x, y, and z directions respectively. Find the direction cosines of a vector $\mathbf{A} = A_x\mathbf{i} + A_y\mathbf{j} + A_z\mathbf{k}$ in terms of its components and its magnitude.

7. What are the direction cosines of $4\mathbf{i} + 2\mathbf{j} + 4\mathbf{k}$? (Use the solution to Problem 6.)

8. Show that $\mathbf{i} + \mathbf{j} + \mathbf{k}$ is perpendicular to the plane $x + y + z = 0$. [Hint: This plane passes through the origin. Show that $\mathbf{i} + \mathbf{j} + \mathbf{k}$ is perpendicular to every vector $x\mathbf{i} + y\mathbf{j} + z\mathbf{k}$ extending from the origin to a point (x,y,z) in the plane.]

9. If $\mathbf{A}$, $\mathbf{B}$, and $\mathbf{C}$ are vectors extending from the origin to points A, B, and C respectively, show that $\frac{1}{3}\mathbf{A} + \frac{1}{3}\mathbf{B} + \frac{1}{3}\mathbf{C}$ extends from the origin to the point of intersection of the medians of the triangle ABC.

1.8 : Equations of a Line

The *position vector* of a point is the vector extending from the origin to the point. Thus the position vector of a point (x,y,z) is the vector $x\mathbf{i} + y\mathbf{j} + z\mathbf{k}$. This correspondence between points and vectors is the fundamental means whereby problems in analytic geometry can be studied by vector methods.

As an elementary example, let us derive the equations of a line passing through a given point (x_0,y_0,z_0) and parallel to a given nonzero vector $\mathbf{V} = a\mathbf{i} + b\mathbf{j} + c\mathbf{k}$.

Let $\mathbf{R}_0$ be the position vector of (x_0,y_0,z_0) and let $\mathbf{R}$ be the position vector of a point (x,y,z). The point (x,y,z) will lie on the desired line if and only if $\mathbf{R} - \mathbf{R}_0$ is parallel to $\mathbf{V}$. A vector will be parallel to $\mathbf{V}$ if and only if it equals some scalar multiple of $\mathbf{V}$, so the condition that (x,y,z) be on the line is that $\mathbf{R} - \mathbf{R}_0 = t\mathbf{V}$ for some number t.

Rewriting this as $\mathbf{R} = \mathbf{R_0} + t\mathbf{V}$ and writing this out in terms of the components of the vectors we obtain

$$x = x_0 + at$$
(1)
$$y = y_0 + bt$$
$$z = z_0 + ct$$

A point (x,y,z) is on the line through (x_0,y_0,z_0) and parallel to $\mathbf{V} = a\mathbf{i} + b\mathbf{j} + c\mathbf{k}$ if and only if its coordinates satisfy all three of the equations (1) for some value of the parameter t.

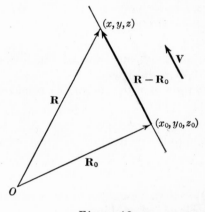

Figure 12

Equations (1) are called the *parametric form* of the equations of the line. The parameter t can be thought of as representing *time;* we can think of equations (1) as giving the position of a moving particle at time t. This particle traverses a line parallel to $\mathbf{V}$ and passes through the point (x_0,y_0,z_0) at time $t = 0$.

If all three coordinates of $\mathbf{V}$ are nonzero, this system of equations can be written in the following form, obtained by eliminating the parameter t:

(2)
$$\frac{x - x_0}{a} = \frac{y - y_0}{b} = \frac{z - z_0}{c}$$

Caution: If any of the coordinates of $\mathbf{V}$ are zero, (2) does not make sense, and (1) must be used instead (see Example 2 following).

EXAMPLE 1: Find equations of the line passing through $(2,0,4)$ and parallel to $2\mathbf{i} + \mathbf{j} + 3\mathbf{k}$, in both parametric and non-parametric form.

Solution: Here $\mathbf{V} = 2\mathbf{i} + \mathbf{j} + 3\mathbf{k}$, so $a = 2$, $b = 1$, and $c = 3$. In parametric form the equations are

$$x = 2 + 2t$$
$$y = t$$
$$z = 4 + 3t$$

In nonparametric form they are

$$\frac{x-2}{2} = y = \frac{z-4}{3}$$

EXAMPLE 2: Find equations of the line passing through $(0,3,-1)$ parallel to $3\mathbf{i} + 4\mathbf{k}$.

Solution: In this case $b = 0$, so (2) would not make sense. In parametric form we have

$$x = 3t$$
$$y = 3$$
$$z = -1 + 4t$$

If we now eliminate the parameter from the first and third equations we obtain

$$\frac{x}{3} = \frac{z+1}{4}, \qquad y = 3$$

This pair of equations can also be written

$$4x - 3z = 3, \qquad y = 3$$

EXAMPLE 3: Find a unit vector parallel to the line

$$\frac{x-4}{2} = y - 3 = \frac{z+1}{2}$$

Solution: By comparison with (2) we have $a = 2$, $b = 1$, and $c = 2$, so a vector parallel to the line is $2\mathbf{i} + \mathbf{j} + 2\mathbf{k}$. Dividing this vector by its own length we obtain a unit vector $\frac{2}{3}\mathbf{i} + \frac{1}{3}\mathbf{j} + \frac{2}{3}\mathbf{k}$. The negative of this vector is also a correct solution.

EXERCISES

1. Find parametric equations of the line passing through the origin parallel to $3\mathbf{i} + 7\mathbf{k} - 2\mathbf{j}$.

2. Find the two unit vectors parallel to the line
$$\frac{x - 1}{3} = \frac{y + 2}{4}, \qquad z = 9$$

3. Find two unit vectors parallel to the line $x = 2y = 3z + 3$. Hint: These equations can be written in form (2) as follows:
$$x = \frac{y}{\frac{1}{2}} = \frac{z + 1}{\frac{1}{3}}$$

4. Find two unit vectors parallel to the line represented by the equations $x + y = 1, x - 3z = 5$.   [Hint: Rewrite in form (2).]

5. Find equations of the line parallel to the z axis passing through the point $(1,2,3)$.

6. Find equations of the line perpendicular to the yz plane, passing through $(1,2,3)$.

7. Find equations of the line passing through the origin and parallel to the line
$$x - 3 = \frac{y + 2}{4} = 1 - z$$

8. Find the angle between the two intersecting lines
$$\frac{x - 1}{3} = \frac{y - 3}{4} = \frac{z}{5} \quad \text{and} \quad \frac{x - 1}{2} = 3 - y = 2z$$

9. Find equations of the line passing through the points $(3,4,5)$ and $(3,4,7)$.

10. Find equations of the line passing through the points $(1,4,-1)$ and $(2,2,7)$.

11. Let A and B be two points with position vectors $\mathbf{A}$ and $\mathbf{B}$ respectively. Show that the line passing through these points may be represented by the vector equation

(3) $\mathbf{R} = s\mathbf{A} + t\mathbf{B},$ $s + t = 1$

12. Solve Problem 10 by making use of (3).

1.9 : Scalar Products

The *scalar product* of two vectors is the number

(1) $$\mathbf{A}\cdot\mathbf{B} = |\mathbf{A}|\,|\mathbf{B}|\cos\theta$$

where θ denotes the angle between the vectors. Although **A** and **B** are *vectors*, $\mathbf{A}\cdot\mathbf{B}$ is a *number*. The scalar product is also sometimes called the *dot product* or the *inner product*.

In a few simple cases, the scalar product of two vectors is easily computed directly from this definition. For example, the scalar product of the vectors shown in Figure 13 is $9\sqrt{3}$.

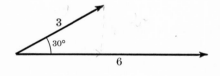

Figure 13

If either **A** or **B** is the zero vector, we have either $|\mathbf{A}| = 0$ or $|\mathbf{B}| = 0$, so by (1) it follows that $\mathbf{A}\cdot\mathbf{B} = 0$. (We ignore the fact that θ is not defined in this case.)

On the other hand, it is possible to have $\mathbf{A}\cdot\mathbf{B} = 0$ even though both **A** and **B** are nonzero vectors. For example, if **A** and **B** are perpendicular, then $\cos\theta = \cos 90° = 0$ and hence $\mathbf{A}\cdot\mathbf{B} = 0$.

In Section 1.7, we derived a formula for $\cos\theta$ in terms of the components of the two vectors. It follows from that formula that

(2) $$\mathbf{A}\cdot\mathbf{B} = A_xB_x + A_yB_y + A_zB_z$$

Memorize (1) and (2) *now*. They are important.

EXAMPLE 1: Find the scalar product of $4\mathbf{i} - 5\mathbf{j} - \mathbf{k}$ and $\mathbf{i} + 2\mathbf{j} + 3\mathbf{k}$.

Solution: $(4)(1) + (-5)(2) + (-1)(3) = -9$. (The negative sign indicates that the angle between the vectors must be greater than 90°.)

EXAMPLE 2: Find the angle between the vectors
$\mathbf{A} = 2\mathbf{i} + 2\mathbf{j} - \mathbf{k}$ and $\mathbf{B} = 3\mathbf{i} + 4\mathbf{j}$.

Solution: Since (1) and (2) have already been memorized, there is no need to look up the formula derived in Section 1.7. We have $|\mathbf{A}| = 3$ and $|\mathbf{B}| = 5$. Using (2), we see that $\mathbf{A} \cdot \mathbf{B} = 14$. Substituting these values in (1) we solve to get $\theta = \cos^{-1}(14/15)$.

EXAMPLE 3: If $\mathbf{F}$ is a constant force acting through a displacement $\mathbf{D}$, the work done by $\mathbf{F}$ is defined to be the product of the magnitude of the displacement with the component of the force in the direction of the displacement. In vector notation this is written

$$\text{Work} = \mathbf{F} \cdot \mathbf{D}$$

The following properties of the scalar product are easily verified from (2):

(3) $$\mathbf{A} \cdot \mathbf{B} = \mathbf{B} \cdot \mathbf{A} \qquad \text{(symmetry)}$$

(4) $$(s\mathbf{A}) \cdot \mathbf{B} = s(\mathbf{A} \cdot \mathbf{B}), \qquad (\mathbf{A} + \mathbf{B}) \cdot \mathbf{C} = \mathbf{A} \cdot \mathbf{C} + \mathbf{B} \cdot \mathbf{C}$$
                                        (linearity in the first factor)

(5) $$\mathbf{A} \cdot (t\mathbf{B}) = t(\mathbf{A} \cdot \mathbf{B}), \qquad \mathbf{A} \cdot (\mathbf{B} + \mathbf{C}) = \mathbf{A} \cdot \mathbf{B} + \mathbf{A} \cdot \mathbf{C}$$
                                        (linearity in the second factor)

(6) $$|\mathbf{A}|^2 = \mathbf{A} \cdot \mathbf{A}$$

EXAMPLE 4: It is interesting to see how the cosine law of trigonometry can be derived by vector methods. By (6), replacing $\mathbf{A}$ by $\mathbf{A} - \mathbf{B}$, we have $|\mathbf{A} - \mathbf{B}|^2 = (\mathbf{A} - \mathbf{B}) \cdot (\mathbf{A} - \mathbf{B})$. By (4) and (5), the right side of this equation is $\mathbf{A} \cdot \mathbf{A} - \mathbf{B} \cdot \mathbf{A} - \mathbf{A} \cdot \mathbf{B} + \mathbf{B} \cdot \mathbf{B}$, which by (3) equals $\mathbf{A} \cdot \mathbf{A} + \mathbf{B} \cdot \mathbf{B} - 2\mathbf{A} \cdot \mathbf{B}$. Using (1) this becomes $|\mathbf{A}|^2 + |\mathbf{B}|^2 - 2|\mathbf{A}| |\mathbf{B}| \cos \theta$. If we interpret $\mathbf{A}$, $\mathbf{B}$, and $\mathbf{A} - \mathbf{B}$ as the sides of a triangle, we obtain the cosine law:

$$|\mathbf{A} - \mathbf{B}|^2 = |\mathbf{A}|^2 + |\mathbf{B}|^2 - 2|\mathbf{A}| |\mathbf{B}| \cos \theta$$

EXAMPLE 5 (A Maximum Principle): Let there be given a nonzero vector $\mathbf{D}$, and let $\mathbf{n}$ denote a variable *unit* vector. Then $|\mathbf{n}| = 1$ and $\mathbf{D} \cdot \mathbf{n} = |\mathbf{D}| |\mathbf{n}| \cos \theta = |\mathbf{D}| \cos \theta$. This will be a maximum when $\cos \theta = 1$, i.e., when $\theta = 0$. Thus we have derived the following maximum principle, which will be useful to us in later sections:

The unit vector making $\mathbf{D} \cdot \mathbf{n}$ a maximum is the unit vector $\mathbf{n}$ pointing in the same direction as $\mathbf{D}$.

EXERCISES

1. Find the scalar product of $3\mathbf{i} + 8\mathbf{j} - 2\mathbf{k}$ with $5\mathbf{i} + \mathbf{j} + 2\mathbf{k}$.

2. Find the scalar product of $2\mathbf{i} + 3\mathbf{j} + 4\mathbf{k}$ with $4\mathbf{i} - 3\mathbf{k} + 9\mathbf{j}$.

3. Find the scalar product of $3\mathbf{i} + 4\mathbf{j}$ with $5\mathbf{j} - 10\mathbf{k}$.

4. Determine the angle between $2\mathbf{i} + \mathbf{j} - 2\mathbf{k}$ and $3\mathbf{i} - 4\mathbf{j}$.

5. Find the angle between $2\mathbf{i}$ and $3\mathbf{i} + 4\mathbf{j}$.

6. Find the component of $8\mathbf{i} + \mathbf{j}$ in the direction of $\mathbf{i} + 2\mathbf{j} - 2\mathbf{k}$.

7. Find the component of $\mathbf{i} + \mathbf{j} + \mathbf{k}$ in the direction of $\mathbf{i} + \mathbf{j}$.

8. Find the vector in the same direction as $\mathbf{i} + \mathbf{j}$ whose component in the direction of $2\mathbf{i} - 4\mathbf{k}$ is unity.

9. If $\mathbf{u}$ and $\mathbf{v}$ are unit vectors, and θ is the angle between them, find $\frac{1}{2}|\mathbf{u} - \mathbf{v}|$ in terms of θ.

10. Prove the parallelogram equality, i.e.: The sum of the squares of the diagonals of a parallelogram equals the sum of the squares of its sides.

11. Let $\mathbf{A} = (\cos\phi)\mathbf{i} + (\sin\phi)\mathbf{j}$ and $\mathbf{B} = (\cos\theta)\mathbf{i} + (\sin\theta)\mathbf{j}$. Draw these vectors in the xy plane. By interpreting the scalar product $\mathbf{A}\cdot\mathbf{B}$ geometrically, prove that $\cos(\phi - \theta) = \cos\phi\cos\theta + \sin\phi\sin\theta$.

12. Find the component of the force $5\mathbf{i} + 7\mathbf{j} - \mathbf{k}$ in the direction of the displacement PQ, where $P(3,0,1)$ and $Q(4,4,4)$ are points in space.

13. By interpreting $2x + 3y + 4z$ as a scalar product, show that $2\mathbf{i} + 3\mathbf{j} + 4\mathbf{k}$ is perpendicular to the plane $2x + 3y + 4z = 0$.

1.10 : *Equation of a Plane*

We shall now derive the equation of a plane by vector methods. We pose the following problem: to find an equation representing the plane passing through a given point (x_0, y_0, z_0) and perpendicular to a given nonzero vector $\mathbf{N} = a\mathbf{i} + b\mathbf{j} + c\mathbf{k}$. Let $\mathbf{R}_0 = x_0\mathbf{i} + y_0\mathbf{j} + z_0\mathbf{k}$ be the position vector of the given point, and let $\mathbf{R} = x\mathbf{i} + y\mathbf{j} + z\mathbf{k}$ be the position vector of some other point (x,y,z). Then (x,y,z) will lie in the plane only if $\mathbf{R} - \mathbf{R}_0$ is perpendicular to $\mathbf{N}$. In terms of scalar products, this condition can be written

(1) $$(\mathbf{R} - \mathbf{R}_0) \cdot \mathbf{N} = 0$$

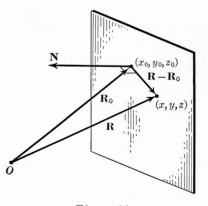

Figure 14

[This derivation assumes that (x,y,z) is not the same as (x_0,y_0,z_0). However, in that case $\mathbf{R} = \mathbf{R}_0$, so $\mathbf{R} - \mathbf{R}_0$ is the zero vector and (1) is still valid.]

Conversely, if (1) is satisfied, then (since $\mathbf{N}$ is nonzero) either $\mathbf{R} - \mathbf{R}_0$ is perpendicular to $\mathbf{N}$ or it is the zero vector. In either case this implies that $\mathbf{R}$ is the position vector of a point in the plane.

Hence (1) is a vector equation of the plane. In terms of components, this becomes

(2) $$a(x - x_0) + b(y - y_0) + c(z - z_0) = 0$$

Lumping the constant terms, this can be written

(3) $$ax + by + cz = d$$

where $d = ax_0 + by_0 + cz_0$.

EXAMPLE 1:   Find an equation of the plane passing through $(1,3,-6)$ perpendicular to the vector $3\mathbf{i} - 2\mathbf{j} + 7\mathbf{k}$.

Solution: By (2) we can write the equation down at once: $3(x - 1) - 2(y - 3) + 7(z + 6) = 0$. This can be simplified to $3x - 2y + 7z = -45$.

EXAMPLE 2:   Find an equation of the plane passing through (1,2,3) perpendicular to the line

$$\frac{x-1}{4} = \frac{y}{5} = \frac{z+5}{6}$$

Solution: We recall from an earlier section that we can find a vector parallel to the given line by reading off the coefficients in the denominators: $4\mathbf{i} + 5\mathbf{j} + 6\mathbf{k}$. This vector is perpendicular to the desired plane, and so the equation of the plane is $4(x - 1) + 5(y - 2) + 6(z - 3) = 0$.

We leave it to the reader to prove that any equation $ax + by + cz = d$, where a, b, and c are not all zero, represents a plane, and that the vector $\mathbf{N} = a\mathbf{i} + b\mathbf{j} + c\mathbf{k}$ is perpendicular to the plane.   [Hint: If $\mathbf{R}_0$ is the position vector of a point whose coordinates satisfy the equation, then $\mathbf{R}_0 \cdot \mathbf{N} = d$. Substituting for d in the equation we get $\mathbf{R} \cdot \mathbf{N} = \mathbf{R}_0 \cdot \mathbf{N}$, so $(\mathbf{R} - \mathbf{R}_0) \cdot \mathbf{N} = 0$.   Interpret geometrically.]

EXAMPLE 3:   Find a unit vector perpendicular to the plane $2x + y - 2z = 7$.

Solution: Reading off the coefficients, we see that $2\mathbf{i} + \mathbf{j} - 2\mathbf{k}$ is perpendicular to the plane. Its magnitude is 3, so the desired unit vector is $\frac{2}{3}\mathbf{i} + \frac{1}{3}\mathbf{j} - \frac{2}{3}\mathbf{k}$. The negative of this vector is also a correct answer.

A vector perpendicular to a plane is sometimes called a *normal*.

EXAMPLE 4:   Find the angle between the two planes $3x + 4y = 0$ and $2x + y - 2z = 5$.

Solution: The desired angle equals the angle between the normals $\mathbf{N}_1 = 3\mathbf{i} + 4\mathbf{j}$ and $\mathbf{N}_2 = 2\mathbf{i} + \mathbf{j} - 2\mathbf{k}$. By the methods of a preceding section,

$$\cos \theta = \frac{\mathbf{N}_1 \cdot \mathbf{N}_2}{|\mathbf{N}_1| \, |\mathbf{N}_2|} = \frac{6 + 4}{(5)(3)} = \frac{2}{3}$$

The desired angle is approximately $48°$.

EXAMPLE 5:   In books on analytic geometry, it is shown that the distance between an arbitrary point (x_1, y_1, z_1) and the plane $ax + by + cz = d$ is given by the expression

$$\frac{|ax_1 + by_1 + cz_1 - d|}{(a^2 + b^2 + c^2)^{\frac{1}{2}}}$$

Derive this expression by vector methods.

Solution: Let $\mathbf{R}_0$ be the position vector of a point in the plane, and let $\mathbf{R}_1 = x_1\mathbf{i} + y_1\mathbf{j} + z_1\mathbf{k}$ and $\mathbf{N} = a\mathbf{i} + b\mathbf{j} + c\mathbf{k}$. The desired distance is the absolute value (distance is never negative!) of the component of $\mathbf{R}_1 - \mathbf{R}_0$ in the direction of $\mathbf{N}$. Hence this distance is

$$\frac{|(\mathbf{R}_1 - \mathbf{R}_0) \cdot \mathbf{N}|}{|\mathbf{N}|} = \frac{|\mathbf{R}_1 \cdot \mathbf{N} - d|}{|\mathbf{N}|}$$

which, written out in terms of components, is the expression given above.

EXAMPLE 6: Find the distance between the pairs of planes $x + y + z = 5$ and $x + y + z = 10$.

Solution: Take an arbitrary point in the first plane, say $(1,1,3)$, and find its distance to the second plane by using the expression derived in Example 5. We obtain

$$\frac{|5 - 10|}{\sqrt{3}} = \frac{5\sqrt{3}}{3}$$

EXERCISES

1. Find unit vectors normal to the planes
   (a) $2x + y + 2z = 8$
   (b) $4x - 4z = 0$
   (c) $-y + 6z = 0$
   (d) $x = 5$
   (e) $y = z + 2$
   (f) $x = y$

2. Find an equation of the plane through the origin perpendicular to $2\mathbf{i} - 8\mathbf{j} + 2\mathbf{k}$.

3. Determine $\cos \theta$, where θ is the angle between the planes $x + y + z = 0$ and $x = 0$.

4. Find the distances between the pairs of planes
   (a) $x + 2y + 3z = 5$ and $x + 2y + 3z = 19$
   (b) $x + y = 4$ and $x + y = 10$
   (c) $x = 5$ and $x = 7$ (no calculations needed here!)

5. Find a plane passing through $(1,3,3)$, parallel to the plane $3x + y - z = 8$.

6. Is it possible to find a plane perpendicular to both **i** and **j**?

7. If **A** is a fixed nonzero vector, interpret geometrically the equation $(\mathbf{R} - \mathbf{A}) \cdot \mathbf{R} = 0$. (Is it a plane?)

8. Find the equation of a line in the xy plane perpendicular to the vector $3\mathbf{i} - \mathbf{j}$.

9. Find the distance between the lines $x + y = 0$ and $x + y = 5$ in the xy plane.

10. Find a line in the xy plane parallel to $3x + 2y = 4$ passing through the point $(3,1)$.

REVIEW PROBLEMS

1. In each case, find a vector with the stated property:
   (a) extending from the point $(2,0,3)$ to the point $(4,-1,8)$
   (b) perpendicular to the plane $2x + 3y - 4z = 18$
   (c) parallel to the line
   $$\frac{x - 2}{3} = y + 4 = \frac{z + 1}{7}$$
   (d) of unit length perpendicular to the plane
   $$2x - 2y + z = 15$$
   (e) of unit length parallel to the vector $2\mathbf{i} - 12\mathbf{k}$
   (f) of unit length parallel to the line
   $$\frac{x - 4}{3} = \frac{y + 1}{4}, \qquad z = 7$$

2. Find the inner product $\mathbf{A} \cdot \mathbf{B}$ of the vectors $\mathbf{A} = 2\mathbf{i} - 3\mathbf{j} + 7\mathbf{k}$ and $\mathbf{B} = 7\mathbf{i} + 2\mathbf{j} - \mathbf{k}$.

3. What are the lengths $|\mathbf{A}|$ and $|\mathbf{B}|$ of the vectors described in Problem 2?

4. Find the cosine of the angle between the two vectors described in Problem 2.

5. By vector methods, find the cosine of the angle between the lines
   $$\frac{x - 1}{3} = \frac{y + 8}{2} = z \quad \text{and} \quad x = y = z$$

6. By vector methods, show that the line $x = y = (z + 2)/3$ is parallel to the plane $2x - 8y + 2z = 5$.

7.   By vector methods find the distance from the point (3,4,7) to
     the plane $2x - y - 2z = 4$.

8.   By vector methods find the angle between the line $x = y = 2z$
     and the plane $x + y + z = 0$.

1.11 : Triple Scalar Products

Let **A**, **B**, and **C** be vectors in space,

$$\mathbf{A} = A_x\mathbf{i} + A_y\mathbf{j} + A_z\mathbf{k}$$
$$\mathbf{B} = B_x\mathbf{i} + B_y\mathbf{j} + B_z\mathbf{k}$$
$$\mathbf{C} = C_x\mathbf{i} + C_y\mathbf{j} + C_z\mathbf{k}$$

Their triple scalar product, denoted [**A**,**B**,**C**], is defined to be the
number

$$(1) \qquad [\mathbf{A},\mathbf{B},\mathbf{C}] = A_xB_yC_z + A_yB_zC_x + A_zB_xC_y - A_zB_yC_x$$
$$- A_yB_xC_z - A_xB_zC_y$$

In determinant form, this may be written

$$(2) \qquad [\mathbf{A},\mathbf{B},\mathbf{C}] = \begin{vmatrix} A_x & A_y & A_z \\ B_x & B_y & B_z \\ C_x & C_y & C_z \end{vmatrix}$$

For example, if $\mathbf{A} = 2\mathbf{i} + \mathbf{k}$, $\mathbf{B} = 3\mathbf{i} + \mathbf{j} + \mathbf{k}$, and $\mathbf{C} = \mathbf{i} + \mathbf{j} + 4\mathbf{k}$, we have

$$[\mathbf{A},\mathbf{B},\mathbf{C}] = [2\mathbf{i} + \mathbf{k}, 3\mathbf{i} + \mathbf{j} + \mathbf{k}, \mathbf{i} + \mathbf{j} + 4\mathbf{k}]$$

$$= \begin{vmatrix} 2 & 0 & 1 \\ 3 & 1 & 1 \\ 1 & 1 & 4 \end{vmatrix} = 8 + 3 - 1 - 2 = 8$$

The geometrical interpretation of the triple scalar product is as
follows. Suppose that **A**, **B**, and **C** are nonzero vectors, not all
parallel to the same plane. Let us represent them by arrows with
initial points at the origin. They can then be considered to be
coterminal edges of a parallelepiped (Fig. 15). *Except perhaps for
the sign,* [**A**,**B**,**C**] *equals the volume of this parallelepiped.*

If one or more of the three vectors **A**, **B**, and **C** is equal to the zero vector, then [**A**,**B**,**C**] will equal zero.   Also, if **A**, **B**, and **C** are all parallel to the same plane, then [**A**,**B**,**C**] will be equal to zero. For example, the vectors **i**, **j**, and **i** + 2**j** are all parallel to the xy plane, and

$$[\mathbf{i}, \mathbf{j}, \mathbf{i} + 2\mathbf{j}] = \begin{vmatrix} 1 & 0 & 0 \\ 0 & 1 & 0 \\ 1 & 2 & 0 \end{vmatrix} = 0$$

In either of these cases we can think of **A**, **B**, and **C** as determining a "degenerate" parallelepiped with zero volume.

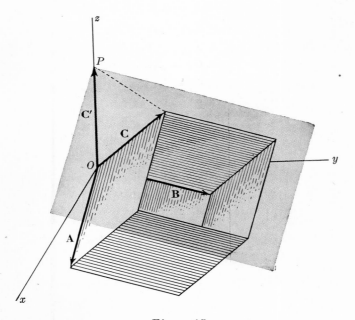

Figure 15

Preparatory to proving these assertions, we list the following properties of the triple scalar product.   These properties are easily verified directly from the definition (1).

(3) $[\mathbf{i}, \mathbf{j}, \mathbf{k}] = 1$

(4) For any three vectors **A**, **B**, and **C**, we have $[\mathbf{A},\mathbf{B},\mathbf{C}] = [\mathbf{B},\mathbf{C},\mathbf{A}] = [\mathbf{C},\mathbf{A},\mathbf{B}] = -[\mathbf{B},\mathbf{A},\mathbf{C}] = -[\mathbf{A},\mathbf{C},\mathbf{B}] = -[\mathbf{C},\mathbf{B},\mathbf{A}]$. In other words, the *absolute value* of the triple scalar product does not depend on the order, but whenever two of the vectors are interchanged the *sign* changes.

(5) If two or more of the vectors **A**, **B**, and **C** are equal, then $[\mathbf{A},\mathbf{B},\mathbf{C}] = 0$. (For example, $[\mathbf{i} + \mathbf{j}, 3\mathbf{i} - \mathbf{k}, \mathbf{i} + \mathbf{j}] = 0$, since the first and third factors are equal.)

(6) The triple scalar product is *homogeneous* in each of its three factors. This means that, for any number s, we have $[s\mathbf{A},\mathbf{B},\mathbf{C}] = s[\mathbf{A},\mathbf{B},\mathbf{C}]$, $[\mathbf{A},s\mathbf{B},\mathbf{C}] = s[\mathbf{A},\mathbf{B},\mathbf{C}]$, and $[\mathbf{A},\mathbf{B},s\mathbf{C}] = s[\mathbf{A},\mathbf{B},\mathbf{C}]$. (For example, $[3\mathbf{i},\mathbf{j},\mathbf{k}] = 3[\mathbf{i},\mathbf{j},\mathbf{k}] = 3$.)

(7) The triple scalar product is additive in each of its three factors. This means that

$$[\mathbf{A} + \mathbf{D}, \mathbf{B}, \mathbf{C}] = [\mathbf{A},\mathbf{B},\mathbf{C}] + [\mathbf{D},\mathbf{B},\mathbf{C}]$$
$$[\mathbf{A}, \mathbf{B} + \mathbf{E}, \mathbf{C}] = [\mathbf{A},\mathbf{B},\mathbf{C}] + [\mathbf{A},\mathbf{E},\mathbf{C}]$$
and
$$[\mathbf{A}, \mathbf{B}, \mathbf{C} + \mathbf{F}] = [\mathbf{A},\mathbf{B},\mathbf{C}] + [\mathbf{A},\mathbf{B},\mathbf{F}]$$

It is interesting to notice that by using properties (3) through (7) it is possible to evaluate any scalar triple product without using (1) or (2). For example, let $\mathbf{A} = \mathbf{i} + 3\mathbf{j}$, $\mathbf{B} = \mathbf{i} + \mathbf{k}$, and $\mathbf{C} = -\mathbf{k}$. Then

$$\begin{aligned}
[\mathbf{A},\mathbf{B},\mathbf{C}] &= [\mathbf{i} + 3\mathbf{j}, \mathbf{i} + \mathbf{k}, -\mathbf{k}] \\
&= [\mathbf{i}, \mathbf{i} + \mathbf{k}, -\mathbf{k}] + [3\mathbf{j}, \mathbf{i} + \mathbf{k}, -\mathbf{k}] \\
&= [\mathbf{i},\mathbf{i},-\mathbf{k}] + [\mathbf{i},\mathbf{k},-\mathbf{k}] + [3\mathbf{j},\mathbf{i},-\mathbf{k}] + [3\mathbf{j},\mathbf{k},-\mathbf{k}] \\
&= -[\mathbf{i},\mathbf{i},\mathbf{k}] - [\mathbf{i},\mathbf{k},\mathbf{k}] - 3[\mathbf{j},\mathbf{i},\mathbf{k}] - 3[\mathbf{j},\mathbf{k},\mathbf{k}] \\
&= -3[\mathbf{j},\mathbf{i},\mathbf{k}] = 3[\mathbf{i},\mathbf{j},\mathbf{k}] = 3
\end{aligned}$$

Notice that the first, second, and fourth terms vanish because they have repeated factors.

(8) If any one of the three vectors is replaced by the sum of that one vector with a linear combination of the other two, the triple scalar product is unchanged. For example, if we replace **A** by $\mathbf{A} + s\mathbf{B} + t\mathbf{C}$, where s and t are any numbers whatsoever, then $[\mathbf{A} + s\mathbf{B} + t\mathbf{C}, \mathbf{B}, \mathbf{C}] = [\mathbf{A},\mathbf{B},\mathbf{C}]$. The proof is easy:

$$[\mathbf{A} + s\mathbf{B} + t\mathbf{C}, \mathbf{B}, \mathbf{C}] = [\mathbf{A},\mathbf{B},\mathbf{C}] + s[\mathbf{B},\mathbf{B},\mathbf{C}] + t[\mathbf{C},\mathbf{B},\mathbf{C}]$$

and the last two terms vanish by (5).

We are now ready to prove the statements made earlier. The "degenerate" cases are almost trivial. For example, suppose that **A**, **B**, and **C** are nonzero coplanar vectors and that **B** is not parallel to **C**. Then there must exist numbers s and t such that $\mathbf{A} = s\mathbf{B} + t\mathbf{C}$ (Fig. 16; notice that in this figure t is negative). Then

$$[\mathbf{A},\mathbf{B},\mathbf{C}] = [s\mathbf{B} + t\mathbf{C},\ \mathbf{B},\ \mathbf{C}] = s[\mathbf{B},\mathbf{B},\mathbf{C}] + t[\mathbf{C},\mathbf{B},\mathbf{C}] = 0$$

since each product has repeated factors.

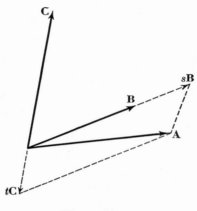

Figure 16

Now suppose that **A**, **B**, and **C** are nonzero vectors, not all parallel to the same plane. Let them be represented by arrows extending from the origin (Fig. 15). Let us call the parallelogram with edges **A** and **B** the *base* of the parallelepiped determined by **A**, **B**, and **C**. Pass a plane through the terminal of **C**, parallel to the base. This plane will intersect at least one of the coordinate axes at some point P. Let **C**′ denote the vector represented by the arrow OP (Fig. 15). Then it is easy to see that (a) the parallelepiped determined by **A**, **B**, and **C**′ has the same volume as the original parallelepiped, since its base and altitude are the same, and (b) **C** = **C**′ + **D**, where **D** is some vector parallel to the base. Since any vector parallel to the base can be written in the form $s\mathbf{A} + t\mathbf{B}$ for a suitable choice of numbers s and t,

$$[\mathbf{A},\mathbf{B},\mathbf{C}] = [\mathbf{A}, \mathbf{B}, \mathbf{C}' + \mathbf{D}] = [\mathbf{A},\mathbf{B},\mathbf{C}'] + [\mathbf{A},\mathbf{B},\mathbf{D}]$$
$$= [\mathbf{A},\mathbf{B},\mathbf{C}'] + [\mathbf{A}, \mathbf{B}, s\mathbf{A} + t\mathbf{B}]$$
$$= [\mathbf{A},\mathbf{B},\mathbf{C}'] + s[\mathbf{A},\mathbf{B},\mathbf{A}] + t[\mathbf{A},\mathbf{B},\mathbf{B}] = [\mathbf{A},\mathbf{B},\mathbf{C}']$$

In this manner *we have obtained a new parallelepiped with the same volume as before, with one edge along a coordinate axis*, and $[\mathbf{A},\mathbf{B},\mathbf{C}'] = [\mathbf{A},\mathbf{B},\mathbf{C}]$.

Now consider this new parallelepiped, taking the side determined by $\mathbf{A}$ and $\mathbf{C}'$ as base. Repeating the above argument, we obtain a new parallelepiped with edges $\mathbf{A}$, $\mathbf{B}'$, and $\mathbf{C}'$, having the same volume, where $\mathbf{B}'$ is along a coordinate axis, and with $[\mathbf{A},\mathbf{B}',\mathbf{C}'] = [\mathbf{A},\mathbf{B},\mathbf{C}'] = [\mathbf{A},\mathbf{B},\mathbf{C}]$. Repeating the argument yet a third time, we obtain a parallelepiped with *all three edges* $\mathbf{A}'$, $\mathbf{B}'$, and $\mathbf{C}'$ along coordinate axes, having the same volume, and with $[\mathbf{A}',\mathbf{B}',\mathbf{C}'] = [\mathbf{A},\mathbf{B},\mathbf{C}]$.

It remains now to show that the volume of the original parallelepiped is $[\mathbf{A},\mathbf{B},\mathbf{C}]$, or perhaps $-[\mathbf{A},\mathbf{B},\mathbf{C}]$. According to the remarks made above, it suffices to show that the volume of a parallelepiped with edges $\mathbf{A}'$, $\mathbf{B}'$, and $\mathbf{C}'$ along coordinate axes is $[\mathbf{A}',\mathbf{B}',\mathbf{C}']$. But this is almost trivial: for example, if $\mathbf{A}' = a\mathbf{i}$, $\mathbf{B}' = b\mathbf{j}$, and $\mathbf{C}' = c\mathbf{k}$, then $[\mathbf{A}',\mathbf{B}',\mathbf{C}'] = abc$, and since the parallelepiped in this case is rectangular with edges $|a|$, $|b|$, and $|c|$, its volume is either abc or $-abc$. This completes the proof of the assertions made earlier.

The above proof may be summarized as follows. We replaced the original vectors $\mathbf{A}$, $\mathbf{B}$, and $\mathbf{C}$ by new vectors $\mathbf{A}'$, $\mathbf{B}'$, and $\mathbf{C}'$. The new vectors were so constructed that they determined a rectangular parallelepiped with the same volume as that of the parallelepiped determined by $\mathbf{A}$, $\mathbf{B}$, and $\mathbf{C}$. Moreover, $[\mathbf{A}',\mathbf{B}',\mathbf{C}'] = [\mathbf{A},\mathbf{B},\mathbf{C}]$. The proof was completed by showing that this volume is equal to $\pm[\mathbf{A}',\mathbf{B}',\mathbf{C}']$, and hence equals $\pm[\mathbf{A},\mathbf{B},\mathbf{C}]$.

EXERCISES

1.   Find the triple scalar product $[\mathbf{A},\mathbf{B},\mathbf{C}]$ given that
   (a) $\mathbf{A} = 2\mathbf{i}$, $\mathbf{B} = 3\mathbf{j}$, $\mathbf{C} = 5\mathbf{k}$
   (b) $\mathbf{A} = \mathbf{i} + \mathbf{j} + \mathbf{k}$, $\mathbf{B} = 3\mathbf{i} + \mathbf{j}$, $\mathbf{C} = 5\mathbf{k} - \mathbf{j}$
   (c) $\mathbf{A} = 2\mathbf{i} - \mathbf{j} + \mathbf{k}$, $\mathbf{B} = \mathbf{i} + \mathbf{j} + \mathbf{k}$, $\mathbf{C} = 2\mathbf{i} + 3\mathbf{k}$
   (d) $\mathbf{A} = \mathbf{k}$, $\mathbf{B} = \mathbf{i}$, $\mathbf{C} = \mathbf{j}$

2.   Find the volume of the parallelepiped whose coterminal edges are arrows representing the vectors $3\mathbf{i} + 4\mathbf{j}$, $2\mathbf{i} + 3\mathbf{j} + 4\mathbf{k}$, $5\mathbf{k}$.

3. Find the volume of the parallelepiped with coterminal edges AB, AC, and AD, where $A = (3,2,1)$, $B = (4,2,1)$, $C = (0,1,4)$, and $D = (0,0,7)$.

4. Find the volume of the tetrahedron with coterminal edges representing the vectors $\mathbf{i} + \mathbf{j}$, $\mathbf{i} - \mathbf{j}$, $2\mathbf{k}$. Illustrate with a sketch. [Note: The volume of the tetrahedron is one sixth the volume of the parallelepiped having the same coterminal edges.]

5. Find the area of the parallelogram in the plane with vertices at $(0,0)$, $(1,1)$, $(3,4)$, $(4,5)$. [Hint: Convert this to a three-dimensional problem, finding the volume of the parallelepiped with this parallelogram as base, taking the third edge to be of unit length along the z axis.]

6. Find the equation of the plane passing through the origin parallel to the vectors $\mathbf{A} = 3\mathbf{i} + \mathbf{j} - 2\mathbf{k}$ and $\mathbf{B} = \mathbf{i} - \mathbf{j} + 5\mathbf{k}$. [Hint: The point (x,y,z) is in this plane if and only if $[\mathbf{R},\mathbf{A},\mathbf{B}] = 0$, where $\mathbf{R} = x\mathbf{i} + y\mathbf{j} + z\mathbf{k}$.]

7. Find the equation of the plane passing through $(3,4,-1)$ parallel to the vectors $\mathbf{A} = 2\mathbf{i} + \mathbf{j} + \mathbf{k}$ and $\mathbf{B} = \mathbf{i} - 3\mathbf{k}$. (Hint: Let $\mathbf{R}_0 = 3\mathbf{i} + 4\mathbf{j} - \mathbf{k}$. Consider $[\mathbf{R} - \mathbf{R}_0,\mathbf{A},\mathbf{B}]$.)

1.12 : Orientation

In working in the xy plane, it is conventional to take the positive x direction to the right and the positive y direction upwards. Angles are then taken to be *positive* in the *counterclockwise* direction.

When working with planes in space, there is no generally accepted convention for determining the positive sense for angles. The choice is quite arbitrary. Given any plane in space, we may arbitrarily decree in which direction we shall consider angles to be positive. The plane is then said to be oriented.

One way of orienting a plane is as follows. Let $\mathbf{A}$ and $\mathbf{B}$ be nonzero vectors, not parallel, represented by arrows in the given plane. Let these arrows extend from the same point. Let $\mathbf{A}$ be rotated through the smallest angle possible to coincide in direction with $\mathbf{B}$. The sense of this rotation is then said to be "positive" and the plane is thereby oriented. *The plane is oriented by giving the vectors $\mathbf{A},\mathbf{B}$ in that order.*

For example, the usual orientation of the xy plane is obtained by giving the vectors **i,j** in that order.   By a 90° rotation the direction of **i** can be made to coincide with that of **j**, and this rotation has the conventional "positive" sense.   We obtain the same orientation by giving the vectors **i** + **j** and **j** in that order (Fig. 17).   On the other hand, if we specified the orientation by giving **j,i** in that order, we would obtain the opposite orientation, whereby angles would be measured positive in the clockwise sense (which is not conventional but is perfectly satisfactory nevertheless).

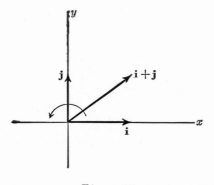

Figure 17

Another way of orienting a plane is as follows.   Let there be given a single vector that is not parallel to the plane.   Let this vector be represented by an arrow that has its initial point in the plane. Then the terminal point of the arrow will be on one side of the plane, which we call (arbitrarily) the *positive* side.   We now take the positive sense for angles in the plane to be such that a right-handed screw with head parallel to the plane and shank perpendicular to the plane would advance in the direction of the positive side of the plane if rotated in the positive sense.   (This is independent of the way in which the screw points.)   Alternatively, if we imagine the right hand grasping the given vector, with thumb pointing in the direction of the arrowhead, the fingers will curl around the shank of the arrow in the positive sense of rotation in the plane.

In Figure 18 both methods of orienting a plane are illustrated for planes perpendicular to the y axis.   At the left, the plane is oriented by prescribing two vectors in the plane, **A** and **B**, in that order.   On the right, the same orientation is achieved by prescribing a vector **C** extending from a point in the plane.

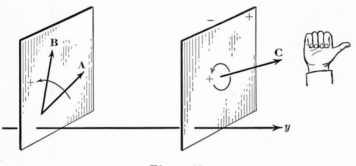

Figure 18

Now let us return to the discussion of the triple scalar product. Let **A**, **B**, and **C** be nonzero vectors, not all parallel to the same plane, represented by arrows with initial points at the origin (Fig. 18). The vectors **A** and **B** determine a plane passing through the origin. If the orientation of this plane, as determined by **A**,**B** in that order, is identical with its orientation as determined by **C**, we say that **A**, **B**, and **C** in that order form a *right-handed system*.   One reason for this terminology is that if the thumb and first two fingers of the right hand are held so they are mutually perpendicular, the thumb, forefinger, and second finger form such a system.   Another reason is that if **A**, **B**, and **C**, in that order, form a *right-handed* system, the rotation of **A** into **B** (through an angle less than 180°) will advance a right-handed screw in the general direction of **C**.   The vectors **A**, **B**, and **C** of Figure 19 form a right-handed system, as do also the vectors **i**, **j**, and **k**.

We shall now outline a proof that *the triple scalar product* [**A**,**B**,**C**] *of three vectors is positive if and only if the three vectors, in that order, form a right-handed system*.   The reader can easily convince himself that the directions of **A**, **B**, and **C** can be continuously modified so as to become aligned with the directions of **i**, **j**, and **k** respectively, without ever becoming coplanar in the process if they form a right-handed system.   (If **A**, **B**, and **C** do not form a right-handed system, this is impossible.)   During this process, the triple scalar product [**A,B,C**] will vary continuously, and since the three vectors

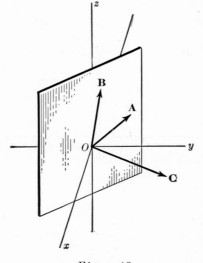

Figure 19

are never coplanar, [**A,B,C**] will not ever be zero.   In the final position [**A,B,C**] is positive.   It follows that [**A,B,C**] must have been positive to begin with, since a continuous function can change from negative to positive values only by passing through zero.   On the other hand, if **A**, **B**, and **C** are not right-handed to begin with, then **B,A,C** in that order will be a right-handed system, whence by the above argument [**B,A,C**] is positive and hence [**A,B,C**] is negative.

EXERCISE

Sketch the vectors **A** = **i** + **j**, **B** = **i** + 2**j** + 2**k**, and **C** = **i** + 3**k**.   Determine whether or not **A**, **B**, and **C** in that order form a right-handed system.   Check by determining the sign of [**A,B,C**].

1.13 : Vector Products

The *vector product* $\mathbf{A} \times \mathbf{B}$ of two vectors is defined by the equation

(1) $\quad \mathbf{A} \times \mathbf{B} = (A_y B_z - A_z B_y)\mathbf{i} + (A_z B_x - A_x B_z)\mathbf{j} + (A_x B_y - A_y B_x)\mathbf{k}$

Sometimes $\mathbf{A} \times \mathbf{B}$ is called the *cross product,* to distinguish it from $\mathbf{A} \cdot \mathbf{B}$ which is then called the *dot product.*

This definition may be conveniently memorized in determinant form:

(1') $\qquad\qquad\qquad \mathbf{A} \times \mathbf{B} = \begin{vmatrix} \mathbf{i} & \mathbf{j} & \mathbf{k} \\ A_x & A_y & A_z \\ B_x & B_y & B_z \end{vmatrix}$

This symbolic determinant is interpreted to be the vector whose x, y, and z components are the cofactors, respectively, of the first, second, and third entries in the first row.

The geometrical interpretation of the vector product will be considered shortly, but first we emphasize that $\mathbf{A} \times \mathbf{B}$ is a *vector,* not a scalar, and that $\mathbf{A} \times \mathbf{B}$ is *not* the same as $\mathbf{B} \times \mathbf{A}$. Thus the vector product differs considerably from the scalar product $\mathbf{A} \cdot \mathbf{B}$, which is a scalar and is independent of the order of its factors.

EXAMPLE 1: Find the vector product $\mathbf{A} \times \mathbf{B}$ if $\mathbf{A} = 3\mathbf{i} + 4\mathbf{j}$ and $\mathbf{B} = \mathbf{i} + 5\mathbf{k} - 2\mathbf{j}$.

Solution:

$$\mathbf{A} \times \mathbf{B} = \begin{vmatrix} \mathbf{i} & \mathbf{j} & \mathbf{k} \\ 3 & 4 & 0 \\ 1 & -2 & 5 \end{vmatrix} = 20\mathbf{i} - 15\mathbf{j} - 10\mathbf{k}$$

EXAMPLE 2: Find $\mathbf{k} \times \mathbf{i}$.

Solution:

$$\mathbf{k} \times \mathbf{i} = \begin{vmatrix} \mathbf{i} & \mathbf{j} & \mathbf{k} \\ 0 & 0 & 1 \\ 1 & 0 & 0 \end{vmatrix} = \mathbf{j}$$

The following properties of the vector product are readily verified directly from the definition (1).

(2) $$\mathbf{A} \times \mathbf{B} = -(\mathbf{B} \times \mathbf{A})$$

(3) $$(\mathbf{A} + \mathbf{B}) \times \mathbf{C} = (\mathbf{A} \times \mathbf{C}) + (\mathbf{B} \times \mathbf{C})$$

(4) $$\mathbf{A} \times (\mathbf{B} + \mathbf{C}) = (\mathbf{A} \times \mathbf{B}) + (\mathbf{A} \times \mathbf{C})$$

(5) $$\mathbf{A} \times (s\mathbf{B}) = s(\mathbf{A} \times \mathbf{B})$$

(6) $$(s\mathbf{A}) \times \mathbf{B} = s(\mathbf{A} \times \mathbf{B})$$

(7) $$(\mathbf{A} \times \mathbf{B}) \cdot \mathbf{C} = [\mathbf{A},\mathbf{B},\mathbf{C}]$$

Properties (2), (5), and (6) are valid for any two vectors $\mathbf{A}$ and $\mathbf{B}$ and any scalar s. Properties (3), (4), and (7) are valid for any three vectors $\mathbf{A}$, $\mathbf{B}$, and $\mathbf{C}$.

If either $\mathbf{A}$ or $\mathbf{B}$ is the zero vector, then $\mathbf{A} \times \mathbf{B}$ is the zero vector. The vector product of any vector with itself is the zero vector, since if $\mathbf{A} = \mathbf{B}$, (2) becomes $\mathbf{A} \times \mathbf{A} = -(\mathbf{A} \times \mathbf{A})$, and the only vector equal to its own negative is the zero vector. More generally, if $\mathbf{A} = a\mathbf{U}$ and $\mathbf{B} = b\mathbf{U}$, we have $\mathbf{A} \times \mathbf{B} = (a\mathbf{U}) \times (b\mathbf{U}) = ab(\mathbf{U} \times \mathbf{U}) = \mathbf{0}$, showing that *if two vectors are parallel, their vector product is the zero vector.* The reader need not memorize these facts; they will be easy to remember from the geometrical interpretation of the vector product, given below.

Property (7) shows that the triple scalar product $[\mathbf{A},\mathbf{B},\mathbf{C}]$ is closely related to both the scalar product and the vector product. [In many textbooks the triple scalar product $[\mathbf{A},\mathbf{B},\mathbf{C}]$ is *defined* to be $(\mathbf{A} \times \mathbf{B}) \cdot \mathbf{C}$.] To verify (7) we simply write out the scalar product of $\mathbf{A} \times \mathbf{B}$ with $\mathbf{C}$, obtaining

$$(\mathbf{A} \times \mathbf{B}) \cdot \mathbf{C} = (A_y B_z - A_z B_y)C_x + (A_z B_x - A_x B_z)C_y + (A_x B_y - A_y B_x)C_z$$

which is equal to the determinant

$$[\mathbf{A},\mathbf{B},\mathbf{C}] = \begin{vmatrix} A_x & A_y & A_z \\ B_x & B_y & B_z \\ C_x & C_y & C_z \end{vmatrix}$$

The position of the dot and the cross can be changed at will,

(8) $$(\mathbf{A} \times \mathbf{B}) \cdot \mathbf{C} = \mathbf{A} \cdot (\mathbf{B} \times \mathbf{C})$$

since

$$(\mathbf{A} \times \mathbf{B}) \cdot \mathbf{C} = [\mathbf{A},\mathbf{B},\mathbf{C}] = [\mathbf{B},\mathbf{C},\mathbf{A}] = (\mathbf{B} \times \mathbf{C}) \cdot \mathbf{A} = \mathbf{A} \cdot (\mathbf{B} \times \mathbf{C})$$

The geometrical interpretation of the vector product is indicated in Figure 20. Let $\mathbf{A}$ and $\mathbf{B}$ be nonzero vectors that are not parallel. Let $\mathbf{n}$ denote the unit vector perpendicular to both $\mathbf{A}$ and $\mathbf{B}$, with sense of direction such that **A**, **B**, and **n**, in that order, form a right-handed system.   In other words, **n** points in the direction in which a right-handed screw would advance under a rotation through angle

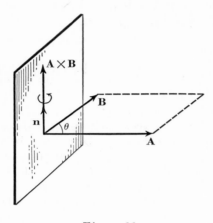

Figure 20

θ carrying **A** into **B**, where θ is a positive angle less than 180°.   Then **A** × **B** is the vector pointing in the same direction as **n**, with *magnitude* equal to the area of the parallelogram determined by **A** and **B**.

Since the area of this parallelogram is $|\mathbf{A}|\,|\mathbf{B}|\sin\theta$, we can summarize this by writing

(9) $$\mathbf{A}\times\mathbf{B} = |\mathbf{A}|\,|\mathbf{B}|\sin\theta\,\mathbf{n}$$

Equation (9) provides an alternative definition of the vector product that is entirely equivalent to the algebraic definition given by (1).   In computing **A** × **B** it is usually easier to use (1), but in geometrical and physical problems it is important to understand (9).

We now proceed to the *proof* that (9) is equivalent to (1).   We note first that [**A**,**B**,**n**] is positive, since **n** was chosen so that **A**, **B**, and **n**, in that order, form a right-handed system.   Moreover, [**A**,**B**,**n**] is numerically equal to the volume of the parallelepiped determined by **A**, **B**, and **n**.   Since **n** is of unit length and is perpendicular to both **A** and **B**, this volume is numerically equal to the area of the parallelogram determined by **A** and **B**.   Since [**A**,**B**,**n**] = (**A** × **B**)·**n**, this shows that (**A** × **B**)·**n** = $|\mathbf{A}|\,|\mathbf{B}|\sin\theta$.

The following reasoning shows that $\mathbf{A} \times \mathbf{B}$ has the same direction as $\mathbf{n}$. Among all unit vectors $\mathbf{n}$, the one chosen above is obviously the one that makes the volume $[\mathbf{A},\mathbf{B},\mathbf{n}]$ of the parallelepiped a maximum. Therefore, since $[\mathbf{A},\mathbf{B},\mathbf{n}] = (\mathbf{A} \times \mathbf{B}) \cdot \mathbf{n}$, the maximum principle (Section 1.9, Example 5, taking $\mathbf{D} = \mathbf{A} \times \mathbf{B}$) shows that $\mathbf{n}$ points in the same direction as $\mathbf{A} \times \mathbf{B}$.

Since $\mathbf{A} \times \mathbf{B}$ and $\mathbf{n}$ have the same direction, $(\mathbf{A} \times \mathbf{B}) \cdot \mathbf{n} = |\mathbf{A} \times \mathbf{B}|$. Hence

$$|\mathbf{A} \times \mathbf{B}| = (\mathbf{A} \times \mathbf{B}) \cdot \mathbf{n} = |\mathbf{A}|\,|\mathbf{B}|\,\sin\theta$$

and this completes the proof.

EXAMPLE 3: Find two unit vectors perpendicular to both $\mathbf{A} = 2\mathbf{i} + 2\mathbf{j} - 3\mathbf{k}$ and $\mathbf{B} = \mathbf{i} + 3\mathbf{j} + \mathbf{k}$.

Solution: We have seen that $\mathbf{A} \times \mathbf{B}$ is perpendicular to both $\mathbf{A}$ and $\mathbf{B}$. We have

$$\mathbf{A} \times \mathbf{B} = \begin{vmatrix} \mathbf{i} & \mathbf{j} & \mathbf{k} \\ 2 & 2 & -3 \\ 1 & 3 & 1 \end{vmatrix} = 11\mathbf{i} - 5\mathbf{j} + 4\mathbf{k}$$

The length of this vector is $9\sqrt{2}$. The desired *unit* vector is therefore

$$\mathbf{n} = \frac{11}{9\sqrt{2}}\mathbf{i} - \frac{5}{9\sqrt{2}}\mathbf{j} + \frac{4}{9\sqrt{2}}\mathbf{k}$$

If we had taken $\mathbf{B} \times \mathbf{A}$ instead we would have obtained the negative of this vector. The two answers are

$$\pm\left(\frac{11\sqrt{2}}{18}\mathbf{i} - \frac{5\sqrt{2}}{18}\mathbf{j} + \frac{2\sqrt{2}}{9}\mathbf{k}\right)$$

EXAMPLE 4: Find the area of the parallelogram determined by $\mathbf{A} = \mathbf{i} + \mathbf{j} - 3\mathbf{k}$ and $\mathbf{B} = 5\mathbf{k} - 6\mathbf{j}$.

Solution:

$$\mathbf{A} \times \mathbf{B} = \begin{vmatrix} \mathbf{i} & \mathbf{j} & \mathbf{k} \\ 1 & 1 & -3 \\ 0 & -6 & 5 \end{vmatrix} = -13\mathbf{i} - 5\mathbf{j} - 6\mathbf{k}$$

$$|\mathbf{A} \times \mathbf{B}| = \sqrt{13^2 + 5^2 + 6^2} = \sqrt{230}$$

which is the desired area.

EXAMPLE 5: Find the equations of the line passing through $(3,2,-4)$ parallel to the line of intersection of the two planes $x + 3y - 2z = 8$, $x - 3y + z = 0$.

Solution: Let $\mathbf{A} = \mathbf{i} + 3\mathbf{j} - 2\mathbf{k}$ and $\mathbf{B} = \mathbf{i} - 3\mathbf{j} + \mathbf{k}$. Since $\mathbf{A}$ is perpendicular to the first plane and $\mathbf{B}$ is perpendicular to the second, and $\mathbf{A} \times \mathbf{B}$ is perpendicular to both $\mathbf{A}$ and $\mathbf{B}$, it follows that $\mathbf{A} \times \mathbf{B}$ is parallel to both planes. Hence $\mathbf{A} \times \mathbf{B}$ is parallel to the line of intersection. We have

$$\mathbf{A} \times \mathbf{B} = \begin{vmatrix} \mathbf{i} & \mathbf{j} & \mathbf{k} \\ 1 & 3 & -2 \\ 1 & -3 & 1 \end{vmatrix} = -3\mathbf{i} - 3\mathbf{j} - 6\mathbf{k}$$

Equations of the desired line are

$$\frac{x-3}{-3} = \frac{y-2}{-3} = \frac{z+4}{-6}$$

or, equivalently,

$$x - 3 = y - 2 = \frac{z+4}{2}$$

EXERCISES

1. Find $\mathbf{A} \times \mathbf{B}$ where
   (a) $\mathbf{A} = 3\mathbf{i} - \mathbf{j} + 2\mathbf{k}$, $\mathbf{B} = \mathbf{i} + \mathbf{j} - 4\mathbf{k}$
   (b) $\mathbf{A} = 2\mathbf{i} + \mathbf{j} + 7\mathbf{k}$, $\mathbf{B} = 3\mathbf{i} + \mathbf{j} - \mathbf{k}$
   (c) $\mathbf{A} = \mathbf{j} + 6\mathbf{k}$, $\mathbf{B} = \mathbf{k} + 2\mathbf{j} - \mathbf{i}$
   (d) $\mathbf{A} = \mathbf{i}$, $\mathbf{B} = \mathbf{j}$
   (e) $\mathbf{B} \times \mathbf{A}$ is known to be $\mathbf{i} - \mathbf{j}$

2. Find the area of the parallelogram determined by $3\mathbf{i} + 4\mathbf{j}$ and $\mathbf{i} + \mathbf{j} + \mathbf{k}$.

3. Find the area of the triangle with vertices $(1,1,2)$, $(2,3,5)$, and $(1,5,5)$.

4. Find $\mathbf{A} \times \mathbf{B}$ if $\mathbf{A} = \mathbf{i} - \mathbf{j} + \mathbf{k}$ and $\mathbf{B} = 3\mathbf{i} - 3\mathbf{j} + 3\mathbf{k}$. What is the geometrical significance of this answer?

5. Find a unit vector perpendicular to both $3\mathbf{i} + \mathbf{j}$ and $2\mathbf{i} - \mathbf{j} - 5\mathbf{k}$.

6. By vector methods, find the equations of the line through $(2,3,7)$ parallel to the line of intersection of the planes $2x + y + z = 0$, $x - y + 7z = 0$.

7. Find equations of a line perpendicular to the lines $x = y = z$, $x = 2y = 3z$, passing through the origin.

8. Compute $(\mathbf{A} \times \mathbf{B}) \times \mathbf{C}$ and also $\mathbf{A} \times (\mathbf{B} \times \mathbf{C})$, given that $\mathbf{A} = 2\mathbf{i} + 2\mathbf{j}$, $\mathbf{B} = 3\mathbf{i} - \mathbf{j} + \mathbf{k}$, and $\mathbf{C} = 8\mathbf{i}$.

9. By vector methods, determine the equation of the plane determined by the points $(2,0,1)$, $(1,1,3)$, and $(4,7,-2)$.

10. Find a unit vector in the plane of the vectors $\mathbf{A} = \mathbf{i} + 2\mathbf{j}$ and $\mathbf{B} = \mathbf{j} + 2\mathbf{k}$, perpendicular to the vector $\mathbf{C} = 2\mathbf{i} + \mathbf{j} + 2\mathbf{k}$.

11. By taking the vector cross product of
$$(\cos \theta)\mathbf{i} + (\sin \theta)\mathbf{j}$$
$$(\cos \psi)\mathbf{i} + (\sin \psi)\mathbf{j}$$
and interpreting geometrically, derive a well-known trigonometric identity.

12. If $\mathbf{A}$, $\mathbf{B}$, and $\mathbf{C}$ are vectors from the origin to points A, B, and C respectively, show that $(\mathbf{A} \times \mathbf{B}) + (\mathbf{B} \times \mathbf{C}) + (\mathbf{C} \times \mathbf{A})$ is perpendicular to the plane ABC. [Hint: Consider $(\mathbf{B} - \mathbf{A}) \times (\mathbf{C} - \mathbf{A})$.]

13. Find the altitude of a parallelepiped determined by $\mathbf{A}$, $\mathbf{B}$, and $\mathbf{C}$, if the base is taken to be the parallelogram determined by $\mathbf{A}$ and $\mathbf{B}$, and if
$$\mathbf{A} = \mathbf{i} + \mathbf{j} + \mathbf{k}$$
$$\mathbf{B} = 2\mathbf{i} + 4\mathbf{j} - \mathbf{k}$$
$$\mathbf{C} = \mathbf{i} + \mathbf{j} + 3\mathbf{k}$$
Hint: Think of the geometrical interpretation of
$$[\mathbf{A},\mathbf{B},\mathbf{C}]/|\mathbf{A} \times \mathbf{B}|$$

1.14 : Physical Applications

Our purpose here is merely to *suggest* the importance of vector methods in physics and engineering. We note that angles are always measured in radians, and angular velocity in radians per unit time; in general, however, we shall ignore units.

The work W done by a constant force $\mathbf{F}$ acting through a displacement $\mathbf{D}$ is

(1) $$W = \mathbf{F} \cdot \mathbf{D}$$

In other words, the work done is the product of the magnitude of the displacement by the scalar component of the force in the direction of the displacement.

EXAMPLE 1:   A force $\mathbf{F} = 3\mathbf{i} + \mathbf{j} + 6\mathbf{k}$ acts through a displacement $\mathbf{D} = 2\mathbf{i} + \mathbf{j} - \mathbf{k}$.   Find the work done.
Solution: $W = \mathbf{F} \cdot \mathbf{D} = 6 + 1 - 6 = 1$ unit of work.

Consider a rigid body rotating about an axis with angular velocity ω.   The angular velocity is represented by a vector $\boldsymbol{\omega}$ of magnitude ω extending along the axis of rotation with sense deter-

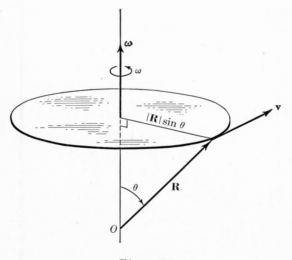

Figure 21

mined by the right-hand rule: if the fingers of the right hand are wrapped about the axis in the direction of rotation, the thumb points in the direction of $\boldsymbol{\omega}$ (Fig. 21).

Let us assume that the origin O is on the axis of rotation and let

R denote the position vector of a particle in the body. Then the velocity **v** of the particle is given by

(2) $\mathbf{v} = \boldsymbol{\omega} \times \mathbf{R}$

To see this, we first note that $|\mathbf{R}| \sin \theta$ is the distance of the particle from the axis of rotation, so **v** has magnitude $\omega |\mathbf{R}| \sin \theta$. Moreover, the velocity **v** is necessarily perpendicular to both **R** and $\boldsymbol{\omega}$, and the sense of $\boldsymbol{\omega}$ is such that **v** equals $\boldsymbol{\omega} \times \mathbf{R}$ rather than $\mathbf{R} \times \boldsymbol{\omega}$, as we see from Figure 21. We omit further details, but we note that (2) is valid even when the axis of rotation is changing in direction (for example, think of a spinning top), provided the axis always passes through the origin.

EXAMPLE 2: A rigid body rotates with constant angular velocity ω about the line $x = y/2 = z/2$. Find the speed of a particle at the instant it passes through the point (2,3,5).

Solution: The vector $\mathbf{i} + 2\mathbf{j} + 2\mathbf{k}$ is parallel to the axis. A unit vector parallel to the axis is $\frac{1}{3}\mathbf{i} + \frac{2}{3}\mathbf{j} + \frac{2}{3}\mathbf{k}$. Therefore

$$\boldsymbol{\omega} = \pm\omega\left(\frac{1}{3}\mathbf{i} + \frac{2}{3}\mathbf{j} + \frac{2}{3}\mathbf{k}\right)$$

(The statement of the problem leaves the sign ambiguous.) The velocity is

$$\mathbf{v} = \boldsymbol{\omega} \times \mathbf{R} = \pm\omega\begin{vmatrix} \mathbf{i} & \mathbf{j} & \mathbf{k} \\ \frac{1}{3} & \frac{2}{3} & \frac{2}{3} \\ 2 & 3 & 5 \end{vmatrix} = \pm\omega\left(\frac{4}{3}\mathbf{i} - \frac{1}{3}\mathbf{j} - \frac{1}{3}\mathbf{k}\right)$$

The speed is

$$|\mathbf{v}| = \omega\left(\frac{16}{9} + \frac{1}{9} + \frac{1}{9}\right)^{\frac{1}{2}} = \frac{\sqrt{18}}{3}\,\omega$$

As an application of the triple scalar product, we consider the moment of a force about an axis. Let us assume the axis to pass through the origin, and let **u** denote either of the two unit vectors directed along this axis. Let **R** denote the position vector of the point of application of a force **F**. The *scalar moment* of **F** about the axis is defined to be

$$M_{\text{axis}} = [\mathbf{R},\mathbf{F},\mathbf{u}]$$

Since $[\mathbf{R},\mathbf{F},\mathbf{u}] = (\mathbf{R} \times \mathbf{F}) \cdot \mathbf{u}$, $|M_{\text{axis}}|$ is the length of the projection of $\mathbf{R} \times \mathbf{F}$ on the given axis. The vector

$$\mathbf{M} = \mathbf{R} \times \mathbf{F}$$

is called the *vector moment* of **F** about the origin.   The vector moment of **F** about the origin depends on the point of application of **F** as well as on the vector **F** itself.   The sign of the scalar moment depends on the choice of unit vector **u**.

  EXAMPLE 3:   An important special case is obtained if **F** and **R** are both parallel to the xy plane and **u** is along the z axis (Fig. 22).

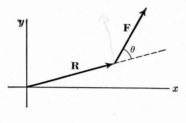

Figure 22

  In the figure, the z axis is not shown; it is directed out of the page towards the reader.   The scalar moment of **F** about the z axis is $M_z = [\mathbf{R},\mathbf{F},\mathbf{k}]$.   Since $\mathbf{R} \times \mathbf{F}$ is parallel to the z axis, we have $M_z = |\mathbf{R}|\,|\mathbf{F}|\sin\theta$, where θ is the angle between **R** and **F**, measured positive in the counterclockwise direction.   In other words, the scalar moment M_z is the product of the distance $|\mathbf{R}|$ between the point of application and the axis, and the component of **F** perpendicular to **R**; it provides a measure of the tendency of **F** to produce rotation about the z axis.

EXERCISES

1. Find the work done by a force $\mathbf{F} = 3\mathbf{i} - 2\mathbf{j} + 10\mathbf{k}$ in moving an object through a displacement $\mathbf{D} = 4\mathbf{i} + 6\mathbf{j} + \mathbf{k}$.

2. If **ω** points in the direction of $\mathbf{i} + \mathbf{j} + \mathbf{k}$ and the body rotates about an axis through the origin with angular velocity $10\sqrt{3}$ radians/sec, find the locus of points having speed 20 ft/sec. What does this locus represent?

3. A force of magnitude F lb is applied in the positive x direction at a point (x_0, y_0, z_0).

   (a) Find the scalar moment of this force about the axis $x = y = z$, taking $\mathbf{u}$ to be a positive scalar multiple of $\mathbf{i} + \mathbf{j} + \mathbf{k}$.

   (b) Show this to be a positive moment if and only if $z_0 > y_0$, by using your answer to (a) and also by drawing a diagram.

1.15 : Vector Identities

Of the following identities, the first two are the most important.

(1) $$\mathbf{A} \times (\mathbf{B} \times \mathbf{C}) = (\mathbf{A} \cdot \mathbf{C})\mathbf{B} - (\mathbf{A} \cdot \mathbf{B})\mathbf{C}$$

(2) $$(\mathbf{A} \times \mathbf{B}) \times \mathbf{C} = (\mathbf{A} \cdot \mathbf{C})\mathbf{B} - (\mathbf{B} \cdot \mathbf{C})\mathbf{A}$$

(3) $$(\mathbf{A} \times \mathbf{B}) \times (\mathbf{C} \times \mathbf{D}) = [\mathbf{A},\mathbf{C},\mathbf{D}]\mathbf{B} - [\mathbf{B},\mathbf{C},\mathbf{D}]\mathbf{A}$$

(4) $$(\mathbf{A} \times \mathbf{B}) \cdot (\mathbf{C} \times \mathbf{D}) = (\mathbf{A} \cdot \mathbf{C})(\mathbf{B} \cdot \mathbf{D}) - (\mathbf{A} \cdot \mathbf{D})(\mathbf{B} \cdot \mathbf{C})$$

If $\mathbf{V} = \mathbf{A} \times (\mathbf{B} \times \mathbf{C})$ is not the zero vector, then it must be perpendicular to $\mathbf{B} \times \mathbf{C}$. Since $\mathbf{B} \times \mathbf{C}$ is itself perpendicular to both $\mathbf{B}$ and $\mathbf{C}$, it follows that $\mathbf{V}$ must be in the plane of $\mathbf{B}$ and $\mathbf{C}$, and since they are nonzero vectors that are not parallel (otherwise $\mathbf{V}$ would be the zero vector), $\mathbf{V}$ must be a linear combination of $\mathbf{B}$ and $\mathbf{C}$. Thus $\mathbf{V} = m\mathbf{B} + n\mathbf{C}$ for suitable scalars m and n. The fact that $m = \mathbf{A} \cdot \mathbf{C}$ and $n = -\mathbf{A} \cdot \mathbf{B}$ is not obvious, of course; we omit the proof. Similarly, one can see that $(\mathbf{A} \times \mathbf{B}) \times \mathbf{C}$ must be a linear combination of $\mathbf{A}$ and $\mathbf{B}$, but it is not obvious what the scalar coefficients will be.

To memorize these formulas, it is convenient to remember the "rule of the middle factor," which states that in each case the middle factor precedes the minus sign,

$$(\mathbf{A} \times \mathbf{B}) \times \mathbf{C} = (\quad)\mathbf{B} - (\quad)\mathbf{A}$$
$$\mathbf{A} \times (\mathbf{B} \times \mathbf{C}) = (\quad)\mathbf{B} - (\quad)\mathbf{C}$$

and the blanks are then filled by the scalar products of the other two vectors, so that each term is linear in $\mathbf{A}$, $\mathbf{B}$, and $\mathbf{C}$ separately.

To derive (3), let $\mathbf{U} = \mathbf{C} \times \mathbf{D}$, whence

$$(\mathbf{A} \times \mathbf{B}) \times \mathbf{U} = (\mathbf{A} \cdot \mathbf{U})\mathbf{B} - (\mathbf{B} \cdot \mathbf{U})\mathbf{A} = [\mathbf{A},\mathbf{C},\mathbf{D}]\mathbf{B} - [\mathbf{B},\mathbf{C},\mathbf{D}]\mathbf{A}$$

To derive (4),

$$(\mathbf{A} \times \mathbf{B}) \cdot \mathbf{U} = [\mathbf{A},\mathbf{B},\mathbf{U}] = \mathbf{A} \cdot (\mathbf{B} \times \mathbf{U}) = \mathbf{A} \cdot [\mathbf{B} \times (\mathbf{C} \times \mathbf{D})]$$
$$= \mathbf{A} \cdot [(\mathbf{B} \cdot \mathbf{D})\mathbf{C} - (\mathbf{B} \cdot \mathbf{C})\mathbf{D}]$$
$$= (\mathbf{B} \cdot \mathbf{D})(\mathbf{A} \cdot \mathbf{C}) - (\mathbf{B} \cdot \mathbf{C})(\mathbf{A} \cdot \mathbf{D})$$

EXERCISES

1. Derive the identity
$$(\mathbf{A} \times \mathbf{B}) \times (\mathbf{C} \times \mathbf{D}) = [\mathbf{A},\mathbf{B},\mathbf{D}]\mathbf{C} - [\mathbf{A},\mathbf{B},\mathbf{C}]\mathbf{D}$$

2. Derive the identity
$$(\mathbf{A} \times \mathbf{B}) \cdot (\mathbf{B} \times \mathbf{C}) \times (\mathbf{C} \times \mathbf{A}) = [\mathbf{A},\mathbf{B},\mathbf{C}]^2$$

3. Verify the identity
$$\mathbf{A} \times (\mathbf{B} \times \mathbf{C}) + \mathbf{B} \times (\mathbf{C} \times \mathbf{A}) + \mathbf{C} \times (\mathbf{A} \times \mathbf{B}) = 0$$

1.16 : Spherical Trigonometry

As an interesting exercise, we shall now derive the basic formulas of spherical trigonometry by vector methods.   It is not our intention, however, to discuss in any detail the practical applications of these formulas.

A spherical triangle is a three-sided figure drawn on the surface of a sphere.   The sides of a spherical triangle are required to be arcs of great circles.

We recall that a great circle is a circle obtained by intersecting the sphere with a plane *passing through its center*.   Two great circles always intersect in two distinct points; their angle of intersection is defined to be the angle between their corresponding planes.   The reader can easily verify that this is equivalent to defining the angle to be equal to the plane angle between two lines tangent to the corresponding great circles at a point of intersection.

The magnitude of a side of a spherical triangle may be measured in two ways.   Either we may take its arc length or we may take the angle it subtends at the center of the sphere.   These two methods give the same numerical result if the radius of the sphere is unity.

We shall adopt consistently the second of these two methods. In other words, if A, B, and C are the vertices of a spherical triangle, with opposite sides a, b, and c respectively, the numerical value of, say, a will be taken to be the plane angle BOC, where O is the center of the sphere (see Fig. 23).

In the following derivations, we assume the sphere to have radius $R = 1$, and we take the center of the sphere at the origin. The unit vectors extending from the center to **A**, **B**, and **C** will be denoted $\boldsymbol{\alpha}$, $\boldsymbol{\beta}$, and $\boldsymbol{\gamma}$ respectively; we label the vertices in such a manner that $\boldsymbol{\alpha}$, $\boldsymbol{\beta}$, and $\boldsymbol{\gamma}$, in that order, are positively oriented.

Let $\boldsymbol{\alpha}'$, $\boldsymbol{\beta}'$, and $\boldsymbol{\gamma}'$ be unit vectors, extending from the origin and so defined that

(1) $$\boldsymbol{\alpha} \times \boldsymbol{\beta} = \sin c \; \boldsymbol{\gamma}'$$

(2) $$\boldsymbol{\beta} \times \boldsymbol{\gamma} = \sin a \; \boldsymbol{\alpha}'$$

(3) $$\boldsymbol{\gamma} \times \boldsymbol{\alpha} = \sin b \; \boldsymbol{\beta}'$$

(In Fig. 24, only $\boldsymbol{\alpha}'$ is shown. All three are shown in Fig. 25.)

The vectors $\boldsymbol{\alpha}'$, $\boldsymbol{\beta}'$, and $\boldsymbol{\gamma}'$ determine a spherical triangle $A'B'C'$, called the *polar triangle* of ABC (Fig. 26).

Let the sides of this triangle be a', b', and c' respectively.

Notice, for example, that B' is a "pole" corresponding to the great circle joining A and C (geographically, think of the North Pole corresponding to the equator). Also, C' is a pole corresponding to the great circle AB. If these great circles are extended to intersect the side $B'C'$, we see that this side is composed of two overlapping segments $B'E$ and DC' each of magnitude $90°$. Their common overlap has magnitude A, so we see that

(4) $$a' + A = \pi$$

Similarly, we have

(5) $$b' + B = \pi$$

(6) $$c' + C = \pi$$

These three formulas are useful in relating the angles of a spherical triangle to the sides of the corresponding polar triangle.

We are now ready to derive the fundamental formulas of spherical trigonometry.

As in ordinary trigonometry, the solution of problems involving triangles can be accomplished by systematic use of a law of sines and

r = 1 unit
$|\alpha| = |\beta| = |\sigma| = 1$

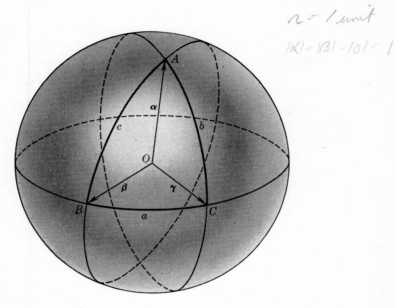

Figure 23

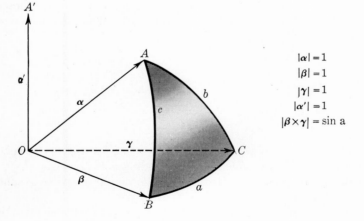

$|\boldsymbol{\alpha}| = 1$
$|\boldsymbol{\beta}| = 1$
$|\boldsymbol{\gamma}| = 1$
$|\boldsymbol{\alpha'}| = 1$
$|\boldsymbol{\beta} \times \boldsymbol{\gamma}| = \sin a$

Figure 24

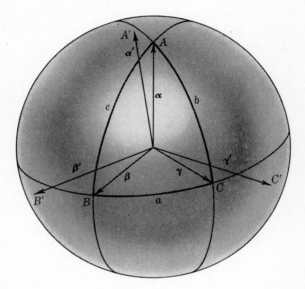

Figure 25

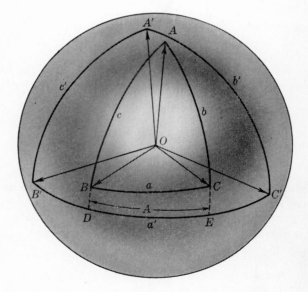

Figure 26

a cosine law.　　These laws are of a somewhat different form for spherical triangles than for triangles in a plane.

　　In the identity

$$(\mathbf{A} \times \mathbf{B}) \cdot (\mathbf{C} \times \mathbf{D}) = (\mathbf{A} \cdot \mathbf{C})(\mathbf{B} \cdot \mathbf{D}) - (\mathbf{A} \cdot \mathbf{D})(\mathbf{B} \cdot \mathbf{C})$$

let us substitute $\boldsymbol{\alpha}$ for $\mathbf{A}$, $\boldsymbol{\beta}$ for $\mathbf{B}$, $\boldsymbol{\alpha}$ for $\mathbf{C}$, and $\boldsymbol{\gamma}$ for $\mathbf{D}$.　　Since $\boldsymbol{\alpha}$ is a unit vector, $\boldsymbol{\alpha} \cdot \boldsymbol{\alpha} = |\boldsymbol{\alpha}|^2 = 1$, so we obtain

$$(7) \qquad (\boldsymbol{\alpha} \times \boldsymbol{\beta}) \cdot (\boldsymbol{\alpha} \times \boldsymbol{\gamma}) = \boldsymbol{\beta} \cdot \boldsymbol{\gamma} - (\boldsymbol{\alpha} \cdot \boldsymbol{\beta})(\boldsymbol{\alpha} \cdot \boldsymbol{\gamma})$$

We see from Figure 24 that $\boldsymbol{\beta} \cdot \boldsymbol{\gamma} = \cos a$, $\boldsymbol{\alpha} \cdot \boldsymbol{\beta} = \cos c$, and $\boldsymbol{\alpha} \cdot \boldsymbol{\gamma} = \cos b$.　　Hence the right side of (7) is

$$\cos a - \cos c \cos b$$

From the way in which $\boldsymbol{\alpha}'$, $\boldsymbol{\beta}'$, and $\boldsymbol{\gamma}'$ were defined, the left side of (7) is

$$(\sin c\ \boldsymbol{\gamma}') \cdot (-\sin b\ \boldsymbol{\beta}')$$
$$= -\sin c \sin b\ (\boldsymbol{\gamma}' \cdot \boldsymbol{\beta}')$$

Now, just as $\boldsymbol{\gamma} \cdot \boldsymbol{\beta}$ is equal to $\cos a$, so also (considering the polar triangle) $\boldsymbol{\gamma}' \cdot \boldsymbol{\beta}'$ is equal to $\cos a'$.　　By (4), this is $\cos(\pi - A)$, which equals $-\cos A$.　　And so the left side of (7) equals

$$\sin c \sin b \cos A$$

Equating the two sides, we obtain the cosine law

$$(8) \qquad \cos a = \cos b \cos c + \sin b \sin c \cos A$$

We can, of course, imagine Figure 24 rotated so that the roles previously played by a, b, and c respectively are now played by b, c, and a, and write

$$(9) \qquad \cos b = \cos c \cos a + \sin c \sin a \cos B$$

and similarly,

$$(10) \qquad \cos c = \cos a \cos b + \sin a \sin b \cos C$$

　　Three more versions of the cosine law are obtained by applying the above law of cosines to the *polar triangle* (just change a to a', b to b', etc.) and then replacing a' by $\pi - A$, b' by $\pi - B$, etc., according to (4), (5), and (6).　　On simplifying, this gives

$$(11) \qquad \cos A = -\cos B \cos C + \sin B \sin C \cos a$$

$$(12) \qquad \cos B = -\cos C \cos A + \sin C \sin A \cos b$$

$$(13) \qquad \cos C = -\cos A \cos B + \sin A \sin B \cos c$$

Now let us turn to the law of sines. Here, we make use of identity (3), Section 1.15, to obtain

$$(\boldsymbol{\alpha} \times \boldsymbol{\beta}) \times (\boldsymbol{\alpha} \times \boldsymbol{\gamma}) = [\boldsymbol{\alpha},\boldsymbol{\beta},\boldsymbol{\gamma}]\boldsymbol{\alpha}$$

The left side of this equals

$$(\sin c\ \boldsymbol{\gamma'}) \times (-\sin b\ \boldsymbol{\beta'})$$
$$= -\sin b \sin c\ (\boldsymbol{\gamma'} \times \boldsymbol{\beta'})$$
$$= -\sin b \sin c\ (-\sin a'\ \boldsymbol{\alpha})$$
$$= (\sin b \sin c \sin A)\boldsymbol{\alpha}$$

(We leave it to the reader to check each of these steps; notice that the polar triangle of $A'B'C'$ is ABC.)

In this manner, we obtain

(14) $(\sin b \sin c \sin A)\boldsymbol{\alpha} = [\boldsymbol{\alpha},\boldsymbol{\beta},\boldsymbol{\gamma}]\boldsymbol{\alpha}$

Similarly,

(15) $(\sin c \sin a \sin B)\boldsymbol{\beta} = [\boldsymbol{\beta},\boldsymbol{\gamma},\boldsymbol{\alpha}]\boldsymbol{\beta}$

(16) $(\sin a \sin b \sin C)\boldsymbol{\gamma} = [\boldsymbol{\gamma},\boldsymbol{\alpha},\boldsymbol{\beta}]\boldsymbol{\gamma}$

Now, it is geometrically obvious that, if $\mathbf{V}$ is any nonzero vector, we can have $s\mathbf{V} = t\mathbf{V}$ only if $s = t$. Applying this principle to (14), (15), and (16), we obtain the scalar equations

(17) $\sin b \sin c \sin A = [\boldsymbol{\alpha},\boldsymbol{\beta},\boldsymbol{\gamma}]$

(18) $\sin c \sin a \sin B = [\boldsymbol{\beta},\boldsymbol{\gamma},\boldsymbol{\alpha}]$

(19) $\sin a \sin b \sin C = [\boldsymbol{\gamma},\boldsymbol{\alpha},\boldsymbol{\beta}]$

Since $[\boldsymbol{\alpha},\boldsymbol{\beta},\boldsymbol{\gamma}] = [\boldsymbol{\beta},\boldsymbol{\gamma},\boldsymbol{\alpha}] = [\boldsymbol{\gamma},\boldsymbol{\alpha},\boldsymbol{\beta}]$, the right sides, and hence the left sides, of (17), (18), and (19) are all equal. So, for example,

$$\sin b \sin c \sin A = \sin c \sin a \sin B$$

This leads to

$$\frac{\sin b}{\sin B} = \frac{\sin a}{\sin A}$$

(provided the triangle is not degenerate). Similarly one can obtain from (17) and (19)

$$\frac{\sin a}{\sin A} = \frac{\sin c}{\sin C}$$

Thus we can finally write down the law of sines,

(20) $$\frac{\sin a}{\sin A} = \frac{\sin b}{\sin B} = \frac{\sin c}{\sin C}$$

valid whenever $\sin A$, $\sin B$, and $\sin C$ are nonzero.

EXERCISES

1. In plane trigonometry, if $C = 90°$, then $\sin A = a/c$. What is the corresponding relation in spherical trigonometry? (Let $C = 90°$ in the law of sines.)

2. An angle of $1'$ at the center of the earth subtends a distance of approximately one nautical mile (about 6080 ft) at the surface of the earth. Thus a $90°$ arc on the earth is $90 \times 60 = 5400$ nautical miles in length. What is the distance between two points on the equator, if one is at longitude $20°$ W and the other $30°$ E?

3. What is the distance between two points on the earth if both are on the same meridian, one at latitude $10°$ N and the other at $35°$ N?

4. A terrestrial triangle is a spherical triangle with vertices at the North Pole and at two other points on the earth. Let the two points in question be New York City, at latitude $41°$ N and longitude $74°$ W, and Moscow, at latitude $56°$ N and longitude $38°$ E. Letting N denote the vertex at New York City and M the vertex at Moscow, with P denoting the North Pole, write down by inspection (a) PM, in degrees and also in nautical miles, (b) PN in degrees and in nautical miles, and (c) angle NPM. Using the cosine law, (d) determine MN in degrees and in nautical miles (i.e., determine the great-circle distance between Moscow and New York City).

5. Take the latitude at Vancouver to be $49°$ N and the longitude $123°$ W. An airplane flies, initially due east, along a great-circle route for 2000 miles. Find the latitude and longitude of the position reached. (1 mile = 5280 ft)

6. An airplane flies from Vancouver (Problem 5) initially due east along a great-circle route:
    (a) What is its longitude when its latitude has decreased $30°$?
    (b) What is its longitude when it crosses the equator?
    (c) At what angle does it cross the equator?

7. Show that $\sin b = \tan a \cot A$, for any spherical right triangle (take $C = 90°$).

8. Find the shortest distance from $(3,4,0)$ to the plane $3x - 4z = 0$, along a path required to be on the sphere $x^2 + y^2 + z^2 = 25$.

REVIEW PROBLEMS

1. Find the area of the parallelogram having as adjacent sides
$$\mathbf{A} = \mathbf{j} - 2\mathbf{i} + 3\mathbf{k}$$
and $$\mathbf{B} = 2\mathbf{j} + 3\mathbf{i} - \mathbf{k}$$

2. Find r and s if $(2\mathbf{i} + 6\mathbf{j} - 27\mathbf{k}) \times (\mathbf{i} + r\mathbf{j} + s\mathbf{k}) = 0$

3. Give an expression for $\mathbf{A} \times (\mathbf{B} \times \mathbf{C})$ not involving vector products. Use this to simplify $(\mathbf{K} \times \mathbf{L}) \times (\mathbf{M} \times \mathbf{B})$.

4. A force $\mathbf{F} = 2\mathbf{i} + 3\mathbf{j} + \mathbf{k}$ acts through a displacement $\mathbf{D} = -2\mathbf{i} + \mathbf{j} - \mathbf{k}$. Find the work done.

5. State which of the following have meaning. Do not evaluate. Assume $\mathbf{B} \neq \mathbf{0}$.
   (a) $\mathbf{A} \times 5\mathbf{B}$
   (b) $[\mathbf{A}, 3\mathbf{B}, \mathbf{C} - \mathbf{D}]$
   (c) $(\mathbf{A} \times \mathbf{B}) \cdot \mathbf{C}$
   (d) $(\mathbf{A} \times \mathbf{B}) \cdot (\mathbf{C} \cdot \mathbf{D})$
   (e) $(\mathbf{A} \cdot \mathbf{B}) \times (\mathbf{C} \times \mathbf{D})$
   (f) $(\mathbf{A} \cdot \mathbf{B}) \times (\mathbf{C} \cdot \mathbf{D})$
   (g) $\mathbf{A} \times [(\mathbf{B} \cdot \mathbf{C})\mathbf{D}]$
   (h) $\dfrac{\mathbf{A}}{|\mathbf{B}|}$
   (i) $\dfrac{\mathbf{A}}{\mathbf{B}}$

6. Four rods of different lengths have their ends loosely joined so as to form a quadrilateral that does not necessarily lie in any plane. Show that the midpoints of the rods form a parallelogram (and, in particular, that these points *will* lie in a plane).

7. Given $\mathbf{A} = \mathbf{i} - 2\mathbf{j}$, $\mathbf{B} = 3\mathbf{j} + 2\mathbf{k}$, $\mathbf{C} = -2\mathbf{i} + 2\mathbf{j} - \mathbf{k}$, find
   (a) $\dfrac{3\mathbf{A} + 2\mathbf{B}}{|\mathbf{C}|}$
   (b) $\mathbf{B} \cdot \mathbf{B} - |\mathbf{B}|^2$
   (c) $\mathbf{C} - \mathbf{C}$
   (d) $[\mathbf{A}, 4\mathbf{B}, \tfrac{1}{2}\mathbf{C}]$

8. Find an equation of the plane perpendicular to $\mathbf{D}$ and through P, where
$$\mathbf{D} = 10\mathbf{i} - 10\mathbf{j} + 5\mathbf{k}$$
and P is $(1,1,-3)$.

9. Find the angle between the plane $x + y + z = 21$ and the line $x - 1 = y + 2 = 2z + 3$.

10. If **A** is a fixed nonzero vector, interpret geometrically
    $(\mathbf{R} - \mathbf{A}) \cdot \mathbf{R} = 0$,
    (a) in the plane, $\mathbf{R} = x\mathbf{i} + y\mathbf{j}$,
    (b) in space, $\mathbf{R} = x\mathbf{i} + y\mathbf{j} + z\mathbf{k}$.

11. Given

$$\mathbf{A} = \cos\theta\,\mathbf{i} - \sin\theta\,\mathbf{j}$$

$$\mathbf{B} = \cos\phi\,\mathbf{i} + \sin\phi\,\mathbf{j}$$

By finding the cosine of the angle between **A** and **B**, derive the trigonometric expression for $\cos(\phi + \theta)$.

12. Consider

$$\mathbf{A} = \mathbf{i} + \mathbf{j} + \mathbf{k} \qquad \mathbf{B} = \mathbf{i}$$

$$\mathbf{C} = C_x\mathbf{i} + C_y\mathbf{j} + C_z\mathbf{k}$$

(a) If $C_x = 1$, $C_y = 2$, find C_z to make the three vectors coplanar.

(b) If $C_y = -1$ and $C_z = 1$, show that no value of C_x can be found to make the three vectors coplanar.

(c) Discuss the geometrical reason for the result in part (b).

T W O

VECTOR FUNCTIONS OF A
SINGLE VARIABLE

2.1 : Differentiation

A vector-valued function $\mathbf{F}$ is a rule that associates with each real number t a vector $\mathbf{F}(t)$. The theory of such functions parallels that of real-valued functions.

For simplicity of exposition, we assume $\mathbf{F}(t)$ to be defined for every real number t, although some of our examples will not satisfy this requirement. (For example, the vector-valued function $\mathbf{F}(t) = (1/t)\mathbf{i}$ is not defined when $t = 0$.)

The expression

$$(1) \qquad\qquad \lim_{t \to t_0} \mathbf{F}(t) = \mathbf{A}$$

means that, given any positive number ε, no matter how small it may be, one can find a positive number δ such that $|\mathbf{F}(t) - \mathbf{A}| < \varepsilon$ whenever $|t - t_0| < \delta$.

This has a simple intuitive meaning. It means that the magnitude of $\mathbf{F}(t)$ is approaching the magnitude of $\mathbf{A}$, and (if $\mathbf{A}$ is nonzero) the angle between them is approaching zero (see Fig. 27).

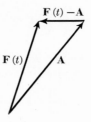

Figure 27

The definition just given is identical to that given in calculus books for real-valued functions, except that the expression $|\mathbf{F}(t) - \mathbf{A}|$ now refers to the magnitude of a vector rather than to the absolute value of a number.

A vector-valued function $\mathbf{F}$ is said to be *continuous* if

$$(2) \qquad \lim_{t \to t_0} \mathbf{F}(t) = \mathbf{F}(t_0)$$

for every real number t_0.   It is said to be *differentiable* if the derivative

$$(3) \qquad \mathbf{F}'(t) = \frac{d\mathbf{F}}{dt}(t) = \lim_{\Delta t \to 0} \frac{\mathbf{F}(t + \Delta t) - \mathbf{F}(t)}{\Delta t}$$

exists for every value of t.   The derivative of a vector function $\mathbf{F}$ is also a vector function.

The fundamental theorems concerning differentiation of vector-valued functions are similar to those for real-valued functions, except that when differentiating the vector product of two vector functions, one must be careful to preserve the order of factors, since the vector product is not a commutative operation.

THEOREM 1:   If $\mathbf{F}$ and $\mathbf{G}$ are differentiable vector functions, then so also is their sum $\mathbf{F} + \mathbf{G}$, and the derivative of the function $\mathbf{F} + \mathbf{G}$ is the sum of the derivatives of $\mathbf{F}$ and $\mathbf{G}$ respectively,

$$(4) \qquad \frac{d}{dt}(\mathbf{F} + \mathbf{G}) = \frac{d\mathbf{F}}{dt} + \frac{d\mathbf{G}}{dt}$$

THEOREM 2: If $\mathbf{F}$ is a differentiable vector function, and s is a differentiable scalar function, then the product $s\mathbf{F}$ is a differentiable vector function, and

$$(5) \qquad \frac{d}{dt}(s\mathbf{F}) = \frac{ds}{dt}\mathbf{F} + s\frac{d\mathbf{F}}{dt}$$

THEOREM 3: If $\mathbf{F}$ and $\mathbf{G}$ are differentiable vector functions, then $\mathbf{F}\cdot\mathbf{G}$ is a differentiable scalar function, and

$$(6) \qquad \frac{d}{dt}(\mathbf{F}\cdot\mathbf{G}) = \frac{d\mathbf{F}}{dt}\cdot\mathbf{G} + \mathbf{F}\cdot\frac{d\mathbf{G}}{dt}$$

THEOREM 4: If $\mathbf{F}$ and $\mathbf{G}$ are differentiable vector functions, then $\mathbf{F}\times\mathbf{G}$ is also a differentiable vector function, and

$$(7) \qquad \frac{d}{dt}(\mathbf{F}\times\mathbf{G}) = \frac{d\mathbf{F}}{dt}\times\mathbf{G} + \mathbf{F}\times\frac{d\mathbf{G}}{dt}$$

The reader who is familiar with the proofs of the sum and product formulas of elementary calculus will have no difficulty filling in the proofs of these theorems. He will need to make use of the following fundamental facts:

$$(8) \qquad |\mathbf{X}| \geq 0, \text{ and } |\mathbf{X}| = 0 \text{ only if } \mathbf{X} \text{ is the zero vector}$$

$$(9) \qquad |s\mathbf{X}| = |s|\,|\mathbf{X}|$$

$$(10) \qquad |\mathbf{X} + \mathbf{Y}| \leq |\mathbf{X}| + |\mathbf{Y}|$$

for all vectors $\mathbf{X}$ and $\mathbf{Y}$ and any scalar s.

It follows from (4) and (5) that if

$$\mathbf{F}(t) = P(t)\mathbf{i} + Q(t)\mathbf{j} + R(t)\mathbf{k}$$

then

$$(11) \qquad \mathbf{F}'(t) = P'(t)\mathbf{i} + Q'(t)\mathbf{j} + R'(t)\mathbf{k}$$

EXAMPLE 1: If $\mathbf{F}(t) = \sin t\,\mathbf{i} + \cos t\,\mathbf{j} + t\mathbf{k}$, then

$$\mathbf{F}'(t) = \cos t\,\mathbf{i} - \sin t\,\mathbf{j} + \mathbf{k}$$

EXAMPLE 2: If $\mathbf{F}(t) = t^3\mathbf{j} - \mathbf{k}$, then $\mathbf{F}'(t) = 3t^2\mathbf{j}$.

EXAMPLE 3: Let $\mathbf{F}(t) = \mathbf{i} + 2\mathbf{j} - \mathbf{k}$. Then $\mathbf{F}$ is a constant vector-valued function, and its derivative with respect to t is identically equal to the zero vector for all t.

EXAMPLE 4:   If $\mathbf{F}'(t) = \mathbf{0}$, then $\mathbf{F}(t) = \mathbf{C}$, where the constant $\mathbf{C}$ is a *vector*.

EXAMPLE 5:   Prove that, if $\mathbf{F}(t)$ has constant nonzero magnitude (varies only in direction), then $\mathbf{F}'(t)$ is either the zero vector or it is a nonzero vector perpendicular to $\mathbf{F}(t)$.

Solution: If $|\mathbf{F}(t)| =$ constant, then we must have

$$\mathbf{F} \cdot \mathbf{F} = \text{constant}$$

and differentiating with respect to t, using (6), we have

$$\frac{d\mathbf{F}}{dt} \cdot \mathbf{F} + \mathbf{F} \cdot \frac{d\mathbf{F}}{dt} = 0$$

$$2\mathbf{F} \cdot \frac{d\mathbf{F}}{dt} = 0$$

Hence the scalar product of $\mathbf{F}$ with $d\mathbf{F}/dt$ is identically zero. This can happen only if the vectors $\mathbf{F}$ and $d\mathbf{F}/dt$ are perpendicular, or if one of them is the zero vector.

EXERCISES

1. Let $\mathbf{F}(t) = \sin t\, \mathbf{i} + \cos t\, \mathbf{j} + \mathbf{k}$.
   (a) Find $\mathbf{F}'(t)$.
   (b) Show that $\mathbf{F}'(t)$ is always parallel to the xy plane.
   (c) For what values of t is $\mathbf{F}'(t)$ parallel to the xz plane?
   (d) Does $\mathbf{F}(t)$ have constant magnitude?
   (e) Does $\mathbf{F}'(t)$ have constant magnitude?
   (f) Compute $\mathbf{F}''(t)$.

2. Find $\mathbf{F}'(t)$ in each of the following cases.
   (a) $\mathbf{F}(t) = 3t\mathbf{i} + t^3\mathbf{j}$
   (b) $\mathbf{F}(t) = \sin t\, \mathbf{i} + e^{-t}\mathbf{j} + 3\mathbf{k}$
   (c) $\mathbf{F}(t) = (e^t\mathbf{i} + \mathbf{j} + t^2\mathbf{k}) \times (t^3\mathbf{i} + \mathbf{j} - \mathbf{k})$
   (d) $\mathbf{F}(t) = (\sin t + t^3)(\mathbf{i} + \mathbf{j} + 2\mathbf{k})$
   (e) $\mathbf{F}(t) = 3\mathbf{i} + \mathbf{k}$

3. Find $f'(t)$ in each of the following cases:
   (a) $f(t) = (3t\mathbf{i} + 5t^2\mathbf{j}) \cdot (t\mathbf{i} - \sin t\, \mathbf{j})$
   (b) $f(t) = |2t\mathbf{i} + 2t\mathbf{j} - \mathbf{k}|$
   (c) $f(t) = [(\mathbf{i} + \mathbf{j} - 2\mathbf{k}) \times (3t^4\mathbf{i} + t\mathbf{j})] \cdot \mathbf{k}$

2.2 : Space Curves

In the first chapter, we showed that the parametric equations of a line can be written in vector form

(1) $$\mathbf{R} = \mathbf{R}_0 + t\mathbf{V}$$

where $\mathbf{R}$ is a vector with components x, y, and z, $\mathbf{R}_0$ is the position vector of a fixed point on the line, and $\mathbf{V} = a\mathbf{i} + b\mathbf{j} + c\mathbf{k}$ is parallel to the line. If $\mathbf{R}$ is taken to be the position vector of a particle at time t, then it is easy to see that $\mathbf{V}$ is the velocity of the particle. It is interesting to note that, if we differentiate (1) with respect to t, we obtain $d\mathbf{R}/dt = \mathbf{V}$.

In this section we consider the more general equation $\mathbf{R} = \mathbf{R}(t)$, of which (1) is simply a special case. In this more general case it is also true that if $\mathbf{R}$ is the position vector of a particle at time t, then $d\mathbf{R}/dt$ gives the velocity of the particle. We also introduce several definitions that will be useful later.

The vector equation $\mathbf{R} = \mathbf{R}(t)$ can be written out in terms of its components, giving the system of equations

(2)
$$x = x(t)$$
$$y = y(t)$$
$$z = z(t)$$

where x, y, and z are functions of a parameter t.

As t increases from some initial value t_1 to some value t_2, the point (x,y,z) traces a path in space. Such a path is called a *space curve*, or *arc*. (The term "curve" is used even if the path is a segment of a straight line.)

Let the point corresponding to $t = t_1$ be denoted P_1, and that corresponding to $t = t_2$ be denoted P_2. Then the arc P_1P_2 is said to be *smooth* if the following conditions are satisfied*:

(*i*) $d\mathbf{R}/dt$ exists and is a continuous function of t, for all values of t in the interval $t_1 \leq t \leq t_2$,

(*ii*) to distinct values of t in the interval $t_1 < t < t_2$ there correspond distinct points,

(*iii*) there is no value of t in the interval $t_1 \leq t \leq t_2$ for which $d\mathbf{R}/dt$ is the zero vector.

---

* Or, P_1P_2 can be said to be smooth if, by a suitable change of variables, these conditions can be fulfilled. For simplicity, we avoid discussion of the effect of a change of parameter.

It is especially useful to think of (x,y,z) as the location of a particle moving through space, with the parameter t representing time. Condition (i) requires that the x, y, and z components of the velocity vary so there will be no sudden changes of direction. Condition (ii) is to ensure that the particle does not occupy the same position twice during the same time interval. In other words, the arc does not cross itself. Condition (iii) requires that the particle is always moving (never at rest).

A smooth arc is said to be *closed* if $R(t_1) = R(t_2)$.

In Figure 28 we give an example of a smooth arc. The arc in Figure 29 is also a smooth arc, and is an example of one that is closed. The arc in Figure 30 is not smooth because at points Q and R the derivatives are not continuous (in a physical case, this might be due to the particle colliding with other particles). The curve in Figure 31 is not smooth, but it consists of three smooth arcs—PS, a closed arc SS, and another smooth arc SQ.

A *regular curve* is a parametrized curve $R = R(t)$ that (i) consists of a finite number of smooth arcs joined together, and (ii) does not cross itself. The curve in Figure 30 is regular; that in Figure 31 is not regular since it crosses itself at S. *Caution:* The term "regular" is used with different meanings by different authors.

In Figures 28, 29, and 30, we have indicated the direction in which the particle is traversing the curve by a small arrow. Strictly speaking, *any curve is nothing more than a collection of points in space.* When, however, we indicate a direction along a smooth arc, as we have in these diagrams, then we say that the arc has been oriented. Obviously, there are only two ways in which a smooth arc can be oriented. The arc in Figure 32 is a replica of that in Figure 28, but is oriented in the opposite way.

When an arc is described by equations such as (2), in terms of a parameter t, the orientation is usually understood to be determined by that parameter: the direction is the direction of increasing t. For example, the closed arc

$$x = \cos t$$

(3) $$y = \sin t$$

$$z = 0$$

is simply a circle of unit radius in the xy plane. As t increases from 0 to 2π, the point moves from its initial position $(1,0,0)$ back to the

P_2

P_1

Figure 28

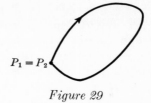

$P_1 = P_2$

Figure 29

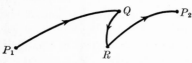

P_1

Q

R

P_2

Figure 30

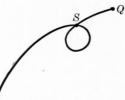

S

Q

P

Figure 31

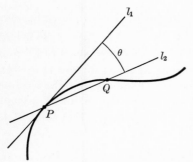

P_2

P_1

Figure 32

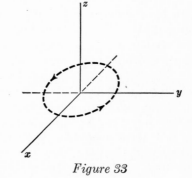

Figure 33

l_1

θ

l_2

Q

P

Figure 34

same position, as shown in Figure 33.   The same arc with opposite orientation can be given parametrically by

$$
\begin{aligned}
x &= \cos t \\
y &= -\sin t \\
z &= 0
\end{aligned}
$$

(4)

The equations (3) specify the same arc as (4), but with opposite orientation, since as t increases from 0 to 2π, the point (x,y,z) traverses the circle in the opposite direction.

The same circle can be represented nonparametrically by the equations

$$
\begin{aligned}
x^2 + y^2 &= 1 \\
z &= 0
\end{aligned}
$$

(5)

There is no way of knowing from (5) which orientation is intended. Note that (5) represents the arc as the intersection of two surfaces, a cylinder and a plane.   When one specifies an oriented arc as the intersection of two surfaces, by giving two equations, it is necessary to specify the orientation separately either verbally or by drawing a diagram.

Again we emphasize that a curve such as that represented by (5) is merely a collection of points (x,y,z) in space.   On the other hand, a parametrized curve such as (3) is a function (a vector-valued function of a parameter t).   Considering them as curves, we do not distinguish between (3) and (4); they are identical and are the same as (5).   But considered as parametrized curves, (3) and (4) are distinct, since the function $\mathbf{R}(t) = x(t)\mathbf{i} + y(t)\mathbf{j} + z(t)\mathbf{k}$ is different in (3) from what it is in (4).

Let $P(x,y,z)$ denote a *fixed* point on a smooth arc corresponding to some value t, and let $Q(x + \Delta x, y + \Delta y, z + \Delta z)$ denote another point on the arc corresponding to another value $t + \Delta t$.   The points P and Q determine a straight line.   A line passing through P is said to be tangent to the arc at point P if the angle θ between this line and the line joining P and Q tends to zero as Δt tends to zero (Fig. 34).

Under the assumption that the arc is smooth, we shall prove that there must exist a tangent to the arc at any point P (except perhaps at the endpoints of a closed arc), and that this tangent is parallel to the vector

$$
\frac{d\mathbf{R}}{dt} = \frac{dx}{dt}\,\mathbf{i} + \frac{dy}{dt}\,\mathbf{j} + \frac{dz}{dt}\,\mathbf{k}
$$

The proof is as follows: Let l_1 denote the line passing through P parallel to $d\mathbf{R}/dt$, and let l_2 denote the line passing through P and Q. Let the vector extending from P to Q be denoted $\Delta\mathbf{R}$. If θ is the angle between these two lines, then by the methods of Section 1.7 we have

$$(6) \qquad \cos\theta = \frac{(d\mathbf{R}/dt)\cdot\Delta\mathbf{R}}{|d\mathbf{R}/dt|\,|\Delta\mathbf{R}|}$$

We wish to show that, as $\Delta\mathbf{R}$ approaches the zero vector, $\cos\theta$ converges to 1. Conditions (i), (ii), and (iii) ensure that $\Delta\mathbf{R}$ approaches zero for t in the range $t_1 < t < t_2$ if and only if Δt approaches zero. Dividing numerator and denominator of (6) by Δt and letting $\Delta t \to 0$, then $\Delta\mathbf{R}/\Delta t \to d\mathbf{R}/dt$ by definition of the derivative, and since the operations of multiplication and division are continuous, the right side of (6) approaches 1. This shows that l_1 is, indeed, tangent to the curve at P.

A vector is said to be tangent to a smooth arc at a point P if it is parallel to the line tangent to the arc at P. Thus the vector

$$(dx/dt)\mathbf{i} + (dy/dt)\mathbf{j} + (dz/dt)\mathbf{k}$$

is tangent to the arc at the point P, provided the derivatives dx/dt, dy/dt, and dz/dt are evaluated at that value of t corresponding to the point P (x,y,z).

It is conventional to denote by the letter $\mathbf{T}$ the *unit vector* tangent to an oriented smooth arc, pointing in the direction determined by the orientation. In other words, $\mathbf{T}$ is defined by the expression

$$(7) \qquad \mathbf{T} = \frac{(dx/dt)\mathbf{i} + (dy/dt)\mathbf{j} + (dz/dt)\mathbf{k}}{\sqrt{(dx/dt)^2 + (dy/dt)^2 + (dz/dt)^2}}$$

obtained by dividing the above vector by its own magnitude.

EXAMPLE 1: Determine the unit vector tangent to the oriented closed arc $x = \cos t$, $y = \sin t$, $z = 0$, at (a) $t = 0$, (b) $t = \pi/2$.

Solution: The answers are obviously (a) $\mathbf{j}$, (b) $-\mathbf{i}$ as can be seen from Figure 35. These answers can be obtained also by use of (7), which gives

$$\mathbf{T} = \frac{-\sin t\,\mathbf{i} + \cos t\,\mathbf{j}}{\sqrt{\sin^2 t + \cos^2 t}} = -\sin t\,\mathbf{i} + \cos t\,\mathbf{j}$$

At $t = 0$, we have $\mathbf{T} = -\sin 0\,\mathbf{i} + \cos 0\,\mathbf{j} = \mathbf{j}$, and at $t = \pi/2$, $\mathbf{T} = -\sin(\pi/2)\,\mathbf{i} + \cos(\pi/2)\,\mathbf{j} = -\mathbf{i}$.

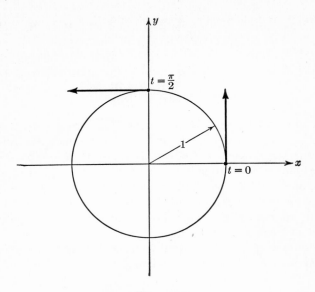

Figure 35

EXAMPLE 2: Find the unit vector tangent to the curve $x = t$, $y = t^2$, $z = t^3$, at the point $(2,4,8)$.
Solution: By (7), we have

$$\mathbf{T} = \frac{\mathbf{i} + 2t\mathbf{j} + 3t^2\mathbf{k}}{\sqrt{1 + 4t^2 + 9t^4}}$$

When $t = 2$ we have $(x,y,z) = (2,4,8)$ and $\mathbf{T} = (1/\sqrt{161})$ $(\mathbf{i} + 4\mathbf{j} + 12\mathbf{k})$.

An arc that is not smooth may not have a tangent at some points. For instance, there is no tangent at Q in Figure 30.

The reader is undoubtedly familiar with the notion of arc length, which is discussed in calculus books (at least for plane curves). This notion generalizes easily to space curves.

Let there be given a smooth space curve C. Let us subdivide C into smaller arcs, and "approximate" it by a polygonal path consisting of n straight-line segments joining the endpoints of the arcs (Fig. 36). That is, we select points $Q_0, Q_1, \ldots, Q_n$ along C, in that order, with Q_0 and Q_n the endpoints of C. For each $k = 0, 1, \ldots, n$, let $\mathbf{R}_k$ be the position vector to the point Q_k, and let $\Delta \mathbf{R}_k = \mathbf{R}_k - \mathbf{R}_{k-1}$, for $k = 1, 2, \ldots, n$. The total length of the polygonal path is then $\sum_{k=1}^{n} |\Delta \mathbf{R}_k|$. The length of the space curve C is then defined to be the limit of sums of this form, where the approximating polygonal

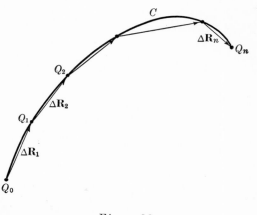

Figure 36

paths are obtained by taking increasingly small subdivisions while n increases without bound. It can be shown that the limit exists, and is independent of the particular subdivisions chosen, provided that the maximum value of the summands $|\Delta \mathbf{R}_k|$ tends to zero. This limit can then be denoted

$$(8) \qquad \int_C |d\mathbf{R}|$$

If the curve is parametrized, with t as a parameter, (8) can be written in the alternative form

$$(9) \qquad \int_{t_1}^{t_2} \left| \frac{d\mathbf{R}}{dt} \right| dt$$

The arc length of a regular curve is defined to be the sum of the lengths of the various smooth curves that constitute it.

In coordinate form, (9) becomes

$$\int_{t_1}^{t_2} \left[\left(\frac{dx}{dt} \right)^2 + \left(\frac{dy}{dt} \right)^2 + \left(\frac{dz}{dt} \right)^2 \right]^{1/2} dt$$

If the arc P_1P_2 lies entirely in the xy plane, which is the simplest case treated in calculus books, then z is identically equal to zero and so $dz/dt = 0$ and, by eliminating the parameter t, (8) may be written in the familiar alternative form

(11)
$$\int_{x_1}^{x_2} \left[1 + \left(\frac{dy}{dx} \right)^2 \right]^{1/2} dx$$

provided the integral exists, or

(12)
$$\int_{y_1}^{y_2} \left[\left(\frac{dx}{dy} \right)^2 + 1 \right]^{1/2} dy$$

provided this integral exists. It is possible that these integrals may not exist. For example, if the arc P_1P_2 contains a segment that is parallel to the y axis, then dy/dx will not exist along this segment (that is, dy/dx is "infinite") and (11) will not make sense.

Equation (8) may be written in coordinate form

(13)
$$\int_{t_1}^{t_2} [(dx)^2 + (dy)^2 + (dz)^2]^{1/2}$$

where it is understood that dx, dy, and dz are expressed in terms of the parameter t and the differential dt (so that t is the variable over which the integration is performed). Sometimes it is possible to write two of the variables, say y and z, in terms of one of the others, say x. In that case dy and dz may be expressed in terms of x and dx, and the integral is taken with respect to x, the limits of integration being the values of x corresponding to t_1 and t_2.

EXAMPLE 3: Find the arc length between $(0,0,1)$ to $(1,0,1)$ of the curve

$$y = \sin 2\pi x \qquad z = \cos 2\pi x$$

(This is a helix winding about the x axis.)

 Solution:

$$dx^2 + dy^2 + dz^2 = dx^2 + 4\pi^2 \cos^2 2\pi x\, dx^2 + 4\pi^2 \sin^2 2\pi x\, dx^2$$
$$= (1 + 4\pi^2)\, dx^2. \quad \text{Hence the integral is}$$
$$\int_0^1 (1 + 4\pi^2)^{1/2}\, dx = (1 + 4\pi^2)^{1/2}$$

Returning to (9), we see that the arc length measured along the curve from some arbitrary initial position $\mathbf{R}(t_1)$ to a variable position $\mathbf{R}(t)$ is given by

$$s(t) = \int_{t_1}^{t_1} \left| \frac{d\mathbf{R}}{dt} \right| dt \qquad (t \geq t_1)$$

By the fundamental theorem of calculus, we then have

$$\frac{ds}{dt} = \left| \frac{d\mathbf{R}}{dt} \right|$$

In coordinate form, this becomes

$$\frac{ds}{dt} = \left[\left(\frac{dx}{dt} \right)^2 + \left(\frac{dy}{dt} \right)^2 + \left(\frac{dz}{dt} \right)^2 \right]^{1/2}$$

Since our assumptions guarantee that $ds/dt \neq 0$, it follows that dt/ds exists and by the chain rule

$$\frac{d\mathbf{R}}{ds} = \frac{d\mathbf{R}}{dt} \frac{dt}{ds}$$

Since $d\mathbf{R}/dt$ is tangent to the curve, this shows $d\mathbf{R}/ds$ is also. Moreover, by (7), we see that

$$\mathbf{T} = d\mathbf{R}/ds$$

The geometrical and physical interpretation of these formulas will be given in the next section.

EXERCISES

1. Suppose that P_1P_2 is a smooth arc in the xy plane. Is it necessarily true that dy/dx exists at every point on this arc?

2. Give at least one reason for imposing condition (*iii*) in the definition of smooth arc.

3. By using identities concerning hyperbolic functions, eliminate the parameter t from the equations
$$x = \cosh t \qquad y = \sinh t$$
$$z = 0$$

4. As t varies from -1 to 1, the point (x,y,z) where
$$x = t, \quad y = |t|, \quad z = 0$$

traces a regular curve. At what point on this curve is there no tangent?

5. Find the unit vector tangent to the curve
$$x = \sin 2\pi t \qquad y = \cos 2\pi t$$
$$z = t$$
at the point $(0,1,1)$.

6. If $\mathbf{T}$ denotes the unit tangent to the curve
$$x = t \qquad y = 2t + 5$$
$$z = 3t$$
show that $d\mathbf{T}/dt = 0$.

7. Find the arc length of the curve described in Exercise 6, between $(0,5,0)$ and $(1,7,3)$, (a) by using (8), and (b) by using a little common sense.

8. What is the arc length of the closed arc described in Example 1 (page 65)?

9. Determine the arc length of the curve
$$x = e^t \cos t \qquad y = e^t \sin t$$
$$z = 0$$
between $t = 0$ and $t = 1$.

10. For the curve
$$x = \sin t - t \cos t$$
$$y = \cos t + t \sin t$$
$$z = t^2$$
find (a) the arc length between $(0,1,0)$ and $(-2\pi,1,4\pi^2)$, (b) $\mathbf{T}(t)$, (c) $\mathbf{T}(\pi)$.

11. Find the unit vector tangent to the oriented closed curve
$$x = a \cos t, \qquad y = b \sin t, \qquad z = 0$$
at $t = \frac{3}{2}\pi$.

2.3 : Velocity and Acceleration

In elementary physics books, it is shown that the acceleration of a particle moving in a *circular path* with *constant speed v* has magnitude v^2/ρ, where ρ is the radius* of the circle. If m is the mass of the particle, the force producing this acceleration has magnitude mv^2/ρ. This force is directed towards the center of the circle and is called the *centripetal force*.†

If the speed of the particle is also changing, then the acceleration is the sum of two components, the centripetal acceleration a_n, which is normal to the path, and a component a_t that is tangential to the path. The magnitude of the centripetal acceleration is v^2/ρ. The magnitude of the tangential acceleration a_t is $a_t = \rho\alpha$, where α is the angular acceleration $d^2\theta/dt^2$. Since arc length measured along a circle of radius ρ is $s = \rho\theta$, and since ρ is constant, we have $d^2s/dt^2 = \rho d^2\theta/dt^2 = \rho\alpha$, so we can also write $a_t = d^2s/dt^2$.

It is important to keep in mind that the acceleration of a particle is defined to be the time rate of change of its velocity. Since velocity is a vector quantity, this acceleration may arise from a change in either the magnitude or the direction of the velocity, or both. In the example just cited, the centripetal acceleration a_n arises entirely from the change in direction of velocity, whereas the tangential acceleration a_t is related entirely to the change in speed. (Recall that the magnitude of the velocity is the speed.)

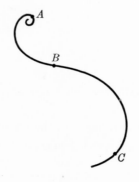

Figure 37

These concepts generalize to motion along any curve. Before giving a rigorous discussion, we shall give a purely heuristic discussion

* The usual notation in such books is R, not ρ.
† The reaction to this force is called the *centrifugal force*.

in which we use such vague terms as "approximately" and "small." This discussion serves as motivation for what follows later.

A small portion of any sufficiently smooth curve may be considered (approximately) as an arc of a circle of radius ρ. The value of ρ may vary with position on the curve. Thus, the more "bent" the curve, the smaller ρ will be. For a straight line, we would have to take ρ to be "infinity" (whatever that may mean; remember this is not a rigorous discussion). In Figure 37, the value of ρ at point A is less than its value at C, and ρ is extremely large in the neighborhood of point B.

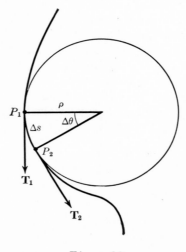

Figure 38

In Figure 38, we consider a portion of a curve between two nearby points P_1 and P_2. Let the arc length of this part of the curve be denoted Δs, and let $\Delta \theta$ denote the angle subtended by this arc at the center of the approximating circle. Clearly $\Delta s = \rho \Delta \theta$ (since we always measure angles in radians), and so $1/\rho = \Delta \theta / \Delta s$. The unit tangent vectors $\mathbf{T}_1$ and $\mathbf{T}_2$ at these two points also make an angle $\Delta \theta$, and the change in the unit tangent as we proceed from P_1 and P_2 is

$$\Delta \mathbf{T} = \mathbf{T}_2 - \mathbf{T}_1$$

For small $\Delta \theta$, the magnitude of $\Delta \mathbf{T}$ is approximately $\Delta \theta$, as we see from Figure 39 (keep in mind that the magnitudes of $\mathbf{T}_1$ and $\mathbf{T}_2$ are unity). Thus

$$\left|\frac{\Delta\mathbf{T}}{\Delta s}\right| \approx \frac{\Delta\theta}{\Delta s} = \frac{1}{\rho}$$

This approximation improves continuously as Δs approaches zero, so we can write

$$\left|\frac{d\mathbf{T}}{ds}\right| = \frac{1}{\rho}$$

This formula gives in principle a means of calculating ρ, the radius of the approximating circle. (But see Example 1, p. 78, before using this formula.)

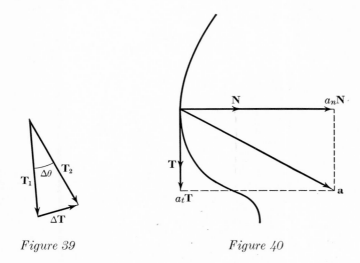

Figure 39   Figure 40

Now, let $\mathbf{N}$ denote a *unit* vector pointing towards the center of the approximating circle, and as usual let $\mathbf{T}$ denote the unit tangent vector (Section 2.2). The directions of both $\mathbf{T}$ and $\mathbf{N}$ may vary at different points along the curve, but they are always at right angles with each other. The preceding discussion suggests that the acceleration $\mathbf{a}$ is a sum of two components,

(1) $$\mathbf{a} = a_t\mathbf{T} + a_n\mathbf{N}$$

where $a_t = d^2s/dt^2$ and $a_n = v^2/\rho = (1/\rho)(ds/dt)^2$. (Again, we suggest that the reader look at Example 1, p. 78, before he uses these formulas.)

We are now ready to give a rigorous treatment of the velocity and acceleration of a moving particle.   The reader should realize that the preceding discussion is not intended to *prove* anything, but simply to serve as *motivation* for some of the following definitions.

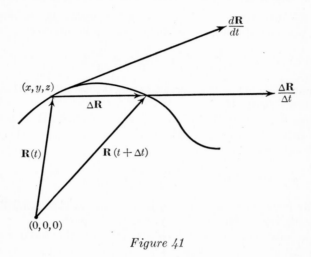

Figure 41

Since we will need to compute second derivatives, we assume that the coordinates x, y, and z are functions of t possessing second derivatives.   We assume also that these functions define a smooth arc (Section 2.2).

The *position* vector of the particle is defined to be

(2) $$\mathbf{R} = x\mathbf{i} + y\mathbf{j} + z\mathbf{k}$$

which we visualize as the directed line segment extending from the origin to the point at which the particle is located.   Clearly, $\mathbf{R}$ is a vector-valued function of the variable t, and the above assumptions ensure that the derivatives $d\mathbf{R}/dt$ and $d^2\mathbf{R}/dt^2$ exist.   These derivatives (which turn out to be the velocity $\mathbf{v}$ and the acceleration $\mathbf{a}$, respectively) are computed as shown in Section 2.1,

(3) $$\frac{d\mathbf{R}}{dt} = \frac{dx}{dt}\mathbf{i} + \frac{dx}{dt}\mathbf{j} + \frac{dy}{dt}\mathbf{k}$$

(4) $$\frac{d^2\mathbf{R}}{dt^2} = \frac{d^2x}{dt^2}\mathbf{i} + \frac{d^2y}{dt^2}\mathbf{j} + \frac{d^2z}{dt^2}\mathbf{k}$$

During a time interval of duration Δt, the position vector of the particle changes from an initial value $\mathbf{R}(t)$ to a new value $\mathbf{R}(t + \Delta t)$. The *displacement* of the particle during this interval of time is defined to be

$$(5) \qquad \Delta \mathbf{R} = \mathbf{R}(t + \Delta t) - \mathbf{R}(t) = \Delta x\, \mathbf{i} + \Delta y\, \mathbf{j} + \Delta z\, \mathbf{k}$$

If the displacement is divided by the scalar Δt, we obtain the average velocity of the particle during the time interval,

$$(6) \qquad \frac{\Delta \mathbf{R}}{\Delta t} = \frac{\Delta x}{\Delta t}\, \mathbf{i} + \frac{\Delta y}{\Delta t}\, \mathbf{j} + \frac{\Delta z}{\Delta t}\, \mathbf{k}$$

(In Figure 41, Δt is less than unity, hence the vector $\Delta \mathbf{R}/\Delta t$ is greater in magnitude than $\Delta \mathbf{R}$.)

Since $\mathbf{R}$ is differentiable, the average velocity $\Delta \mathbf{R}/\Delta t$ tends to a limit as Δt tends to zero. This limit is, by definition, the (instantaneous) velocity,

$$(7) \qquad \mathbf{v}(t) = \mathbf{R}'(t) = \frac{d\mathbf{R}}{dt} = \frac{dx}{dt}\, \mathbf{i} + \frac{dy}{dt}\, \mathbf{j} + \frac{dz}{dt}\, \mathbf{k}$$

It is clear from the diagram (and it was proved in Section 2.2) that the velocity vector $d\mathbf{R}/dt$ is tangential to the path.

It is convenient always to picture $\mathbf{v}(t)$ as a directed line segment with its tail at the point where the particle is located. As t varies, the corresponding vector $\mathbf{v}(t)$ may vary either in direction or magnitude or in both (Fig. 42). The speed of the particle is defined to be

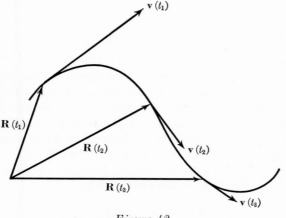

Figure 42

the magnitude of the velocity. From the definition of arc length (Section 2.2) we see that the speed is ds/dt, where s is arc length measured along the curve from some arbitrary initial point:

$$(8) \qquad |\mathbf{v}(t)| = \left[\left(\frac{dx}{dt}\right)^2 + \left(\frac{dy}{dt}\right)^2 + \left(\frac{dz}{dt}\right)^2\right]^{1/2} = \frac{ds}{dt}$$

As noted in that section, the unit tangent vector $\mathbf{T}$ may be obtained by dividing the velocity $\mathbf{v}(t)$ by the speed $|\mathbf{v}(t)|$, since our assumptions guarantee that $|\mathbf{v}(t)|$ is never zero.

$$(9) \qquad \mathbf{T} = \frac{\mathbf{v}(t)}{|\mathbf{v}(t)|}$$

We recall that $\mathbf{T}$ is also given by the expression

$$(10) \qquad \mathbf{T} = d\mathbf{R}/ds$$

This may be *seen* geometrically by noting that $|\Delta\mathbf{R}|$ is approximately equal to Δs, when Δs is small, so that $d\mathbf{R}/ds$ is a unit vector; the *rigorous* proof that $d\mathbf{R}/ds$ is tangent to the curve and of unit magnitude has already been given.

The *curvature* k of the curve at any point is defined to be the *magnitude* of the vector $d\mathbf{T}/ds$ at that point:

$$(11) \qquad k = \left|\frac{d\mathbf{T}}{ds}\right|$$

If $k \neq 0$, the *radius of curvature* ρ is defined to be the reciprocal of the curvature,

$$(12) \qquad \rho = 1/k$$

The motivation for this definition of ρ has already been given. By introducing k we will be able to avoid using the term "infinite radius of curvature." Thus, the curvature of a straight line is $k = 0$. In Figure 37, we see that $k = 0$ at point B, and we note that the curvature at point A is greater than the curvature at C.

Since $\mathbf{T}$ has constant *magnitude*, the derivative of $\mathbf{T}$ with respect to t is either the zero vector or it is a nonzero vector perpendicular to $\mathbf{T}$. This was proved in Example 5, Section 2.1. This is clear geometrically from Figure 39, where we see that $\Delta\mathbf{T}$ is approximately perpendicular to $\mathbf{T}$ if $\Delta\mathbf{T}$ is small.

If $d\mathbf{T}/dt$ is not the zero vector, we define the unit vector $\mathbf{N}$ to be $d\mathbf{T}/dt$ divided by its own magnitude,

$$(13) \qquad \mathbf{N} = \frac{d\mathbf{T}/dt}{|d\mathbf{T}/dt|}$$

If we apply the chain rule $d\mathbf{T}/dt = (d\mathbf{T}/ds)(ds/dt)$ to both numerator and denominator of this fraction, we can cancel ds/dt and obtain the alternative expression

$$\mathbf{N} = \frac{d\mathbf{T}/ds}{|d\mathbf{T}/ds|}$$

and since $k = |d\mathbf{T}/ds|$ we can write

$$d\mathbf{T}/ds = k\mathbf{N}$$

Now we are ready to discuss the acceleration of the particle. This is defined, of course, as the time rate of change of the velocity,

(14) $$\mathbf{a}(t) = \mathbf{v}'(t) = \frac{d\mathbf{v}}{dt} = \frac{d^2x}{dt^2}\mathbf{i} + \frac{d^2y}{dt^2}\mathbf{j} + \frac{d^2z}{dt^2}\mathbf{k}$$

Since $|\mathbf{v}(t)| = ds/dt$, we can write

(15) $$\mathbf{v}(t) = \frac{ds}{dt}\mathbf{T}$$

By the product rule for derivatives (Section 2.1),

$$\mathbf{a}(t) = \mathbf{v}'(t) = \frac{d^2s}{dt^2}\mathbf{T} + \frac{ds}{dt}\frac{d\mathbf{T}}{dt} = \frac{d^2s}{dt^2}\mathbf{T} + \frac{ds}{dt}\frac{d\mathbf{T}}{ds}\frac{ds}{dt}$$

$$= \frac{d^2s}{dt^2}\mathbf{T} + \left(\frac{ds}{dt}\right)^2 k\mathbf{N}$$

In other words, we have

(16) $$\mathbf{a} = a_t\mathbf{T} + a_n\mathbf{N}$$

where $a_t = d^2s/dt^2$ and $a_n = kv^2$. This is what we desired to prove. We note that at any point on the curve where $k = 0$, the normal vector $\mathbf{N}$ is not defined, but that doesn't matter since we have $a_n = 0$ in that case and hence have no need for $\mathbf{N}$ in (16). In the special case that $k \neq 0$, we can write $a_n = v^2/\rho$, the way we did in the heuristic discussion given previously.

Since $\mathbf{T}$ and $\mathbf{N}$ are mutually perpendicular vectors, at any point where they are defined we have, by the Pythagorean theorem,

(17) $$a^2 = a_t^2 + a_n^2$$

To compute a, one need only find $d^2\mathbf{R}/dt^2$ by differentiation, and calculate the magnitude of this vector. To compute a_t we need only find $v = d\mathbf{R}/dt$, calculate its magnitude $|d\mathbf{R}/dt| = ds/dt$, and differentiate this with respect to t. Having computed a and a_t, it is then easy to obtain a_n by using (17).

In many problems this is more practical than using the expression kv^2, since it is not always easy to compute k.

EXAMPLE 1: The position of a particle moving around the circle $x^2 + y^2 = r^2$ in the xy plane, with angular velocity ω, is

$$x = r \cos \omega t \qquad y = r \sin \omega t$$
$$z = 0$$

Find the normal and tangential components of acceleration of the particle, and determine the curvature of the circle.

Solution: We have

$$\mathbf{R} = r \cos \omega t\, \mathbf{i} + r \sin \omega t\, \mathbf{j}$$
$$d\mathbf{R}/dt = -r\omega \sin \omega t\, \mathbf{i} + r\omega \cos \omega t\, \mathbf{j}$$
$$d^2\mathbf{R}/dt^2 = -r\omega^2 \cos \omega t\, \mathbf{i} - r\omega^2 \sin \omega t\, \mathbf{j}$$

The magnitudes of these vectors are

$$v = ds/dt = |d\mathbf{R}/dt| = (r^2\omega^2 \sin^2 \omega t + r^2\omega^2 \cos^2 \omega t)^{\frac{1}{2}}$$
$$= \omega r$$
$$a = |d^2\mathbf{R}/dt^2| = \omega^2 r$$

Since ds/dt is a constant, $a_t = d^2s/dt^2 = 0$, and $a = a_n$. Therefore $kv^2 = \omega^2 r$, and since $v = \omega r$, we have $k = \omega^2 r/\omega^2 r^2 = 1/r$. This proves that the curvature of a circle is the reciprocal of its radius. The answers are: $a_n = \omega^2 r$, $a_t = 0$, $k = 1/r$.

EXAMPLE 2: The coordinates of a particle at time t are

$$x = \sin t - t \cos t$$
$$y = \cos t + t \sin t$$
$$z = t^2$$

Find the speed, the normal and tangential components of acceleration, and the curvature of the path, in terms of t.

Solution:

$$\mathbf{R} = (\sin t - t \cos t)\mathbf{i} + (\cos t + t \sin t)\mathbf{j} + t^2\mathbf{k}$$
$$d\mathbf{R}/dt = (t \sin t)\mathbf{i} + (t \cos t)\mathbf{j} + 2t\mathbf{k}$$
$$d^2\mathbf{R}/dt^2 = (t \cos t + \sin t)\mathbf{i} + (-t \sin t + \cos t)\mathbf{j} + 2\mathbf{k}$$

The speed is $ds/dt = |d\mathbf{R}/dt| = (t^2 \sin^2 t + t^2 \cos^2 t + 4t^2)^{1/2} = \sqrt{5}\,t$. The tangential component of acceleration is $a_t = d^2s/dt^2 = \sqrt{5}$. From (17),

$$a_n = [a^2 - a_t{}^2]^{1/2}$$
$$= [(t \cos t + \sin t)^2 + (-t \sin t + \cos t)^2 + 2^2 - 5]^{1/2} = t$$

Since $a_n = kv^2$ we have $k = a_n/v^2 = t/5t^2 = 1/5t$.

EXERCISES

In the first four problems below, the coordinates of a moving particle are given as a function of the time t. Find (a) the speed, (b) the tangential and normal components of acceleration, (c) the unit tangent vector $\mathbf{T}$, and (d) the curvature of the curve, as functions of time.

1. $x = e^t \cos t, \quad y = e^t \sin t, \quad z = 0$

2. $x = 3t \cos t, \quad y = 3t \sin t, \quad z = 4t$

3. $x = e^t \cos t, \quad y = e^t \sin t, \quad z = e^t$

4. $x = 5 \sin 4t, \quad y = 5 \cos 4t, \quad z = 10t$

5. If $\mathbf{F}$ is a function of t possessing derivatives of all orders, find the derivative of

$$\mathbf{F} \times \frac{d\mathbf{F}}{dt} \cdot \frac{d^2\mathbf{F}}{dt^2}$$

6. By inspection, write down the values of each of the following:

  (a) $\dfrac{d\mathbf{R}}{ds} \cdot \mathbf{T}$

  (b) $\dfrac{d}{ds}(\mathbf{T} \cdot \mathbf{T})$

  (c) $\dfrac{d^2\mathbf{R}}{dt^2} \cdot \mathbf{T}$

  (d) $\mathbf{T} \cdot \mathbf{N}$

  (e) $\dfrac{d\mathbf{R}}{dt} \cdot \mathbf{T}$

7. Find the curvature of the space curve

$$x = 3t^2 - t^3$$
$$y = 3t^2$$
$$z = 3t + t^3$$

8.   A space curve that lies in a plane is called a plane curve. What can you say about $\mathbf{T} \times \mathbf{N}$ if you know that the curve is a plane curve? (The vector $\mathbf{T} \times \mathbf{N}$ is called the *binormal*.)

2.4 : Planar Motion in Polar Coordinates

In this section we consider the motion of a particle in the xy plane in which the position of the particle is given in polar coordinates. We assume the polar coordinates (r,θ) are given as functions of the time t, and that these functions possess second derivatives.

Although it is possible to change from polar coordinates to Cartesian coordinates, this may be inconvenient for various reasons, which is one reason for treating this case separately. The main reason for considering polar coordinates separately will become clear as we proceed.

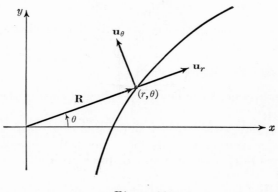

Figure 43

In order to work directly with polar coordinates, it is convenient to introduce unit vectors $\mathbf{u}_r$ and $\mathbf{u}_\theta$ which point respectively along the position vector and at right angles to it (in the direction of increasing θ), as shown in Figure 43.

It is easy to see that $\mathbf{u}_r$ and $\mathbf{u}_\theta$ can be written in terms of $\mathbf{i}$ and $\mathbf{j}$ as follows:

(1)
$$\mathbf{u}_r = \cos \theta \, \mathbf{i} + \sin \theta \, \mathbf{j}$$
$$\mathbf{u}_\theta = -\sin \theta \, \mathbf{i} + \cos \theta \, \mathbf{j}$$

Note that $\mathbf{u}_r$ and $\mathbf{u}_\theta$ are functions of θ and are defined at every point in space except the origin. Unlike $\mathbf{i}$ and $\mathbf{j}$, $\mathbf{u}_r$ and $\mathbf{u}_\theta$ are not constants. For example, along the positive x axis, $\mathbf{u}_r = \mathbf{i}$, but along the positive y axis, $\mathbf{u}_r = \mathbf{j}$. It follows that we must be careful in differentiating vector fields written in terms of $\mathbf{u}_r$ and $\mathbf{u}_\theta$.

Directly from (1) we see that

(2)
$$d\mathbf{u}_r/d\theta = \mathbf{u}_\theta$$
$$d\mathbf{u}_\theta/d\theta = -\mathbf{u}_r$$

These formulas will be used repeatedly in the following discussion.

The position vector of a particle located at a point (r,θ) is

(3)
$$\mathbf{R} = r\mathbf{u}_r$$

We obtain the velocity by differentiating (3) and using the chain rule,

$$\frac{d\mathbf{R}}{dt} = \frac{dr}{dt}\mathbf{u}_r + r\frac{d\mathbf{u}_r}{dt}$$

$$= \frac{dr}{dt}\mathbf{u}_r + r\frac{d\mathbf{u}_r}{d\theta}\frac{d\theta}{dt}$$

Hence, by (2), the velocity is given by

(4)
$$\mathbf{v} = \frac{d\mathbf{R}}{dt} = \frac{dr}{dt}\mathbf{u}_r + r\frac{d\theta}{dt}\mathbf{u}_\theta$$

This expresses the velocity as the sum of a radial component, directed away from or towards the origin with magnitude $|dr/dt|$, and a transverse component with magnitude $|r\,d\theta/dt|$.

EXAMPLE 1: A particle moves around the circle $r = 2$ with angular velocity $d\theta/dt = 5$ radians/second. Find its speed.

Solution: Since r is a constant, $dr/dt = 0$. Hence

$$\mathbf{v} = r(d\theta/dt)\mathbf{u}_\theta = 10\mathbf{u}_\theta$$

Hence $|\mathbf{v}| = 10$.

EXAMPLE 2: A circular disk rotates with constant angular velocity 3 rad/sec. A fly walks from the center of the disk outwards to the rim at a rate of 2 cm/sec (relative to the disk).   Find the speed of the fly 4 seconds after he starts at the center.

Solution: Since $dr/dt = 2$ we have $r = r_0 + 2t$.   Since the fly starts at the center, $r_0 = 0$.   Hence by (4)

$$\mathbf{v} = 2\mathbf{u}_r + 3r\mathbf{u}_\theta$$

At time $t = 4$, $r = 2t = 8$, so $\mathbf{v} = 2\mathbf{u}_r + 24\mathbf{u}_\theta$.   The speed is then $(2^2 + 24^2)^{\frac{1}{2}} = (580)^{\frac{1}{2}}$ cm/sec.

Returning to (4), we differentiate again to obtain the acceleration:

$$\mathbf{a} = \frac{d\mathbf{v}}{dt} = \frac{d^2r}{dt^2}\mathbf{u}_r + \frac{dr}{dt}\frac{d\mathbf{u}_r}{dt} + \frac{dr}{dt}\frac{d\theta}{dt}\mathbf{u}_\theta + r\frac{d^2\theta}{dt^2}\mathbf{u}_\theta + r\frac{d\theta}{dt}\frac{d\mathbf{u}_\theta}{dt}$$

$$= \frac{d^2r}{dt^2}\mathbf{u}_r + \frac{dr}{dt}\frac{d\mathbf{u}_r}{d\theta}\frac{d\theta}{dt} + \frac{dr}{dt}\frac{d\theta}{dt}\mathbf{u}_\theta + r\frac{d^2\theta}{dt^2}\mathbf{u}_\theta + r\frac{d\theta}{dt}\frac{d\theta}{dt}\frac{d\mathbf{u}_\theta}{d\theta}$$

$$= \frac{d^2r}{dt^2}\mathbf{u}_r + 2\frac{dr}{dt}\frac{d\theta}{dt}\mathbf{u}_\theta + r\frac{d^2\theta}{dt^2}\mathbf{u}_\theta - r\left(\frac{d\theta}{dt}\right)^2\mathbf{u}_r$$

Combining terms,

$$(5) \qquad \mathbf{a} = \left[\frac{d^2r}{dt^2} - r\left(\frac{d\theta}{dt}\right)^2\right]\mathbf{u}_r + \left[r\frac{d^2\theta}{dt^2} + 2\frac{dr}{dt}\frac{d\theta}{dt}\right]\mathbf{u}_\theta$$

The first term in (5), $(d^2r/dt^2)\mathbf{u}_r$, is just what we would expect to have, and the third term, $r(d^2\theta/dt^2)\mathbf{u}_\theta$, is also familiar from elementary physics (where the abbreviation α is sometimes used to denote the angular acceleration $d^2\theta/dt^2$).   In the special case that r is a constant, we have motion in a circle with center at the origin, a special case in which $\mathbf{u}_\theta$ and $\mathbf{u}_r$ are, respectively, the vectors $\mathbf{T}$ and $-\mathbf{N}$ of the preceding section.   In this special case, the second term is the centripetal acceleration term.

The fourth term,

$$2\frac{dr}{dt}\frac{d\theta}{dt}\mathbf{u}_\theta$$

sometimes called the *Coriolis acceleration*, is more complicated and is usually not discussed in elementary physics textbooks.   As a careful examination of the above derivation will show, this term is due partly to the change in *direction* of the radial component of velocity, and partly to the fact that, as r changes, the transverse component of velocity changes, even if the angular velocity $d\theta/dt$ is constant.

According to Newton's second law, $\mathbf{F} = m\mathbf{a}$, where $\mathbf{F}$ is the resultant force acting on the particle. This force $\mathbf{F}$ may be written as the sum of two components,

$$\mathbf{F} = F_r\mathbf{u}_r + F_\theta\mathbf{u}_\theta$$

The motion of the particle is then governed by the two differential equations

$$(6) \qquad F_r = m\frac{d^2r}{dt^2} - mr\left(\frac{d\theta}{dt}\right)^2$$

$$(7) \qquad F_\theta = mr\frac{d^2\theta}{dt^2} + 2m\frac{dr}{dt}\frac{d\theta}{dt}$$

If both sides of (7) are multiplied by r, (7) can be written in the form

$$(8) \qquad torque \quad rF_\theta = \frac{d}{dt}\left(mr^2\frac{d\theta}{dt}\right) \quad angular\ momentum$$

which in some cases may be interpreted as stating that the torque applied to the particle equals the time rate of change of its angular momentum.

If $F_\theta = 0$, (8) may be integrated to yield $mr^2\,d\theta/dt = C$. In other words, if the force is always directed radially towards or away from the origin (a "central force field"), then the angular momentum of the particle will be constant. This immediately implies Kepler's second law of planetary motion, that the radius vector in a central force field sweeps over area at a constant rate, since the rate at which the vector $\mathbf{R}$ sweeps out area is

$$\frac{dA}{dt} = \frac{1}{2}r^2\frac{d\theta}{dt}$$

EXERCISES

1. Find $d^3\mathbf{R}/dt^3$ in terms of $\mathbf{u}_r$ and $\mathbf{u}_\theta$.

2. A particle moves in a plane with constant angular velocity ω about the origin. The rate of increase of its acceleration is parallel to the position vector $\mathbf{R}$.
   (a) What is the transverse component of $d^3\mathbf{R}/dt^3$?
   (b) Show that $d^2r/dt^2 = r\omega^2/3$.

3. Find $\mathbf{v}$ and $\mathbf{a}$ if a particle moves so that

$$r = b(1 - \cos\theta)$$

and

$$\frac{d\theta}{dt} = 4$$

4. Find **v** and **a** if
$$r = b(1 + \sin t)$$
$$\theta = e^{-t} - 1$$

5. Which terms in (5) will be nonzero, in each of the following cases:
    (a) a particle moves around a circle with center at the origin with constant nonzero angular velocity;
    (b) a particle moves around a circle with center at the origin with constant nonzero angular acceleration;
    (c) a particle moves along a straight line not passing through the origin, with constant speed;
    (d) a person is walking from the center of a merry-go-round towards its outer edge (discuss various possibilities).

6. A particle moves along a straight line, not passing through the origin.
    (a) Is $r(d\theta/dt)^2$ nonzero?
    (b) Can $r(d\theta/dt)^2$ be called the centripetal acceleration in this case?

7. A particle moves with constant radial speed 2 cm/sec away from the center of a platform rotating with uniform angular velocity of 30 revolutions per minute.
    (a) What is its radial acceleration?
    (b) What is its Coriolis acceleration?

8. Find the magnitude of the Coriolis acceleration of a particle moving in the xy plane with position given by
$$x = 3t \cos 4\pi t$$
$$y = 3t \sin 4\pi t$$

T H R E E

SCALAR AND VECTOR FIELDS

3.1 : Scalar Fields;   Isotimic Surfaces;   Gradient

If to each point (x,y,z) of a region in space there is made to correspond a number $f(x,y,z)$, we say that f is a *scalar field*. In other words, a scalar field is simply a scalar-valued function of three variables.

For the sake of fixing ideas, the following scalar fields are given as examples that will be referred to repeatedly:

EXAMPLE 1: $f(x,y,z) = x + 2y - 3z$

EXAMPLE 2: $f(x,y,z) = x^2 + y^2 + z^2$

EXAMPLE 3: $f(x,y,z) = x^2 + y^2$

EXAMPLE 4: $f(x,y,z) = \dfrac{x^2}{4} + \dfrac{y^2}{9} + z^2$

EXAMPLE 5: $f(x,y,z) = \sqrt{x^2 + y^2} - z$

EXAMPLE 6: $f(x,y,z) = \dfrac{1}{x^2 + y^2}$

The fields in Examples 1 through 5 are defined at every point in space. The field in Example 6 is defined at every point (x,y,z) except where $x^2 + y^2 = 0$, that is, everywhere except on the z axis.

If f is a scalar field, any surface defined by $f(x,y,z) = C$, where C is a constant, is called an *isotimic surface* (from the Greek *isotimos*, meaning *of equal value*). Sometimes, in physics, more specialized terms are used. For instance, if f denotes either electric or gravitational field potential, such surfaces are called *equipotential surfaces*. If f denotes temperature, they are called *isothermal surfaces*. If f denotes pressure, they are called *isobaric surfaces*.

In the above examples, the isotimic surfaces are:

EXAMPLE 1:   All planes perpendicular to the vector $\mathbf{i} + 2\mathbf{j} - 3\mathbf{k}$.

EXAMPLE 2:   All spheres with center at the origin.

EXAMPLE 3:   All right circular cylinders with the z axis as axis of symmetry.

EXAMPLE 4:   A family of ellipsoids.

EXAMPLE 5:   A family of cones.

EXAMPLE 6:   The same as in Example 3.

It is impossible for distinct isotimic surfaces of the same scalar field to intersect, since only one number $f(x,y,z)$ is associated with any one point (x,y,z).

Here are some physical examples of scalar fields: the mass density of the atmosphere, the temperature at each point in an insulated wall, the water pressure at each point in the ocean, the gravitational potential of points in astronomical space, the electrostatic potential of the region between two condenser plates. Such scalar fields as density and pressure are only approximate idealizations of a complicated physical situation, since they take no account of the atomic properties of matter.

Let us consider the behavior of a scalar field in the neighborhood of a point (x_0,y_0,z_0) within its region of definition. Let us imagine a line segment passing through (x_0,y_0,z_0) parallel to a given vector $\mathbf{u}$. Let s denote displacement measured along the line segment in the direction of $\mathbf{u}$ (Fig. 44) with $s = 0$ corresponding to (x_0,y_0,z_0). To each value of the parameter s there corresponds a point (x,y,z) on the line segment, and hence a corresponding scalar $f(x,y,z)$. The derivative df/ds at $s = 0$, if this derivative exists, is called the *directional derivative* of f at (x_0,y_0,z_0), in the direction of the vector $\mathbf{u}$.

In other words, the directional derivative of f is simply the rate of change of f, per unit distance, in some prescribed direction. The directional derivative df/ds will generally depend on the location of the point (x_0, y_0, z_0) and also on the direction prescribed.

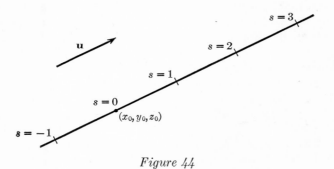

Figure 44

The directional derivative of a scalar field f in a direction parallel to the x axis, with s measured as increasing in the positive x direction, is conventionally denoted $\partial f/\partial x$, and is called the partial derivative of f with respect to x. Similarly, the directional derivative of f in the positive y direction is called $\partial f/\partial y$, and that in the positive z direction, $\partial f/\partial z$. We assume that the reader has had some experience with partial derivatives.

The directional derivative of a scalar field f in a direction that is not parallel to any of the coordinate axes is conventionally denoted df/ds, but of course this symbol is ambiguous; it would not make sense to ask "what is df/ds" without specifying the direction in which s is to be measured.

A convenient way of specifying the desired direction is by prescribing a vector $\mathbf{u}$ pointing in that direction. Although the magnitude of $\mathbf{u}$ is immaterial, it is conventional to take $\mathbf{u}$ to be a unit vector. We have already seen (Section 2.3) that a unit vector in a desired direction can be obtained by computing $d\mathbf{R}/ds$ in that direction, where $\mathbf{R} = x\mathbf{i} + y\mathbf{j} + z\mathbf{k}$. That is,

$$(1) \qquad \mathbf{u} = \frac{dx}{ds}\mathbf{i} + \frac{dy}{ds}\mathbf{j} + \frac{dz}{ds}\mathbf{k}$$

is a unit vector pointing in the direction in which s is measured. Here we are thinking of x, y, and z as functions of the parameter s, for points (x,y,z) on the line segment.

If the partial derivatives $\partial f/\partial x$, $\partial f/\partial y$, and $\partial f/\partial z$ exist and are continuous throughout a region, then it can be shown (see any book on advanced calculus) that the following chain rule is valid:

(2)
$$\frac{df}{ds} = \frac{\partial f}{\partial x}\frac{dx}{ds} + \frac{\partial f}{\partial y}\frac{dy}{ds} + \frac{\partial f}{\partial z}\frac{dz}{ds}$$

If we define the *gradient* of f to be the vector

(3)
$$\mathbf{grad}\, f = \frac{\partial f}{\partial x}\mathbf{i} + \frac{\partial f}{\partial y}\mathbf{j} + \frac{\partial f}{\partial z}\mathbf{k}$$

we see that the right side of (2) is the dot product of $\mathbf{u}$ with $\mathbf{grad}\, f$,

(2′)
$$\frac{df}{ds} = \mathbf{u}\cdot\mathbf{grad}\, f$$

Since $\mathbf{u}$ is a unit vector, $\mathbf{u}\cdot\mathbf{grad}\, f = |\mathbf{u}|\,|\mathbf{grad}\, f|\cos\theta = |\mathbf{grad}\, f|\cos\theta$, where θ is the angle between $\mathbf{grad}\, f$ and $\mathbf{u}$. This gives us the first fundamental property of the gradient:

> The scalar component of $\mathbf{grad}\, f$ in any given direction gives the rate of change df/ds in that direction.

By the maximum principle (Section 1.9), the largest possible value of $\mathbf{u}\cdot\mathbf{grad}\, f$, for unit vectors $\mathbf{u}$, is obtained when $\mathbf{u}$ is in the same direction as $\mathbf{grad}\, f$ (assuming $\mathbf{grad}\, f \neq \mathbf{0}$). Since $\mathbf{u}\cdot\mathbf{grad}\, f = df/ds$, it follows that the maximum value of df/ds is obtained in the direction of $\mathbf{grad}\, f$. This is the second fundamental property of the gradient:

> $\mathbf{grad}\, f$ points in the direction of the maximum rate of increase of the function f.

If $\mathbf{u}$ points in the direction of $\mathbf{grad}\, f$, then

$$\mathbf{u}\cdot\mathbf{grad}\, f = |\mathbf{u}|\,|\mathbf{grad}\, f|\cos 0 = |\mathbf{grad}\, f|,$$

which gives the third fundamental property of the gradient:

> The magnitude of $\mathbf{grad}\, f$ equals the maximum rate of increase of f per unit distance.

The wording of these fundamental properties has been chosen in a manner that experience shows makes them rather easy to memorize [and they *should* be memorized, together with the definition (3)].

The fourth fundamental property of the gradient of a function makes it possible to use the gradient concept in solving geometrical problems:

> Through any point (x_0, y_0, z_0) where **grad** $f \neq \mathbf{0}$, there passes an isotimic surface $f(x, y, z) = C$; **grad** f is normal (i.e., perpendicular) to this surface at the point (x_0, y_0, z_0).

The constant C is, of course, equal to $f(x_0, y_0, z_0)$. The fourth fundamental property applies only to points where **grad** $f \neq \mathbf{0}$. If **grad** $f = \mathbf{0}$ it may be that no isotimic surface can be found that contains the point (x_0, y_0, z_0). The property holds only when $\partial f / \partial x$, $\partial f / \partial y$, and $\partial f / \partial z$ exist and are continuous in a neighborhood of the point in question.

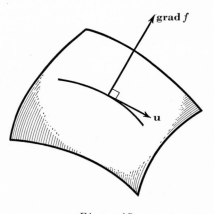

Figure 45

We omit a detailed proof of this property, but the following discussion may make it seem reasonable. Let C denote the value of f at (x_0, y_0, z_0). Since **grad** $f \neq \mathbf{0}$, it follows from the preceding fundamental properties that df/ds will be positive in some direction. If, then, we proceed away from (x_0, y_0, z_0) in that direction, the value of $f(x, y, z)$ will increase, and if we proceed in the opposite direction, its value will decrease. Since f and its partial derivatives are continuous, it seems reasonable that there will be a surface passing through (x_0, y_0, z_0) on one side of which the values of f will be greater than (and on the other less than) C. Now suppose we consider any smooth arc passing through (x_0, y_0, z_0) and entirely contained in this surface. Then $f(x,y,z) = C$ for all points on this arc and so $df/ds = 0$, where s is measured along this arc. Since $df/ds = \mathbf{u} \cdot \mathbf{grad}\, f$, and in this case $\mathbf{u}$ is a unit vector tangent to this arc, we see that $\mathbf{u} \cdot \mathbf{grad}\, f = df/ds = 0$, implying that $\mathbf{grad}\, f$ is perpendicular to $\mathbf{u}$. This reasoning applies to any smooth arc in the surface passing through (x_0, y_0, z_0). Hence $\mathbf{grad}\, f$ is perpendicular to every such arc, at that point, which can be the case only if $\mathbf{grad}\, f$ is perpendicular to the surface (Fig. 45).

We now return to the six examples given previously. In each case the gradient is easily computed using the definition (3):

EXAMPLE 1: $\mathbf{grad}\, f = \mathbf{i} + 2\mathbf{j} - 3\mathbf{k}$

EXAMPLE 2: $\mathbf{grad}\, f = 2x\mathbf{i} + 2y\mathbf{j} + 2z\mathbf{k}$

EXAMPLE 3: $\mathbf{grad}\, f = 2x\mathbf{i} + 2y\mathbf{j}$

EXAMPLE 4: $\mathbf{grad}\, f = \dfrac{x}{2}\mathbf{i} + \dfrac{2y}{9}\mathbf{j} + 2z\mathbf{k}$

EXAMPLE 5: $\mathbf{grad}\, f = \dfrac{x\mathbf{i} + y\mathbf{j}}{\sqrt{x^2 + y^2}} - \mathbf{k}$

EXAMPLE 6: $\mathbf{grad}\, f = -\dfrac{2x}{(x^2 + y^2)^2}\mathbf{i} - \dfrac{2y}{(x^2 + y^2)^2}\mathbf{j}$

The following remarks may be instructive concerning these examples.

Example 1. (This is the only one of the six examples for which $\mathbf{grad}\, f$ is a constant.) We already know from Section 1.10 that $\mathbf{i} + 2\mathbf{j} - 3\mathbf{k}$ is perpendicular to any plane of the form $x + 2y - 3z = C$. We see that $\mathbf{grad}\, f = \mathbf{i} + 2\mathbf{j} - 3\mathbf{k}$. Thus we have verified the fourth fundamental property, in this special case.

Example 2. In this case the isotimic surfaces are spheres centered at the origin, so the normals to these surfaces must be vectors pointing directly away from the origin. Sure enough, we have $\mathbf{grad}\, f = 2x\mathbf{i} + 2y\mathbf{j} + 2z\mathbf{k} = 2\mathbf{R}$, and we know that the vector $2\mathbf{R}$ always points directly away from the origin. To see the significance of the number 2 here, let r denote the distance from the origin to the point (x,y,z). Then we can, in this example, write the function in terms of r: it is simply r^2. Moreover, if we move away from any point in the direction of maximum increase of r^2, which obviously means moving directly away from the origin, then the element of arc length is simply dr. In this direction, the derivative df/ds is df/dr, and $(d/dr)(r^2) = 2r$. Also, $|2\mathbf{R}| = 2r$, so we have verified the third fundamental property in this special case.

Example 3. The reader familiar with cylindrical coordinates can do the same thing here as we just did with Example 2. Let $\rho = (x^2 + y^2)^{1/2}$, the distance from the point (x,y,z) to the z axis. The function f in this example is simply ρ^2, and obviously increases most rapidly in a direction perpendicular to the z axis. Its derivative in this direction is 2ρ, which is also the magnitude $|\mathbf{grad}\, f| = (4x^2 + 4y^2)^{1/2}$. This direction is clearly normal to the isotimic surfaces, since the latter are right circular cylinders centered on the z axis. The second, third, and fourth fundamental properties are extremely transparent in this case, as they were in Example 2.

Example 5. (We skip Example 4.) All we care to note here is the elementary geometrical significance of the $-\mathbf{k}$ term in $\mathbf{grad}\, f$. The isotimic surfaces of this function are conical; each has an apex on the z axis and spreads outward with increasing z. Thus, we see easily that the normal to one such surface will not point directly away from the z axis, as it does in Example 3, but will have an additional component in the negative z direction.

The following are some sample problems that illustrate the use of the fundamental properties of the gradient of a scalar field.

PROBLEM 1: Find df/ds in the direction of the vector $4\mathbf{i} + 4\mathbf{j} - 2\mathbf{k}$, at the point $(1,1,2)$, if $f(x,y,z) = x^2 + y^2 - z$.

Solution: $\mathbf{grad}\, f = 2x\mathbf{i} + 2y\mathbf{j} - \mathbf{k} = 2\mathbf{i} + 2\mathbf{j} - \mathbf{k}$ at $(1,1,2)$. A unit vector in the desired direction is $\mathbf{u} = \frac{2}{3}\mathbf{i} + \frac{2}{3}\mathbf{j} - \frac{1}{3}\mathbf{k}$ (obtained by dividing $4\mathbf{i} + 4\mathbf{j} - 2\mathbf{k}$ by its own length). The first fundamental property then gives $df/ds = \mathbf{u} \cdot \mathbf{grad}\, f = \frac{4}{3} + \frac{4}{3} + \frac{1}{3} = 3$. This means that the value of the function f is increasing 3 units per unit distance, if we proceed from $(1,1,2)$ in the direction stated.

PROBLEM 2: The temperature of points in space is given by $f(x,y,z) = x^2 + y^2 - z$. A mosquito located at $(1,1,2)$ desires to fly in such a direction that he will get warm as soon as possible. In what direction should he move?

Solution: As we saw in Problem 1, $\mathbf{grad}\, f = 2\mathbf{i} + 2\mathbf{j} - \mathbf{k}$ at $(1,1,2)$. The mosquito should move in the direction of this vector.

PROBLEM 3: A mosquito is flying at a speed of 5 units of distance per second, in the direction of the vector $4\mathbf{i} + 4\mathbf{j} - 2\mathbf{k}$. The temperature is given by $f(x,y,z) = x^2 + y^2 - z$. What is his rate of increase of temperature, per unit time, at the instant he passes through the point $(1,1,2)$?
Solution: As shown in the first problem above, df/ds in this direction is 3 units per unit distance. The rate of increase of temperature per unit time is thus $df/dt = (df/ds)(ds/dt) = (3)(5) = 15$ degrees per second.

PROBLEM 4: What is the maximum possible df/ds, if $f(x,y,z) = x^2 + y^2 - z$, at the point $(1,4,2)$?
Solution: $|\mathbf{grad}\, f| = |2\mathbf{i} + 8\mathbf{j} - \mathbf{k}| = \sqrt{69}$. The answer is approximately 8.31 units per unit distance.

PROBLEM 5: Find a unit vector normal to the surface $x^2 + y^2 - z = 6$ at the point $(2,3,7)$.
Solution: This is an isotimic surface for the function $f(x,y,z) = x^2 + y^2 - z$. At $(2,3,7)$, we have $\mathbf{grad}\, f = 2x\mathbf{i} + 2y\mathbf{j} - \mathbf{k} = 4\mathbf{i} + 6\mathbf{j} - \mathbf{k}$. The length of this vector is $\sqrt{53}$. Thus, an answer is $(\sqrt{53}/53)(4\mathbf{i} + 6\mathbf{j} - \mathbf{k})$. (The negative of this vector is also a correct answer.)

An error commonly made in the preceding problem, for some psychological reason this author cannot fathom, is writing $\mathbf{grad}\, f = 4\mathbf{i} + 6\mathbf{j} - 7\mathbf{k}$, at $(2,3,7)$, as though $\mathbf{grad}\, f$ were $2x\mathbf{i} + 2y\mathbf{j} - z\mathbf{k}$ instead of $2x\mathbf{i} + 2y\mathbf{j} - \mathbf{k}$.

EXERCISES

1.   Find the derivative of $f(x,y,z) = x + xyz$ at the point $(1,-2,2)$ in the direction of (a) $2\mathbf{i} + 2\mathbf{j} - \mathbf{k}$, (b) $2\mathbf{i} + 2\mathbf{j} + \mathbf{k}$.

2.   Given $f(x,y,z) = x^2 + y^2 + z^2$, find the maximum value of df/ds at the point $(3,0,4)$,
     (a) by using the gradient of f;
     (b) by interpreting f geometrically.

3   Find the directional derivative df/ds at $(1,3,-2)$ in the direction
     of $-\mathbf{i} + 2\mathbf{j} + 2\mathbf{k}$ if
     (a) $f(x,y,z) = yz + xy + xz$
     (b) $f(x,y,z) = x^2 + 2y^2 + 3z^2$
     (c) $f(x,y,z) = xy + x^3y^3$
     (d) $f(x,y,z) = \sqrt{x^2 + y^2 + z^2}$

4.   Compute **grad** f if $f(x,y,z) = \sin x + e^{xy} + z$.

5.   If $f(x,y,z) = x^2 + y^2$, what is the locus of points in space for
     which **grad** f is parallel to the y axis?

6.   Find all functions $f(x,y,z)$ such that **grad** $f = 2x\mathbf{i} + z\mathbf{j} + y\mathbf{k}$.

7.   Find the magnitude of the greatest rate of change of $f(x,y,z) =$
     $(x^2 + z^2)^3$ at $(1,3,-2)$.   Interpret geometrically.

8.   Find a vector normal to the surface $x^2 + yz = 5$ at $(2,1,1)$.

9.   Find an equation of the plane tangent to the sphere
     $x^2 + y^2 + z^2 = 21$ at $(2,4,-1)$.

10. Find a vector normal to the cylinder $x^2 + z^2 = 8$ at $(2,0,2)$
     (a) by inspection (draw a diagram);
     (b) by finding the gradient of the function $f(x,y,z) = x^2 + z^2$
          at $(2,0,2)$.

11. Find an equation of the plane tangent to the surface $z^2 - xy =$
     14 at $(2,1,4)$.

12. Find equations of the line normal to the sphere $x^2 + y^2 + z^2 = 2$
     at $(1,1,0)$,
     (a) by inspection (draw a diagram);
     (b) by computing the gradient of $f(x,y,z) = x^2 + y^2 + z^2$ at
          $(1,1,0)$, and using this to find the normal.

13. Find a unit vector normal to the plane $3x - y + 2z = 3$,
     (a) by the methods of Section 1.10;
     (b) by the methods of the preceding section.

14. Find an equation of the plane tangent to the surface $z = x^2 + y^2$
     at $(2,3,13)$. [Hint: Consider the function $f(x,y,z) =$
     $x^2 + y^2 - z$.]

15. Find a unit vector tangent to the curve of intersection of the
     cylinder $x^2 + y^2 = 4$ and the sphere $x^2 + y^2 + z^2 = 9$ at the
     point $(\sqrt{2}, \sqrt{2}, \sqrt{5})$,
     (a) by drawing a diagram, obtaining the answer by inspection;

(b) by finding the vector product of the normals to the two surfaces at that point;

(c) by writing the equations of the curve in parametric form, letting $x = 2 \sin t$ and $y = 2 \cos t$.

16. Determine the angle between the normals to the intersecting spheres $x^2 + y^2 + z^2 = 16$ and $(x - 1)^2 + y^2 + z^2 = 16$, at the point $(1/2, 3/2, 3\sqrt{6}/2)$.

17. At what angle does the line $2x = y = 2z$ intersect the ellipsoid $2x^2 + y^2 + 2z^2 = 8$?

3.2 : Vector Fields and Flow Lines

A vector field $\mathbf{F}$ is a rule associating with each point (x,y,z) in a region a vector $\mathbf{F}(x,y,z)$. In other words, a vector field is a vector-valued function of three variables.

Some vector fields are not defined for all points in space. For example, the vector field

$$\mathbf{F}(x,y,z) = \frac{x\mathbf{i} + y\mathbf{j}}{x^2 + y^2}$$

is not defined along the z axis, since $x^2 + y^2 = 0$ for points on the z axis.

In visualizing a vector field, we imagine that from each point in the region there extends a vector. Both direction and magnitude may vary with position (Fig. 46).

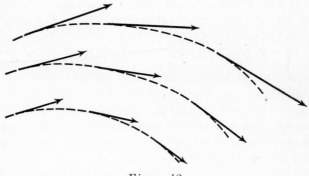

Figure 46

Any vector field may be written in terms of its components:

$$\mathbf{F}(x,y,z) = F_x(x,y,z)\mathbf{i} + F_y(x,y,z)\mathbf{j} + F_z(x,y,z)\mathbf{k}$$

EXAMPLE 1: If $f(x,y,z)$ is a *scalar* field, **grad** f is a *vector* field.

EXAMPLE 2: Each of the "vectors" $\mathbf{u}_r$ and $\mathbf{u}_\theta$ (Section 2.4) is a vector field defined in the plane.

EXAMPLE 3: In hydrodynamics, one associates with each point of a region the velocity of the fluid passing that point. In that manner one obtains, at any instant of time, a vector field describing the instantaneous velocity of the fluid at every point.

EXAMPLE 4: In theoretical physics, there is associated with each point in space an electric intensity vector, representing the force that would be exerted, per unit charge, on a charged particle, if it were located at that point. This electric field, at any instant of time, constitutes a vector field.

EXAMPLE 5: Magnetic fields and gravitational fields also provide examples of vector fields defined in space.

Let us consider a vector field $\mathbf{F}$ that is defined and nonzero at every point of a region in space. Any curve passing through this region is called a *flow line* of $\mathbf{F}$ provided that, at every point on the curve, a vector $\mathbf{T}$ tangent to the curve is parallel to $\mathbf{F}$. (Some authors call them *stream lines* or *characteristic curves* of $\mathbf{F}$. If $\mathbf{F}$ is a field of force, the flow lines are commonly called *lines of force*.) In Figure 46, three flow lines are indicated as dotted curves.

This may be looked at another way. The vector field $\mathbf{F}$ determines, at each point in the region, a direction. If a particle moves in such a manner that its direction at any point coincides with the direction of the vector field $\mathbf{F}$ at that point, the space curve traced out is a flow line.

If the vector field $\mathbf{F}(x,y,z)$ describes the velocity at each point in a hydrodynamic system, the flow lines are the paths which are traversed by the component particles of the fluid. We are assuming here that $\mathbf{F}$ is not a function of the time t.

Note that, if $g(x,y,z)$ is a scalar field that is not zero at any point, the flow lines of the vector field $g(x,y,z)\mathbf{F}(x,y,z)$ will be the same as those of $\mathbf{F}(x,y,z)$, since only the *direction* of $\mathbf{F}$ at any point is relevant in determining the flow lines.

Since the direction of a flow line is uniquely determined by the field $\mathbf{F}$, it is impossible to have two different directions at the same point, and therefore it is impossible for two flow lines to intersect. If the magnitude of $\mathbf{F}$ is zero at some point in space, then no direction is defined at that point and no flow line passes through that point.

If $\mathbf{R}$ is the position vector to an arbitrary point of a flow line, and if s represents arc length measured along the curve, then the unit vector tangent to the curve at that point is given by

$$(1) \qquad \mathbf{T} = \frac{d\mathbf{R}}{ds} = \frac{dx}{ds}\mathbf{i} + \frac{dy}{ds}\mathbf{j} + \frac{dz}{ds}\mathbf{k}$$

The requirement that $\mathbf{T}$ have the same direction as $\mathbf{F}$ can be written

$$(2) \qquad \mathbf{T} = \beta\mathbf{F}$$

where β is a scalar-valued function of x, y, and z. This can be written in terms of components,

$$(3) \qquad \beta F_x = \frac{dx}{ds}, \quad \beta F_y = \frac{dy}{ds}, \quad \beta F_z = \frac{dz}{ds}$$

If F_x, F_y, and F_z are all nonzero, we may eliminate β and write (3) in differential form,

$$(4) \qquad \frac{dx}{F_x} = \frac{dy}{F_y} = \frac{dz}{F_z}$$

If exactly one of these functions (say F_z) is identically zero in a region, then we obtain directly from (3) that the curve lies in a plane (say, $z = $ constant) parallel to one of the coordinate planes.

EXAMPLE 5: If $\mathbf{F} = x\mathbf{i} + y\mathbf{j} + \mathbf{k}$, then $F_x = x$, $F_y = y$, and $F_z = 1$, giving $dx/x = dy/y = dz$. Solving the differential equations $dx/x = dz$ and $dy/y = dz$ we obtain $x = C_1 e^z$, $y = C_2 e^z$. Thus the equations of the flow line passing through the point (3,4,7) are $x = 3e^{z-7}$, $y = 4e^{z-7}$. The equations of the flow line passing through the origin are $x = 0$, $y = 0$—i.e., the z axis.

EXAMPLE 6: If $\mathbf{F} = x\mathbf{i} + y\mathbf{j}$, then $F_x = x$, $F_y = y$, and $F_z = 0$. In this case (3) becomes $\beta x = dx/ds$, $\beta y = dy/ds$, and $0 = dz/ds$. Eliminating β from the first two equations we obtain $dx/x = dy/y$, and solving we obtain $y = Cx$. From the third equation we obtain $z =$ constant. The field is zero when both x and y equal zero, and so the flow lines are not defined along the z axis. The flow lines are straight half-lines parallel to the xy plane, extending outwards from the z axis.

EXAMPLE 7: If $\mathbf{F} = -y\mathbf{i} + x\mathbf{j}$, then $-\beta y = dx/ds$, $\beta x = dy/ds$, and $0 = dz/ds$. Thus $dx/-y = dy/x$ and hence $x^2 + y^2 =$ constant. Also, we have $z =$ constant. The flow lines are circles surrounding the z axis and parallel to the xy plane. As in Example 6, no flow lines pass through points on the z axis.

Flow lines may be infinite in extent, as in Examples 5 and 6, or they may close upon themselves, as in Example 7.

EXERCISES

1. A vector field $\mathbf{F}$ is defined in the xy plane by $\mathbf{F} = -y\mathbf{i} + x\mathbf{j}$. Draw a diagram similar to Figure 46, showing the values of $\mathbf{F}$ at the points $(1,0)$, $(0,1)$, $(-1,0)$, $(0,-1)$, $(1,1)$, $(-1,1)$, $(-1,-1)$, $(1,-1)$, and a scattering of other points. Indicate flow lines.

2. Let $\mathbf{F} = x^2\mathbf{i} + y^2\mathbf{j} + \mathbf{k}$. (a) Find the general equation of a flow line. (b) Find the flow line through the point $(1,1,2)$.

3.3 : Divergence

The concept of *gradient*, as we have presented it, applies only to scalar fields. We now consider the more complicated problem of describing the rate of change of a *vector* field. There are two fundamental measures of the rate of the change of a vector field: the *divergence* and the *curl*.

Roughly speaking, the divergence of a vector field is a scalar field that tells us, at each point, the extent to which the field diverges away from that point. The curl of a vector field is a vector field that gives us, at each point, an indication of how the field swirls in the vicinity of that point. However, to describe divergence and curl in such a brief manner is not only useless but a bit dangerous, since (if taken literally) both of these preceding sentences are not only vague but technically incorrect.   As we shall see, it is possible for a field to have a positive divergence without appearing to "diverge" at all, and it is possible for a field to have a nontrivial curl and yet have flow lines that do not bend at all.

In this section, we consider only the divergence.   We shall first take up the simple problem of computing the divergence, and then we will describe in greater detail its geometrical and physical significance.

The *divergence* of a *vector* field

(1) $$\mathbf{F} = F_x\mathbf{i} + F_y\mathbf{j} + F_z\mathbf{k}$$

is a *scalar* field, denoted div $\mathbf{F}$, defined by

(2) $$\operatorname{div}\mathbf{F} = \frac{\partial F_x}{\partial x} + \frac{\partial F_y}{\partial y} + \frac{\partial F_z}{\partial z}$$

This definition should be memorized, although at this point the student cannot appreciate the importance of the concept of divergence.

Note especially that the divergence of a vector field is a *scalar* field.

Later on, we shall consider other definitions of divergence.   All these definitions lead eventually to formula (2).   The advantage of taking (2) as the definition right away is that it is easy to learn and simple to use for actual computation, when $\mathbf{F}$ is given in form (1). The disadvantage of this definition is that it gives absolutely no idea of the physical or geometrical meaning of the concept of divergence. A student could stare at (2) for a long time and still not discover for himself its significance.

From definition (2), it is easy to compute the divergence of a vector field, as we now demonstrate with examples.   *Warning:* It makes no sense to speak of the divergence of a scalar field.

EXAMPLE 1:   Find div $\mathbf{F}$, if $\mathbf{F} = x\mathbf{i} + y^2z\mathbf{j} + xz^3\mathbf{k}$.

Solution: $\operatorname{div}\mathbf{F} = \dfrac{\partial}{\partial x}(x) + \dfrac{\partial}{\partial y}(y^2z) + \dfrac{\partial}{\partial z}(xz^3)$

$$= 1 + 2yz + 3xz^2$$

EXAMPLE 2:   Find div $\mathbf{F}$, if $\mathbf{F} = xe^y\mathbf{i} + e^{xy}\mathbf{j} + \sin yz\ \mathbf{k}$.

Solution: $\operatorname{div}\mathbf{F} = \dfrac{\partial}{\partial x}(xe^y) + \dfrac{\partial}{\partial y}(e^{xy}) + \dfrac{\partial}{\partial z}(\sin yz)$

$$= e^y + xe^{xy} + y\cos yz$$

EXAMPLE 3:   Give an example of a vector field **F** that has divergence equal to 3 at every point in space.

Solution: Many solutions can be given, for instance **F** = 3x**i** or **F** = x**i** + y**j** + z**k**.

EXAMPLE 4:   In Figure 47, is the divergence of **F** at point P positive or negative?   Assume no variation of **F** in the z direction and that F_z is identically zero.

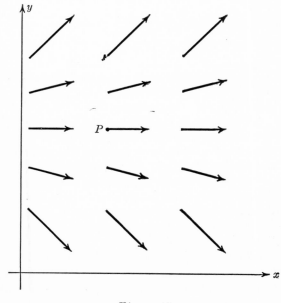

Figure 47

Solution: We see from the diagram that F_x is approximately constant, so $\partial F_x/\partial x = 0$.   Below P, F_y is negative, and above P, F_y is positive, so $\partial F_y/\partial y$ is positive.   Since $F_z = 0$, we have $\partial F_z/\partial z = 0$. It follows that div **F** is positive at point P.

EXAMPLE 5:   In Figure 48, is the divergence of **F** at point P positive or negative?   Assume no variation of **F** in the z direction and that F_z is identically zero.

Solution: We see from the diagram that F_x is decreasing with increasing x, hence $\partial F_x / \partial x$ is negative. F_y and F_z are zero at every point. It follows that the divergence of **F** is negative at every point.

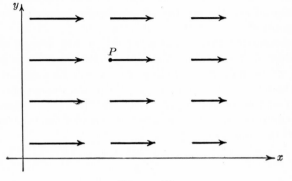

Figure 48

Now let us consider the geometrical meaning of divergence. To fix ideas, let us consider a vector field $\mathbf{F} = F_x\mathbf{i} + F_y\mathbf{j} + F_z\mathbf{k}$ representing the instantaneous velocity of a compressible fluid (say, a gas). Let us consider a region in the neighborhood of a point P. Let V denote the volume of this region. During a time interval Δt, the fluid in this region moves to a new location, where presumably the shape as well as the volume occupied by this body of fluid will be different. In other words, we are considering a fixed body of fluid whose volume is subject to change as the particles making up the body move along the flow lines. If Δt and V are small, the displacement of the center of gravity of this portion of fluid is, to a first approximation, $\mathbf{F}\Delta t$, where **F** is the velocity at P. Let ΔV denote the change in volume of this portion of the fluid. Then $\Delta V / \Delta t$ gives the rate of change of volume, per unit time, during this time interval. If now we pass to the limit, letting Δt tend to zero, we obtain the instantaneous rate of change of volume per unit time, for this portion of fluid, located in the vicinity of point P.

We denote this time rate of change of volume by dV/dt. That is,

(3) $$\frac{dV}{dt} = \lim_{\Delta t \to 0} \frac{\Delta V}{\Delta t}$$

Now the reader should have no difficulty imagining that this time
rate of change of volume dV/dt may depend on the location of the
point P. If, for example, the fluid is expanding in the region surrounding P, dV/dt will be positive. If the fluid is being compressed,
dV/dt will be negative. If the fluid is incompressible, say if it is
water, then dV/dt will be (for all practical purposes) equal to zero,
at *every* point P.

However, and this is important, dV/dt will depend not only on
the location of the point P but also on the magnitude of V. For
instance, if the fluid is expanding, dV/dt will be larger for a larger
volume than for a small volume. (We would expect the change in
volume of a cubic inch of fluid to be greater than the change in volume
of a cubic millimeter.) Let us therefore consider the *fractional* change
of volume per unit time,

$$(4) \qquad\qquad \frac{1}{V}\frac{dV}{dt}$$

The expression (4) represents the time rate of change of volume *per
unit volume*, for a quantity of fluid occupying a region of volume V in
the vicinity of point P. For instance, if the fluid is expanding in such
a way that a cubic millimeter of fluid expands to four cubic millimeters
during two seconds, then the time rate of change of volume per unit
volume is $3/2$ cubic millimeters per cubic millimeter per second (the
physicist would simply say $3/2$ per second, since the unit "cubic
millimeters" cancels out in both numerator and denominator).

What we have just said is somewhat oversimplified. It may be,
especially if the volume V we had to begin with is very large, that
the fluid in some parts of the region is expanding but in other parts is
contracting, or perhaps expanding at a different rate. If we are to
describe what is happening at point P, we must consider a very small
region about P. Or, to put it more precisely, we must take the limit
of (4) as we let V tend to zero. When we do this, we obtain the
divergence of $\mathbf{F}$:

$$(5) \qquad\qquad \operatorname{div}\mathbf{F} = \lim_{V \to 0}\frac{1}{V}\frac{dV}{dt}$$

We now have two definitions of divergence. The first one (2)
is strictly computational, and expresses the divergence as the sum of
three partial derivatives. The second one is geometrically more
meaningful: We imagine the field to represent the velocity of a fluid,
and define the divergence as the "time rate of change of volume per

unit volume." In Figure 47, the divergence is positive at point P, and we see easily that the volume occupied by a given amount of fluid is also increasing as the fluid passes through point P. The lines of flow are diverging in the neighborhood of P. This is the picture that motivates the common (incorrect) statement that "positive divergence means the field is diverging, negative divergence means the field is converging." Note that in Figure 48, the divergence is negative, but the flow lines are *not* converging. The divergence is negative because the volume occupied by a given amount of fluid is decreasing (more fluid enters a given region from the left than leaves it to the right).

We are not yet in a position to show that definitions (2) and (5) are equivalent. Instead, we shall pass on to a discussion of the divergence of another kind of vector field that arises in physics. Here we imagine that the vector field represents the *flux density* of a compressible fluid. It is important to distinguish between the velocity of a fluid and its flux density, so let us digress a moment to discuss this concept, which is of fundamental importance in fluid dynamics.

As before, let $\mathbf{F}$ denote the velocity field of a fluid. At each point in space, $\mathbf{F}$ is a vector representing the velocity of a particle of fluid that is passing through that point. Let ρ denote the density of the fluid. Thus, ρ is a scalar field giving at each point the mass per unit volume of the fluid at that point. Since we assume the fluid to be compressible, the density ρ may vary from one point to another. At any instant of time, $\mathbf{F}$ is a vector field and ρ is a scalar field. The *flux density* $\mathbf{D}$ of the fluid is defined to be the vector field obtained by multiplying $\mathbf{F}$ by ρ:

$$(6) \qquad\qquad \mathbf{D} = \rho\mathbf{F}$$

Roughly speaking, flux density represents the "mass flow" of the liquid. It is not hard to see that the mass of fluid per unit time crossing any small plane area of magnitude dA is, to a first approximation, $\mathbf{D}\cdot\mathbf{n}\,dA$, where $\mathbf{n}$ is a unit vector perpendicular to the area pointing in the same general direction as the fluid crossing the area. In other words, the scalar component of $\mathbf{D}$ in any direction gives the mass per unit area and per unit time that crosses an area perpendicular to that direction.

Now let us assume that no chemical or other processes are going on, in the region we consider, that would tend to create or destroy any fluid. Then it can be shown that

$$(7) \qquad\qquad \operatorname{div} \mathbf{D} = -\partial\rho/\partial t$$

Thus the divergence of the flux density is simply the negative of the time rate of change of fluid density. Because of the negative sign in (7), the divergence of the flux density is negative wherever the mass density of the fluid is increasing, and is positive in regions where the mass density is decreasing. For an incompressible fluid, i.e., a fluid whose mass density ρ is a constant, we must always have div **D** = 0, an important theoretical property in the analysis of the flow of such fluids.

Keep in mind that (7) is not intended as a definition of divergence, but simply as an interesting example of the many formulas from physics that can be expressed quite simply in terms of divergence. The same formula can be written

$$\frac{\partial D_x}{\partial x} + \frac{\partial D_y}{\partial y} + \frac{\partial D_z}{\partial z} + \frac{\partial \rho}{\partial t} = 0$$

but to anyone not expert in partial differential equations this formula is almost meaningless. One of the main features of vector analysis is that it provides a simple and convenient *language* for expressing basic laws of physics.

After we have studied the divergence theorem in the next chapter, formulas such as (7) will take on much more meaning. Meanwhile we shall go on the concept of the *curl*.

EXERCISES

Find the divergence of the following vector fields:

1. $\mathbf{F} = x\mathbf{i} + y^2\mathbf{j} - xz\mathbf{k}$
2. $\mathbf{F} = e^{xy}\mathbf{i} + \sin xy\,\mathbf{j} + \cos^2 zx\,\mathbf{k}$
3. $\mathbf{F} = 3\mathbf{i} + 4\mathbf{j} - 5xy\mathbf{k}$
4. $\mathbf{F} = 3x\mathbf{i} + 4z\mathbf{j} - 7x^2\mathbf{k}$
5. $\mathbf{F} = x^2 \sin y\,\mathbf{i} + y^2 \sin yz\,\mathbf{j} + xy \sin 3z^4\,\mathbf{k}$
6. Give an example of a field with a constant negative divergence.
7. Give an example of a field whose divergence depends only on x, is always positive, and increases with increasing x. [Hint: The function e^x is positive for every x.]
8. Find the divergence of the field

$$\frac{x\mathbf{i} + y\mathbf{j} + z\mathbf{k}}{(x^2 + y^2 + z^2)^{3/2}}$$

Is the divergence of this field defined at every point in space?

9.   What can you say about the divergence of the vector field in
      Figure 49 at points P, Q, and R?

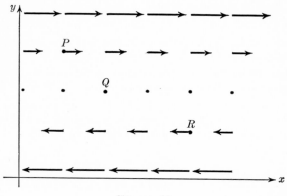

Figure 49

10.   What can you say about the divergence of the vector field in
      Figure 50 at points P, Q, and R?   Assume no variation of **F**
      in the z direction and that F_z is identically zero.

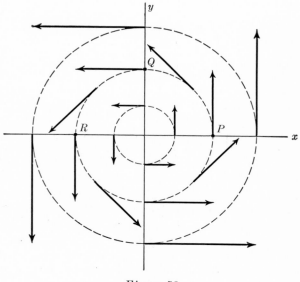

Figure 50

3.4 : Curl

The *curl* of a vector field $\mathbf{F} = F_x\mathbf{i} + F_y\mathbf{j} + F_z\mathbf{k}$ is the vector field

(1) $\left(\dfrac{\partial F_z}{\partial y} - \dfrac{\partial F_y}{\partial z}\right)\mathbf{i} + \left(\dfrac{\partial F_x}{\partial z} - \dfrac{\partial F_z}{\partial x}\right)\mathbf{j} + \left(\dfrac{\partial F_y}{\partial x} - \dfrac{\partial F_x}{\partial y}\right)\mathbf{k}$

Rather than memorize (1), the student is advised to write the curl in the form of a symbolic determinant:

(2) $\mathbf{curl\ F} = \begin{vmatrix} \mathbf{i} & \mathbf{j} & \mathbf{k} \\ \partial/\partial x & \partial/\partial y & \partial/\partial z \\ F_x & F_y & F_z \end{vmatrix}$

EXAMPLE 1: Find **curl F**, if $\mathbf{F} = xyz\mathbf{i} + x^2y^2z^2\mathbf{j} + y^2z^3\mathbf{k}$.
Solution:

$$\mathbf{curl\ F} = \begin{vmatrix} \mathbf{i} & \mathbf{j} & \mathbf{k} \\ \partial/\partial x & \partial/\partial y & \partial/\partial z \\ xyz & x^2y^2z^2 & y^2z^3 \end{vmatrix}$$

$$= (2yz^3 - 2x^2y^2z)\mathbf{i} + (xy)\mathbf{j} + (2xy^2z^2 - xz)\mathbf{k}$$

EXAMPLE 2: Find **curl F** if $\mathbf{F} = x\mathbf{i} + y\mathbf{j} + z\mathbf{k}$.
Solution:

$$\mathbf{curl\ F} = \begin{vmatrix} \mathbf{i} & \mathbf{j} & \mathbf{k} \\ \partial/\partial x & \partial/\partial y & \partial/\partial z \\ x & y & z \end{vmatrix} = \mathbf{0}$$

EXAMPLE 3: In what direction is **curl F** at points P and Q in Figure 51? Assume that F_z is identically zero and that there is no variation in **F** in the z-direction. (This is the velocity field for a rigid rotation, and is the same as that shown in Figure 50.)

Solution: At point P, F_y is increasing in the x direction, so $\partial F_y/\partial x$ is positive. Although F_x is zero at P, it is positive below P and negative above, so F_x is decreasing as we move through P in the y direction, that is, $\partial F_x/\partial y$ is negative. Since we assume F_z identically zero, the derivatives $\partial F_z/\partial y$ and $\partial F_z/\partial x$ are also zero, and since we assume no variation in the z direction, $\partial F_y/\partial z$ and $\partial F_x/\partial z$ are zero. It follows that the only term in (1) that does not vanish is the

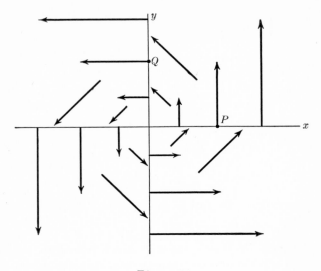

Figure 51

last term, and that the last term is positive. In other words, the curl of this vector field at P is a vector parallel to the z axis (directed towards the reader, perpendicular to the page).

At point Q, F_y is zero, but it is negative to the left of Q and positive to the right, hence $\partial F_y/\partial x$ is positive. F_x is negative at Q and is becoming even more negative with increasing y, and so $\partial F_x/\partial y$ is negative. The term $(\partial F_y/\partial x - \partial F_x/\partial y)$ is therefore positive. The other derivatives in (1) equal zero. It follows that **curl F** at point Q is also perpendicular to the xy plane, directed towards the reader. (In fact, a little reflection will convince the reader that **curl F** at point P is equal to **curl F** at point Q.)

EXAMPLE 4: In what direction is **curl F**, if **F** is as shown in Figure 52?

Solution: Since **F** is directed parallel to the y axis and appears to have magnitude proportional to x, we can guess $\mathbf{F} = Cx\mathbf{j}$, where C is a negative constant. Hence

$$\mathbf{curl\ F} = \begin{vmatrix} \mathbf{i} & \mathbf{j} & \mathbf{k} \\ \partial/\partial x & \partial/\partial y & \partial/\partial z \\ 0 & Cx & 0 \end{vmatrix} = C\mathbf{k}$$

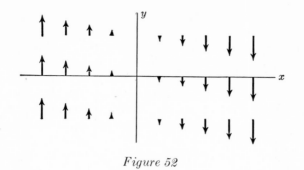

Figure 52

Since C is negative, the curl is directed into the page (negative z direction).

EXAMPLE 5:   Let us imagine that **F** represents the velocity field of a fluid of constant mass density rotating with uniform angular velocity ω about the z axis.   Find **curl F**.   (Assume the angular velocity vector $\boldsymbol{\omega}$ to point in the positive z direction.)

Solution: Since $\boldsymbol{\omega} = \omega\mathbf{k}$, we have (Section 1.14) $\mathbf{F} = \omega\mathbf{k} \times R$, where $\mathbf{R} = x\mathbf{i} + y\mathbf{j} + z\mathbf{k}$.   Hence $\mathbf{F} = -\omega y\mathbf{i} + \omega x\mathbf{j}$.   Using (2) we find that **curl F** $= 2\omega\mathbf{k}$.   In other words, the curl of **F** is just twice the angular velocity vector, and is the same at every point in space.

In connection with the last example, we note once again that the curl of a vector field is a vector field, not just a vector.   Although it is conventional to draw the angular velocity vector along the axis of rotation (in this case, the z axis), **F** and hence the curl of **F** is defined at every point in space, not just for points along the z axis. Example 5 is somewhat unusual; in this special case **curl F** turns out to be a constant (independent of x, y, and z).

Now let us consider the geometrical significance of the curl of a vector field **F**.   As before, it is convenient to imagine that **F** represents the velocity field of a fluid.   Let us for convenience think of the fluid as an incompressible liquid having a fairly high mass density. Now let us imagine we have a little paddle wheel, something like that shown in Figure 53, that is free to rotate about its axis AA'.

Now imagine that we immerse this paddle wheel in the liquid. Because of the flow of the liquid, it will tend to rotate with some angular velocity.   This angular velocity will vary, depending on where we locate the paddle wheel and on the positioning of its axis. For instance, if it is located at the origin in Figure 52, it will rotate most rapidly with its axis parallel to the z axis, and will not tend to rotate at all if its axis is parallel to the x axis.

Let us imagine that the paddle wheel is located at some point P and is so oriented that it is rotating at its maximum possible angular velocity. In other words, suppose that it is not possible to increase its angular velocity by changing the direction of its axis AA'. Then the axis AA' will be parallel to the curl of **F**, and the curl of **F** will have magnitude just twice the angular velocity of the paddle wheel. If the paddle wheel does not tend to rotate at all, no matter what position it is in, then **curl F** is the zero vector.

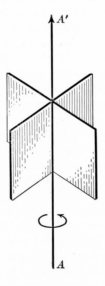

Figure 53

The author assumes that the originators of the definition of **curl F** must have undergone some soul-searching when they encountered this factor of 2 between the magnitude of **curl F** and the angular velocity. It is possible, by changing the definition of curl, to eliminate this factor, but this would require having a factor of $\frac{1}{2}$ in the definition, which would also be inconvenient.

To determine the actual direction of the curl, in this imaginary experiment with the paddle wheel, we use the right-hand rule. If the fingers of the right hand are curled in the same general direction as the blades of the wheel are rotating, then the thumb points in the direction of **curl F**. Thus, if the velocity field were like that shown in Figure 51, the paddle wheel would rotate counterclockwise, so **curl F** would point up from the page rather than into it. The reader with an even more fanciful imagination might think of the axis of the paddle wheel as equipped with the usual right-handed thread, in which case the paddle wheel, while rotating, would tend to pull in the direction of the curl, as though it were trying to screw its way through the liquid.

In Figure 52, the paddle wheel would tend to rotate the most rapidly with its axis perpendicular to the page; it will rotate because the velocity of the fluid is greater on one side than on the other. The direction of the curl is into the page, because the paddle wheel will tend to rotate clockwise. This example shows that it is possible for a vector field to have nonzero curl even when the flow lines are straight lines; hence, to describe **curl F** as "a measure of the rate of swirling of **F**" is not completely accurate.

We hope that this discussion gives the reader some intuitive feeling for the concept of curl. It is not a very rigorous discussion, to be sure. We shall now proceed to another description of the geometrical significance of the curl that some students (but very few) prefer to that given above. It is even more questionable from a rigorous point of view than the one just given.

The reader may be familiar with practice golf balls that an occasional golfer uses in his back yard. Such a ball is hollow with numerous holes punched through its surface. (If you prefer, think of a punctured ping-pong ball.) Imagine such a ball, in miniature, floating in a liquid with velocity field **F**. Since the ball is punctured it is filled with liquid, so that buoyant forces are negligible and the ball will rotate freely with the liquid. As the ball moves through a point P, its angular velocity is described by a vector $\boldsymbol{\omega}$ (Section 1.1) along its axis of rotation. Then **curl F** at point P is approximately equal to $2\boldsymbol{\omega}$. The approximation improves with smaller balls, and as we let the radius of the ball tend to zero, the approximation $2\boldsymbol{\omega}$ tends to **curl F**. Readers familiar with the concept of angular momentum will realize what an oversimplification this picture is; we are assuming a sort of instantaneous response on the part of the ball to the angular velocity of the fluid surrounding it, which is about as naive as assuming that the path of a ball dropped into a fluid will coincide with a flow line.

Because of this connection with rotation, some textbooks write **rot F** rather than **curl F**.

The statements made here will be justified in Section 5.14.

EXERCISES

In Exercises 1 through 3, find **curl F**:

1. $\mathbf{F} = xy^2\mathbf{i} + xy\mathbf{j} + xy\mathbf{k}$

2. $\mathbf{F} = e^{xy}\mathbf{i} + \sin xy\ \mathbf{j} + \cos yz^2\ \mathbf{k}$

3. $\mathbf{F} = z^2x\mathbf{i} + y^2z\mathbf{j} - z^2y\mathbf{k}$

4.   Draw a rough picture of the vector field $\mathbf{F} = x\mathbf{i} + y\mathbf{j} + z\mathbf{k}$ and, thinking of the paddle-wheel interpretation of **curl F**, explain why **curl F** is identically zero in this case.

5.   Give an example of a vector field with curl identically equal to **2i**.

6.   Is it possible to tell anything about **curl F**, given only a description of the flow lines of **F**?

REVIEW EXERCISE

Write down, in your own words, the geometrical or physical significance of **grad** f, div **F**, and **curl F**. Avoid vague nonsense such as "divergence is represented by water spraying out of a nozzle" or "curl is what you get when you stir coffee in a cup."

3.5 : Del Notation

To properly understand the notion of an "operator" is it necessary to take a broader look at the concept of a "function." For this reason we digress momentarily to consider what is meant by a function.

In elementary calculus, the functions considered are usually "real-valued functions of a real variable." That is, a function f is a rule that associates with every real number x in its domain of definition a single real number $f(x)$. For example, the exponential function is defined for all x, and to each real number x associates a single real number e^x. We define this function by writing $f(x) = e^x$. Other functions are defined by writing, say, $f(x) = x^2$ or $f(x) = \sin x$. Most mathematicians nowadays distinguish rather carefully between the symbol f and the notation $f(x)$. The former denotes the function and the latter denotes the value of the function (which is a number and not a function). Thus if $f(x) = x^2$, the function f is the *rule* "square the given number," but $f(3)$ is the *number* 9.

In more advanced courses we meet functions of two or three variables. In this book "scalar fields" are simply real-valued functions of three real variables. Thus, the function f defined by $f(x,y,z) = x^2y^2z^2$ says "multiply together the squares of the given numbers." When used alone, in this context, the letter f denotes this *rule*, but if we write, say, $f(2,1,3)$, we mean the *value* of the function at the point $(2,1,3)$, which in this case is the number 36.

Most of the functions we have been considering in this chapter are described by expressions involving x, y, and z. In studying vector analysis it is useful to "visualize" such functions in geometrical or physical terms. Thus, the engineering student may think of "an arbitrary function f" as meaning "an arbitrary electric potential," or "an arbitrary temperature distribution," and the mathematics major may think of this as meaning "a rule whereby we tag each point in space with a number." The student who thinks of a function as a jumble of x's, y's, and z's doesn't have much fun, and misses much of the point.

The *vector* fields we discuss are *vector-valued* functions of three real variables. But the idea is still much the same. In this context, a function $\mathbf{F}$ is a *rule* that associates with each point (x,y,z) a single vector $\mathbf{F}(x,y,z)$.

But now we come to what is a big hurdle for some students: passing to the *general* notion of a function. Much of the mystery of modern mathematics vanishes when we realize that a mathematician uses the word "function" in a much more general way, to denote any rule that associates an object with each one of a class of objects. Thus we have not only functions that associate numbers with numbers (the functions of elementary calculus), number with points in space (scalar fields), and vectors with points in space (vector fields), but also those that associate *functions* with *functions*!

For reasons of convenience partly, but mostly we suspect because so many people have old-fashioned ideas of what the word "function" means, such functions are usually called "operators." An operator is simply a rule that associates a function of some kind with each one of a class of functions.

To take an example from elementary calculus, the process of differentiation defines what is called the derivative operator. This is the operator that associates with every differentiable function f its derivative df/dx. This operator is sometimes denoted d/dx or sometimes even more simply D. It converts each differentiable function f into its derivative. We may formally write this

$$D(f) = df/dx$$

It is customary in some textbooks to assume that the reader is incapable of understanding even so simple a concept as the derivative operator. In these textbooks it is said that D is simply an abbreviation for d/dx, and that the symbol d/dx means nothing by itself, having meaning only when it is applied to some function f. Then we may write df/dx, which of course we all understand. Other differential operators, such as $L = (d^2/dx^2) + 2(d/dx) + 4$, are similarly interpreted as symbols that are meaningless unless followed by a function. In this case we have

$$L(f) = \frac{d^2f}{dx^2} + 2\frac{df}{dx} + 4f$$

But this is to miss the whole point of the operator concept. It would be much better to visualize this operator as a sort of meatgrinder, into which we drop the function f, turn the handle, and out drops the function $(d^2f/dx^2) + 2(df/dx) + 4f$. There is really no insurmountable difficulty in understanding that an operator T is a *rule* that associates with a function f some other function (or possibly even the same function) $T(f)$. It is certainly idiotic to say that the symbol d/dx means nothing by itself. It means a great deal: It represents the rule whereby we associate with a differentiable function its derivative. There is no point in recounting here the basic definition of "derivative" or the innumerable techniques involved in actually computing a derivative. The point is that a differentiable function has a derivative and the derivative operator pairs the derivative with the function. (The excellent concept of "pairing" is used in many modern books in discussing the function concept. The derivative of a function is just another function, and the derivative operator is the mathematical twine that binds the two together.)

Another example of an operator is the *gradient*. We recall that the gradient of a scalar field f is a vector field **grad** f. The gradient operator may be written, symbolically,

$$\mathbf{i}\frac{\partial}{\partial x} + \mathbf{j}\frac{\partial}{\partial y} + \mathbf{k}\frac{\partial}{\partial z}$$

Divergence is also an operator. It is an operator that converts a vector field into a scalar field. Similarly, *curl* is an operator, but it is an operator that changes a vector field into another vector field.

The three operators that concern us most are gradient, divergence, and curl. Although they may be written **grad**, div, and **curl**, there is a suggestive and convenient symbolic way of writing them that is commonly used. For this purpose, we introduce the symbol ∇, called "del" (sometimes "nabla"), which is an abbreviation for $\mathbf{i}(\partial/\partial x) + \mathbf{j}(\partial/\partial y) + \mathbf{k}(\partial/\partial z)$. In terms of this symbol, we can write **grad** f as ∇f. Working with ∇ purely formally, pretending for the moment it is a vector, we see that if we form the scalar product of ∇ with a vector field $\mathbf{F}$, we obtain

$$\nabla \cdot \mathbf{F} = \left(\mathbf{i}\frac{\partial}{\partial x} + \mathbf{j}\frac{\partial}{\partial y} + \mathbf{k}\frac{\partial}{\partial z}\right) \cdot (\mathbf{i}F_x + \mathbf{j}F_y + \mathbf{k}F_z)$$

$$= \frac{\partial F_x}{\partial x} + \frac{\partial F_y}{\partial y} + \frac{\partial F_z}{\partial z}$$

which is the divergence of $\mathbf{F}$. Similarly, if we imagine ∇ to be a vector and form the vector cross product of ∇ with $\mathbf{F}$, we obtain the curl of $\mathbf{F}$:

$$\nabla \times \mathbf{F} = \left(\mathbf{i}\frac{\partial}{\partial x} + \mathbf{j}\frac{\partial}{\partial y} + \mathbf{k}\frac{\partial}{\partial z}\right) \times (\mathbf{i}F_x + \mathbf{j}F_y + \mathbf{k}F_z)$$

$$= \begin{vmatrix} \mathbf{i} & \mathbf{j} & \mathbf{k} \\ \partial/\partial x & \partial/\partial y & \partial/\partial z \\ F_x & F_y & F_z \end{vmatrix} = \mathbf{curl\ F}$$

To recapitulate, ∇ is an abbreviation,

$$(1) \qquad \nabla = \mathbf{i}\frac{\partial}{\partial x} + \mathbf{j}\frac{\partial}{\partial y} + \mathbf{k}\frac{\partial}{\partial z}$$

The symbols ∇f, $\nabla \cdot \mathbf{F}$ and $\nabla \times \mathbf{F}$ are defined by

$$(2) \qquad \nabla f = \mathbf{grad}\ f$$

(3) $\nabla \cdot \mathbf{F} = \text{div } \mathbf{F}$

(4) $\nabla \times \mathbf{F} = \textbf{curl } \mathbf{F}$

After (1) is memorized, formulas (2), (3), and (4) provide very convenient ways of remembering the expressions for gradient, divergence, and curl.   We just operate with ∇ as though it were a vector. Henceforth we will frequently make use of these abbreviations.

It may be well to point out that ∇ by itself is not an operator, although it may be used as a convenient symbol in representing many different operators (of which **grad**, div, and **curl** are but three).   Nevertheless, ∇ is sometimes called a "vector differential operator," and some books even make the statement "this operator possesses properties analogous to those of ordinary vectors."   Just what these mysterious properties may be is never discussed.   In actual fact, ∇ has few properties analogous to those of ordinary vectors.   This matter will be discussed further in Chapter Five.   For the moment it will suffice to mention that $\nabla \times \mathbf{F}$ is not necessarily perpendicular to $\mathbf{F}$, as one might mistakenly suppose if ∇ were thought of as a vector.

EXERCISES

1.   If $f(x,y,z) = x^2y + z$, what is $f(2,3,4)$?

2.   If $f(x,y,z) = x^2y + z$, what is the value of ∇f at $(2,3,4)$?

3.   If $g(t) = t^3$ and $f(x,y,z) = x^2 + y^2z$, what is $g[f(1,1,3)]$?

4.   Given $\mathbf{F}(x,y,z) = x^2y\mathbf{i} + z\mathbf{j} - (x + y - z)\mathbf{k}$, find
      (a) $\nabla \cdot \mathbf{F}$
      (b) $\nabla \times \mathbf{F}$
      (c) $\nabla(\nabla \cdot \mathbf{F})$

5.   If $\mathbf{F}$ is a vector field, is $\nabla \cdot (\nabla \times \mathbf{F})$ a scalar field or a vector field?

6.   If $\mathbf{F}$ is a vector field, is $\nabla \times (\nabla \times \mathbf{F})$ a scalar field or a vector field?

7.   Find $\nabla \cdot \mathbf{R}$ and $\nabla \times \mathbf{R}$ where $\mathbf{R} = x\mathbf{i} + y\mathbf{j} + z\mathbf{k}$.

8.   If $f(x,y,z) = xyz + e^{xz}$, find $\nabla \cdot (\nabla f)$.

9.   (a) Compute $\nabla \times (\nabla f)$ for the scalar field f defined in Problem 8.

(b) Now do the same thing for another scalar field f (use any of the scalar fields defined in preceding problems, or make one up yourself).

(c) What can you conjecture from this?

10. (a) Compute $\nabla \cdot (\nabla \times \mathbf{F})$ for the vector field $\mathbf{F}$ defined in Problem 4.

(b) Do the same for a vector field $\mathbf{F}$ that you have made up yourself.

(c) What can you conjecture from this?

3.6 : The Laplacian

In electrostatics, the gradient of the electric potential is a scalar multiple of the electric field intensity, and the divergence of the electric intensity is related to the charge density. For this and other reasons it is convenient to introduce a single operator that is the composite of the two operators **grad** and div. This operator is called the *Laplacian*.

The Laplacian of a scalar field f is defined to be div (**grad** f). Note that **grad** f is a vector field and the divergence of **grad** f is a scalar field; hence the Laplacian of a scalar field f is a scalar field. In del notation this is $\nabla \cdot (\nabla f)$ and for simplicity is frequently written $\nabla^2 f$.

We have

(1) $$\text{Laplacian } (f) = \nabla^2 f = \nabla \cdot (\nabla f) = \frac{\partial^2 f}{\partial x^2} + \frac{\partial^2 f}{\partial y^2} + \frac{\partial^2 f}{\partial z^2}$$

since

$$\nabla \cdot (\nabla f) = \nabla \cdot \left(\frac{\partial f}{\partial x} \mathbf{i} + \frac{\partial f}{\partial y} \mathbf{j} + \frac{\partial f}{\partial z} \mathbf{k} \right) = \frac{\partial^2 f}{\partial x^2} + \frac{\partial^2 f}{\partial y^2} + \frac{\partial^2 f}{\partial z^2}$$

The symbol ∇^2 may be considered to be simply an abbreviation for

$$\frac{\partial^2}{\partial x^2} + \frac{\partial^2}{\partial y^2} + \frac{\partial^2}{\partial z^2}$$

The equation

(2) $$\nabla^2 f = 0$$

is called *Laplace's equation*. Any function satisfying this equation in a given region is said to be *harmonic* in that region. For example, the electric potential of a static distribution of charges is harmonic in any region where the charge density is zero. A function describing the steady-state temperature distribution of a homogeneous material is harmonic in the interior of the region occupied by the material.

From the purely mathematical viewpoint, we may say that the Laplacian is a sort of three-dimensional counterpart of the ordinary second derivative operator. For example, if the second derivative of a function of one variable is equal to zero, the function must be of the simple linear form $f(x) = mx + b$. Such a function f has the property that if we average the values of the function at the endpoints of an interval we obtain the value of the function at the center of the interval. Analogously, we may compute the average value of a function of three variables over the surface of a sphere. If the Laplacian of such a function is zero, i.e., if the function is harmonic, then the average value of the function over the surface of a sphere equals its value at the center of the sphere. Unfortunately, this similarity must not be taken too literally; for example, harmonic functions need not be linear functions of x, y, and z. They may be quite complex; whole books have been written about the properties of harmonic functions.

The formal differential operator

$$\nabla^2 = \frac{\partial^2}{\partial x^2} + \frac{\partial^2}{\partial y^2} + \frac{\partial^2}{\partial z^2}$$

may also be applied to *vector* fields to obtain new vector fields, since if $\mathbf{F}$ is a *vector* field, $(\partial^2 \mathbf{F}/\partial x^2) + (\partial^2 \mathbf{F}/\partial y^2) + (\partial^2 \mathbf{F}/\partial z^2)$ makes perfectly good sense. For example, if

$$\mathbf{F} = x^2 y \mathbf{i} + y^2 z^3 \mathbf{j} + xyz^4 \mathbf{k}$$

then we have

$$\frac{\partial^2 \mathbf{F}}{\partial x^2} = 2y\mathbf{i}$$

$$\frac{\partial^2 \mathbf{F}}{\partial y^2} = 2z^3\mathbf{j}$$

$$\frac{\partial^2 \mathbf{F}}{\partial z^2} = 6y^2 z\mathbf{j} + 12xyz^2\mathbf{k}$$

whence $\nabla^2 \mathbf{F} = 2y\mathbf{i} + (2z^3 + 6y^2 z)\mathbf{j} + 12xyz^2\mathbf{k}$. When used in this sense, to operate on vector fields to produce vector fields, we will call ∇^2 the *vector* Laplacian operator. But note that ∇^2 used in this context no longer is the same as div **grad**, since if **F** is a *vector* field, **grad F** (and hence div **grad F**) does not make sense within the context of vector analysis.

EXERCISES

1. Find $\nabla^2 f$ in each case:
    (a) $f(x,y,z) = x^5 y z^3$
    (b) $f(x,y,z) = e^{xyz}$
    (c) $f(x,y,z) = \sin x + \cos y + e^z$
    (d) $f(x,y,z) = \dfrac{1}{(x^2 + y^2 + z^2)^{1/2}}$
    (e) $f(x,y,z) = x + 3y - z$

2. Find $\nabla^2 \mathbf{F}$ in each case:
    (a) $\mathbf{F}(x,y,z) = e^x \mathbf{i} + e^{xz}\mathbf{j} - \mathbf{k}$
    (b) $\mathbf{F}(x,y,z) = x\mathbf{i} + y\mathbf{j} + z\mathbf{k}$
    (c) $\mathbf{F}(x,y,z) = e^x \mathbf{i} + e^y \mathbf{j} + e^z \mathbf{k}$
    (d) $\mathbf{F}(x,y,z) = e^z \mathbf{i} + e^y \mathbf{j} + e^x \mathbf{k}$
    (e) $\mathbf{F}(x,y,z) = 3\mathbf{i} + \mathbf{j} - x^2 y^3 z^4 \mathbf{k}$

3. Tell whether each of the following is a vector field or a scalar field, given that f is a scalar field and $\mathbf{F}$ is a vector field. Two of the expressions are meaningless; determine which two.
    (a) ∇f (f) $\nabla \times f$
    (b) $\nabla \cdot \mathbf{F}$ (g) $\nabla^2 \mathbf{F}$
    (c) $\nabla \times \mathbf{F}$ (h) $\nabla \times (\nabla^2 \mathbf{F})$
    (d) $\nabla \cdot (\nabla f)$ (i) $\nabla \times (\nabla^2 f)$
    (e) $\nabla \times (\nabla f)$ (j) $\nabla (\nabla^2 f)$

3.7 : Vector Identities

Although we continue to use the del notation, formally manipulating

$$\nabla = \mathbf{i}\frac{\partial}{\partial x} + \mathbf{j}\frac{\partial}{\partial y} + \mathbf{k}\frac{\partial}{\partial z}$$

as though it were a vector, this practice has certain hazards. To avoid difficulty, we adopt the convention that unless indicated otherwise the derivative operators appearing in the del operator act only on functions appearing to the right of the del operator.

For example, supposing that

$$\mathbf{F} = x^3 y \mathbf{i} + y^2 \mathbf{j} + x^2 z \mathbf{k}, \qquad \mathbf{R} = x \mathbf{i} + y \mathbf{j} + z \mathbf{k},$$

let us compare the two expressions $(\nabla \cdot \mathbf{R})\mathbf{F}$ and $(\mathbf{R} \cdot \nabla)\mathbf{F}$. For the first of these we have

$$(\nabla \cdot \mathbf{R})\mathbf{F} = 3\mathbf{F} = 3x^3 y \mathbf{i} + 3y^2 \mathbf{j} + 3x^2 z \mathbf{k}$$

On the other hand, in the second expression, $\mathbf{R}$ is to the left of ∇, and therefore the derivatives in the del operator do not act on $\mathbf{R}$. We have

$$(\mathbf{R} \cdot \nabla)\mathbf{F} = \left(x \frac{\partial}{\partial x} + y \frac{\partial}{\partial y} + z \frac{\partial}{\partial z} \right) (x^3 y \mathbf{i} + y^2 \mathbf{j} + x^2 z \mathbf{k})$$

$$= x(3x^2 y \mathbf{i} + 2xz \mathbf{k}) + y(x^3 \mathbf{i} + 2y \mathbf{j}) + z(x^2 \mathbf{k})$$

$$= 4x^3 y \mathbf{i} + 2y^2 \mathbf{j} + 3x^2 z \mathbf{k}$$

To further confuse matters, parentheses are sometimes omitted; the reader must supply such parentheses as necessary to make the expression meaningful. For example, $\nabla \cdot \mathbf{RF}$ and $\mathbf{R} \cdot \nabla \mathbf{F}$ must mean $(\nabla \cdot \mathbf{R})\mathbf{F}$ and $(\mathbf{R} \cdot \nabla)\mathbf{F}$ respectively, since $\nabla \cdot (\mathbf{RF})$ and $\mathbf{R} \cdot (\nabla \mathbf{F})$ do not make sense within the framework of vector analysis. (Some books introduce the notion of a *dyadic* in order to assign a meaning to such expressions as $\nabla \mathbf{F}$. We do not discuss dyadics in this book.)

Similarly, $\nabla \cdot f \mathbf{F}$ means $\nabla \cdot (f \mathbf{F})$, simply the divergence of $f \mathbf{F}$, since $\nabla \cdot f$, and hence $(\nabla \cdot f)\mathbf{F}$, is meaningless.

In some cases where parentheses are omitted, two interpretations are possible, both of which make sense. For example, if $\mathbf{A} = A_1 \mathbf{i} + A_2 \mathbf{j} + A_3 \mathbf{k}$ is a vector field and f is a scalar field, both $(\mathbf{A} \cdot \nabla)f$ and $\mathbf{A} \cdot (\nabla f)$ are meaningful and are sometimes written $\mathbf{A} \cdot \nabla f$. This is because both interpretations lead to exactly the same final result. We have

$$(\mathbf{A} \cdot \nabla)f = \left(A_1 \frac{\partial}{\partial x} + A_2 \frac{\partial}{\partial y} + A_3 \frac{\partial}{\partial z} \right) f = A_1 \frac{\partial f}{\partial x} + A_2 \frac{\partial f}{\partial y} + A_3 \frac{\partial f}{\partial z}$$

and also

$$\mathbf{A} \cdot (\nabla f) = \mathbf{A} \cdot \left(\frac{\partial f}{\partial x} \mathbf{i} + \frac{\partial f}{\partial y} \mathbf{j} + \frac{\partial f}{\partial z} \mathbf{k} \right) = A_1 \frac{\partial f}{\partial x} + A_2 \frac{\partial f}{\partial y} + A_3 \frac{\partial f}{\partial z}$$

both of them equal.

Because of the convention adopted above it is especially important to preserve order in working with ∇. For instance, $\nabla \cdot \mathbf{A}$ is a scalar field, simply the divergence of $\mathbf{A}$, but $\mathbf{A} \cdot \nabla$ is the formal differential operator

$$A_1 \frac{\partial}{\partial x} + A_2 \frac{\partial}{\partial y} + A_3 \frac{\partial}{\partial z}$$

a horse of quite a different color.

We now list a number of identities. Here $\mathbf{F}$ and $\mathbf{G}$ denote vector fields, ϕ denotes a scalar field, and $\mathbf{R} = x\mathbf{i} + y\mathbf{j} + z\mathbf{k}$. We shall not have to make much use of these identities, so we omit their proofs; these proofs are routine but in some cases rather tedious. Nor do we give the precise conditions under which these identities are valid. For example, (6) is valid whenever all second partial derivatives of ϕ are continuous, but the reason for this condition is more appropriately discussed in the next chapter when the significance of (6) is considered.

(1) $\nabla \cdot \phi \mathbf{F} = \phi \nabla \cdot \mathbf{F} + \mathbf{F} \cdot \nabla \phi$

(2) $\nabla \times \phi \mathbf{F} = \phi \nabla \times \mathbf{F} + \nabla \phi \times \mathbf{F}$

(3) $\nabla \cdot (\mathbf{F} \times \mathbf{G}) = \mathbf{G} \cdot (\nabla \times \mathbf{F}) - \mathbf{F} \cdot (\nabla \times \mathbf{G})$

(4) $\nabla \times (\mathbf{F} \times \mathbf{G}) = (\mathbf{G} \cdot \nabla)\mathbf{F} - (\mathbf{F} \cdot \nabla)\mathbf{G} + (\nabla \cdot \mathbf{G})\mathbf{F} - (\nabla \cdot \mathbf{F})\mathbf{G}$

(5) $\nabla(\mathbf{F} \cdot \mathbf{G}) = (\mathbf{F} \cdot \nabla)\mathbf{G} + (\mathbf{G} \cdot \nabla)\mathbf{F}$
$$+ \mathbf{F} \times (\nabla \times \mathbf{G}) + \mathbf{G} \times (\nabla \times \mathbf{F})$$

(6) $\nabla \times (\nabla \phi) = \mathbf{0}$

(7) $\nabla \cdot (\nabla \times \mathbf{F}) = 0.$

(8) $(\mathbf{F} \cdot \nabla)\mathbf{R} = \mathbf{F}$ (where $\mathbf{R} = x\mathbf{i} + y\mathbf{j} + z\mathbf{k}$)

Of these identities, the most interesting are (6) and (7).

Identity (6) states that the curl of the gradient of a scalar field is the zero vector field. In other words, if we know that a vector field is the gradient of some scalar field, then the curl of this field at any point is zero.

Identity (7) states that the divergence of a vector field is zero throughout a region if that field is the curl of a vector field $\mathbf{F}$.

These identities will be discussed in greater detail in the next chapter.

EXERCISES

1.   Derive identity (1). [Hint: Let $\mathbf{F} = F_1\mathbf{i} + F_2\mathbf{j} + F_3\mathbf{k}$ and write out $\nabla \cdot (\phi\mathbf{F})$.]

2.   Derive (2).

3.   Derive (6). Why does this derivation require that ϕ have continuous second partial derivatives?

4.   Derive (8).

5.   Why is the following "identity" obviously not valid?

$$\nabla \cdot (\mathbf{F} \times \mathbf{G}) = \mathbf{G} \cdot (\nabla \times \mathbf{F}) + \mathbf{F} \cdot (\nabla \times \mathbf{G})$$

F O U R

LINE AND SURFACE INTEGRALS

4.1 : Work. Line Integrals

The work done by a *constant* force $\mathbf{F}$ in moving a particle through a displacement $\mathbf{S}$ is $\mathbf{F} \cdot \mathbf{S}$, simply the product of the magnitude of the displacement with the component of the force in the direction of that displacement. If, however, the force is not constant, one must in general integrate to obtain the work done. Letting W denote the work done, we have

$$(1) \qquad\qquad W = \int_a^b F_s \, ds$$

where s denotes arc length measured along the path traversed by the particle, F_s denotes the component of $\mathbf{F}$ in the direction of motion, and the limits a and b are chosen appropriately. Assuming the path is smooth (Section 2.2) we may let $\mathbf{T}$ denote a unit tangent to the path, so that $F_s = \mathbf{F} \cdot \mathbf{T}$, and then we have

$$W = \int_a^b \mathbf{F} \cdot \mathbf{T} \, ds$$

In this integral $\mathbf{F}$ and $\mathbf{T}$ may both vary as the particle moves along the curve from the point where $s = a$ to the point where $s = b$.

There are yet other ways in which (1) can be written. Letting **R** denote the position vector of the particle, i.e., $\mathbf{R} = x\mathbf{i} + y\mathbf{j} + z\mathbf{k}$ where (x,y,z) is the position of the particle, we have (Section 2.2) that $d\mathbf{R} = \mathbf{T}\,ds$, so we may write alternatively

$$W = \int_C \mathbf{F} \cdot d\mathbf{R}$$

The letter C, standing for curve, is a reminder that we must supply the definite integral with appropriate limits of integration. If **F** and **R** are both given as functions of the time t, then we write $\mathbf{F} \cdot d\mathbf{R}$ in terms of t and dt, and the limits of integration will be the values of t corresponding to $s = a$ and $s = b$.

If $\mathbf{F} = F_1\mathbf{i} + F_2\mathbf{j} + F_3\mathbf{k}$, then since $d\mathbf{R} = dx\,\mathbf{i} + dy\,\mathbf{j} + dz\,\mathbf{k}$, we have $\mathbf{F} \cdot d\mathbf{R} = F_1 dx + F_2 dy + F_3 dz$, and we may write

$$W = \int_C (F_1 dx + F_2 dy + F_3 dz)$$

This integral may be split up into three separate integrals, but before evaluating them it is necessary to write each integrand in terms of a single variable and supply the limits of integration appropriate to that variable.

Thus we have four different ways of writing the integral representing the work done by a force field **F** as a particle moves along a curve C joining two points. From a physical point of view it is obvious that these integrals all yield the same value. Whether we write the integral in terms of s or t or even one of the variables x, y, z, we still get the same value for the work done, provided we are careful about our limits of integration. From the strictly mathematical viewpoint it is not obvious that changing variables does not modify the final numerical answer, and by studying the mathematical literature one finds that the theorems justifying this are not always easy to prove. Since this book is not primarily concerned with integration theory, the *proofs* of theorems about vector integration will be omitted. We shall, however, state precise *conditions* sufficient to ensure that these theorems are valid. After finishing this book the reader may wish to study more advanced texts to learn these proofs and also more general conditions under which some of the theorems are valid.

(This paragraph should be omitted by any reader who has not studied electric field theory.) We suggest that while reading the first part of this chapter the reader think of the vector field **F** as giving, at each point in space, the force that would be exerted on a point charge q in an electrostatic field $\mathbf{E}$, that is, $\mathbf{F} = q\mathbf{E}$. The curves we discuss are possible paths along which we force this point charge to move. The line integrals give the work done by the field on the charged particle as it moves along the prescribed path. Don't worry about what it is that produces the electrostatic field, just imagine that the field somehow exists throughout space and will exert a force $\mathbf{F}$ on a charge, a force that varies with position in space. But by all means *forget* any notions you may have about the work done (in moving a charge from one point to another) being independent of the path. For most vector fields the integral will depend not only on the endpoints but also on the path joining those endpoints. In other words, think of electrostatic fields if that is helpful, but forget that special property of electrostatic fields. (Any mathematics teacher who has taught this subject to a class of students who have just studied electrostatic fields in their physics course will appreciate why this paragraph was written!)

Turning to the general case, let $\mathbf{F}$ denote a vector field and let C denote a curve joining two points P_1 and P_2. Let us assume that this curve is represented by parametric equations $x = x(t)$, $y = y(t)$, $z = z(t)$ in such a manner that the position vector $\mathbf{R} = x\mathbf{i} + y\mathbf{j} + z\mathbf{k}$ is a continuously differentiable function of t, with t_1 corresponding to the point P_1 and t_2 corresponding to P_2. Let us further suppose that $\mathbf{F} = F_1\mathbf{i} + F_2\mathbf{j} + F_3\mathbf{k}$ is continuous along C, that is, F_1, F_2, and F_3 are continuous in some region containing C, so that along the curve these functions are continuous functions of t. Then the integral

$$\int_{t_1}^{t_2} \mathbf{F} \cdot d\mathbf{R}$$

makes sense when we write $\mathbf{F}$ as a vector function of t and $d\mathbf{R}$ is expressed in terms of t and dt. This is the integral of the tangential component of $\mathbf{F}$ along C from P_1 to P_2 and is called a *line integral*. This is a misnomer, of course, since the curve C need not be a line.

A fundamental theorem states that under the conditions stated the value of the integral will depend only on the field $\mathbf{F}$ and the oriented curve C, not on the choice of the parameter t. (In the first paragraph of this section, we took the parameter to be arc length, and wrote s instead of t.) If we are given a curve joining P_1 to P_2 consisting of a finite number of curves for which these conditions are satisfied, we can still form a line integral by summing the integrals along the separate curves.

As already noted, the notations

$$\int_C \mathbf{F} \cdot d\mathbf{R}$$

and

$$\int_C (F_1 dx + F_2 dy + F_3 dz)$$

are also used. If the curve is *closed*, i.e., if $P_1 = P_2$, the notation $\oint \mathbf{F} \cdot d\mathbf{R}$ is frequently used. The line integral of $\mathbf{F}$ around a closed curve C is called the *circulation* of $\mathbf{F}$ about C.

EXAMPLE 1: Compute the line integral $\int \mathbf{F} \cdot d\mathbf{R}$ from $(0,0,0)$ to $(1,2,4)$ if

$$\mathbf{F} = x^2 \mathbf{i} + y\mathbf{j} + (xz - y)\mathbf{k}$$

(a) along the line segment joining these two points,

(b) along the curve given parametrically by $x = t^2$, $y = 2t$, $z = 4t^3$.

Solution: (a) Parametric equations for the line segment joining $(0,0,0)$ to $(1,2,4)$ are $x = t, y = 2t, z = 4t$ (Section 1.8). We have

$$\int_C \mathbf{F} \cdot d\mathbf{R} = \int_C x^2 \, dx + y \, dy + (xz - y) \, dz$$

$$= \int_0^1 t^2 \, dt + (2t)(2 \, dt) + (4t^2 - 2t)(4 \, dt)$$

$$= \int_0^1 (17t^2 - 4t) \, dt = \tfrac{11}{3}$$

(b) In this case we have

$$\int_C \mathbf{F} \cdot d\mathbf{R} = \int_0^1 (t^4)(2t \, dt) + (2t)(2 \, dt) + (4t^5 - 2t)(12t^2 \, dt)$$

$$= \int_0^1 (2t^5 + 4t + 48t^7 - 24t^3) \, dt = \tfrac{7}{3}$$

EXAMPLE 2: Find the line integral of the tangential component of $\mathbf{F} = x\mathbf{i} + x^2\mathbf{j}$ from $(-1,0)$ to $(1,0)$ in the xy plane (a) along the x axis, (b) along the semicircle $y = \sqrt{1 - x^2}$, (c) along the dotted polygonal path shown in Figure 54.

Solution:

(a) Along the x axis, $y = 0$, hence $dy = 0 \cdot dx$ and

$$\int \mathbf{F} \cdot d\mathbf{R} = \int (x \, dx + x^2 \, dy)$$

$$= \int_{-1}^{1} x \, dx = \tfrac{1}{2} x^2 \Big|_{-1}^{1} = 0$$

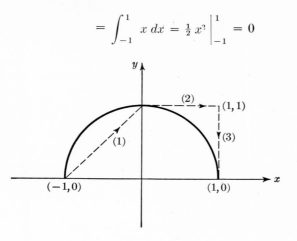

Figure 54

(b) Along the semicircle, a convenient parameter is the polar co-ordinate θ. Since the radius of the circle is unity, we have, for points (x,y) on this path, $x = \cos \theta$, $y = \sin \theta$, hence $dx = -\sin \theta \, d\theta$, $dy = \cos \theta \, d\theta$, and

$$\int \mathbf{F} \cdot d\mathbf{R} = \int (x \, dx + x^2 \, dy)$$

$$= \int [(\cos \theta)(-\sin \theta \, d\theta) + (\cos^2 \theta)(\cos \theta \, d\theta)]$$

$$= \int_{\pi}^{0} (-\sin \theta \cos \theta + \cos^3 \theta) \, d\theta$$

$$= \left[-\frac{\sin^2 \theta}{2} - \sin \theta - \frac{\sin^3 \theta}{2} \right]_{\pi}^{0} = 0$$

(c) Along the path labeled (1), $y = x + 1$, so that $dy = dx$ and

$$\int (x \, dx + x^2 \, dy) = \int_{-1}^{0} [x \, dx + x^2 \, dx] = -\tfrac{1}{6} \qquad \frac{x^2}{2} + \frac{x^3}{3} \Big|_{-1}^{0} = \tfrac{0}{2} + \tfrac{1}{3} = -\tfrac{1}{6}$$

Along (2), $y = 1$, so that $dy = 0 \cdot dx$ and

$$\int (x \, dx + x^2 \, dy) = \int_{0}^{1} x \, dx = \tfrac{1}{2}$$

Along (3), $x = 1$, so that $dx = 0 \cdot dy$ and

$$\int (x \, dx + x^2 \, dy) = \int_{1}^{0} dy = -1$$

[Note that we use y instead of x as the parameter along (3).] The value of the integral is $-\frac{1}{6} + \frac{1}{2} - 1 = -\frac{2}{3}$.

Many students feel queasy about line integrals, at first, because they don't see "what good" they are. A common question is "What do you have after you have computed a line integral?" The answer is: you have a number. Depending on the type of problem, this number may represent work done, change in potential energy, total heat flow, change in entropy, circulation of a fluid, and so on, but at this point the student is advised to concentrate simply on *learning how to compute* line integrals.

EXERCISES

1. In Example 2 above (refer to Figure 54),
   (a) what is **T** along path (1), in the direction shown, in terms of **i** and **j**?
   (b) what is **T** along dotted path (2), in the direction shown?
   (c) along (3), in the direction shown?

2. In Example 2, what is ds, in terms of dx or dy,
   (a) along dotted path (1),
   (b) along dotted path (2),
   (c) along dotted path (3)?

3. Show that $d\mathbf{R} = dx\,\mathbf{i} + dy\,\mathbf{j}$ is the same as **T** ds in each of the three special cases referred to in the preceding two problems. (This illustrates the general rule that, in practice, it is easier to find $d\mathbf{R}$ directly than to find **T** and ds separately and multiply.)

4. Let

$$\mathbf{F} = \frac{y}{x^2 + y^2}\,\mathbf{i} - \frac{x}{x^2 + y^2}\,\mathbf{j}$$

   Find the line integral of the tangential component of **F**, from $(-1,0)$ to $(1,0)$,
   (a) along the semicircle $y = \sqrt{1 - x^2}$;
   (b) along the dotted polygonal path shown in Figure 54.

5. By changing to polar coordinates, find the answers to Problem 4 by inspection.

6. Find $\int \mathbf{F} \cdot d\mathbf{R}$ from $(1,0,0)$ to $(1,0,4)$, if $\mathbf{F} = x\mathbf{i} - y\mathbf{j} + z\mathbf{k}$,
   (a) along the line segment joining $(1,0,0)$ and $(1,0,4)$;
   (b) along the helix $x = \cos 2\pi t$, $y = \sin 2\pi t$, $z = 4t$.

7. Find $\int \mathbf{R} \cdot d\mathbf{R}$ from $(1,2,2)$ to $(3,6,6)$, along the line segment joining these points,
   (a) in a straightforward manner;
   (b) by observing that $\mathbf{R} \cdot d\mathbf{R} = s \, ds$, where $s = (x^2 + y^2 + z^2)^{\frac{1}{2}}$ is the distance from the origin, and computing $\int_3^9 s \, ds$.

8. Find the value of $\oint [(3x + 4y) \, dx + (2x + 3y^2) \, dy]$ around the circle $x^2 + y^2 = 4$.

9. Find the line integral $\int \mathbf{F} \cdot d\mathbf{R}$ along the line segment from $(1,0,2)$ to $(3,4,1)$ where $\mathbf{F} = 2xy\mathbf{i} + (x^2 + z)\mathbf{j} + y\mathbf{k}$.

10. Find the line integral $\oint \mathbf{F} \cdot d\mathbf{R}$ around the circumference of the circle $x^2 - 2x + y^2 = 2$, $z = 1$, where $\mathbf{F} = y\mathbf{i} + x\mathbf{j} + xyz^2\mathbf{k}$.

$$x(x-2) + y^2 - 2$$

4.2 : Domains; Simply-Connected Domains

We recall from elementary calculus that many of the functions that arise are not defined for all values of x, but only for certain intervals. For example, the function $f(x) = 1/x$ is not defined at $x = 0$, and the function $f(x) = \csc x$ is not defined when x is an integral multiple of π.

Similarly, the vector fields that arise in practice are frequently not defined at all points (x,y,z) in space, but only in certain regions of space.

For instance, we learn in elementary physics that the magnitude of the magnetic field intensity due to a current flowing along a straight line varies inversely with the distance from that line. As we get nearer to the line the magnetic intensity increases in magnitude. The magnetic field is not defined along the line itself. The region of definition consists of all points in space except those along the line.

Similarly, the electric intensity due to a system of n point charges is defined everywhere in space except at the n points in question.

To be sure, the fields that arise in elementary physics are rather hypothetical (how can a charge be concentrated at a point?) but they are useful in theoretical discussions and their study is essential to more advanced work.

The reader with limited knowledge of electric or magnetic field theory may imagine instead that the fields we consider are the velocity fields of fluids that are in some container. Obviously it is nonsense to speak of the velocity vector at any point outside the container. The region of definition in this case consists of all points within the container.

The vector fields that usually arise, both in theory and in practice, have two important properties. First, such a field is defined in the interior of a given region but not on the boundary of the region. Secondly, if the field is defined at two points P and Q, it is possible to find a smooth arc C joining P to Q along which the field is everywhere defined.

For instance, the velocity field of a fluid in a container is not defined for points on the surface of the container, but only for points in the interior of the container. Moreover, it is unusual to consider a container with separate compartments; we usually assume that if there is fluid at two points P and Q, it is possible to move from P to Q without passing through any separating walls.

Motivated by these ideas, we now give several precise definitions.

If P is any given point and ε is any positive number (zero is excluded), we say that an *ε-neighborhood of P* is the set of all points that are *less* than ε in distance away from P. Thus, if we are speaking of points in the plane, an ε-neighborhood of a point P consists of all points in the interior (but not on the circumference) of a circle of radius ε and center at P. If we are speaking of points in space, an ε-neighborhood of P consists of all points in the interior (but not on the surface) of a sphere of radius ε and center at P.

Given a region R, we say that P is an *interior point* of R if it is possible to find an ε-neighborhood of P that lies completely within R. We say that P is a *boundary point* of R if, no matter how small we take the positive number ε, the ε-neighborhood of P contains at least one point in R and one point not in R. So, by definition, an interior point cannot be a boundary point, nor can a boundary point be an interior point.

A region is said to be *open* if every point in the region is an interior point of the region. Thus, if the region of definition of a vector field is an open region, we can say: if the field is defined at a point P, it will also be defined in some ε-neighborhood of P. Of course, if P is very near the boundary of the region, ε may have to be very small.

By definition, an open region does not include its boundary. (For example, the set of all points *within* a cube is an open region in space, but the set consisting of all those points either within or on the surface of a cube is not an open region.) If we say an arc C lies in an open region, then by definition C cannot intersect or even touch the boundary of the region.

Henceforth, we shall consider only open regions.

An open region R is said to be *connected* if, given any two points P and Q in R, there can be found a smooth arc in R that joins P to Q.

In Figure 55, we show a region in the plane that is *not* connected. Obviously we cannot join P to Q by a smooth arc that lies completely within the region. We shall have no occasion to consider such regions; henceforth we consider only connected regions.

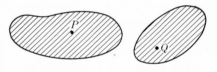

Figure 55

A region that is both open and connected is called a *domain*.

The region of definition of the magnetic field due to a steady current flowing along the z axis consists of all points except those on the z axis. The region of definition of the electric field due to a system of n fixed point charges consists of all points other than the given n points. It is easy to see that in either case the region is both open and connected, so that the word "domain" applies.

In Figure 56, we give an example of a region in the plane. If we let D denote the set of points within the shaded region, not including any points on either of the curves C_1 and C_2, then D is a domain. The points on the curves C_1 and C_2 constitute the boundary of the domain.   In the figure we give an example of a smooth arc joining two points P and Q.

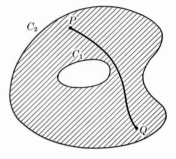

Figure 56

Of special importance are those domains that are simply-connected.   In Figure 57, we show a region in the plane that is simply-connected.   The regions indicated in Figures 56 and 58 are not simply-connected.

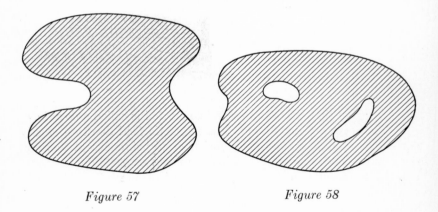

Figure 57   *Figure 58*

Roughly speaking, a domain is said to be simply-connected if every closed curve lying in the domain can be continuously shrunk to a point in the domain without any part of the curve passing through regions outside the domain.   The plane regions indicated in Figures

56 and 58 are not simply-connected because no closed curve surrounding one of the "holes" could be shrunk to a point while still always remaining in the domain. Thus, in the special case of a domain of points in the plane, this simply means that, given any closed curve in the domain, all points within the closed curve are also in the domain. In other words, there are no "holes" in the domain.

Simply-connected domains in space are, very roughly speaking, those domains through which no holes have been bored. Thus the set of points in the interior of a torus (doughnut) is not simply-connected, since a closed curve within the torus surrounding the hole cannot be shrunk to a point while remaining always within the torus.

A closed curve C, in the process of being shrunk to a point, will generate a surface having the original curve C as its boundary. Thus, another way of wording the definition is as follows: a domain is simply-connected if, given any closed curve lying in the domain, there can be found a surface within the domain that has that curve as its boundary.

The domain consisting of all points in the interior of a sphere is simply-connected. As another example, suppose we are given two concentric spheres; then the set of points outside the inner sphere but inside the outer sphere comprises a simply-connected domain.

As a further example, consider the cylinder $x^2 + y^2 = 1$. This is a cylinder of radius 1, concentric with the z axis. Every point outside the cylinder has coordinates (x,y,z) satisfying the inequality $x^2 + y^2 > 1$ (z arbitrary), and the set of all such points is a domain that is *not* simply-connected. The set of points in the interior of the cylinder, $x^2 + y^2 < 1$, *is* simply-connected.

Vector fields defined in simply-connected regions have much simpler properties, in general, than those having domains of definition that are not simply-connected. Domains that are not simply-connected may be very complicated; the reader may wish to contemplate the region of space within an old-fashioned steam radiator, which is very far indeed from being simply-connected.

EXERCISES

In each of the following cases, a region D is defined. Tell whether the region is a domain. If it is a domain, determine whether or not it is simply-connected. If it is not a domain, explain why not.

1.   The region of definition of a magnetic field due to a steady current flowing along the z axis [in other words, the region consisting of all points (x,y,z) such that $x^2 + y^2 > 0$].

2.   The region of definition of an electric field due to n point charges.

3.   The region consisting of all points above the xy plane, i.e., all points (x,y,z) such that $z > 0$.

4.   The region D consisting of all points (x,y,z) for which $z \geq 0$.

5.   The region D consisting of all points (x,y,z) such that

$$x^2 + y^2 + z^2 > 4$$

6.   The region D consisting of all points (x,y,z) for which

$$1 < x^2 + y^2 < 4$$

(i.e., all points outside a cylinder of radius 1 and within a cylinder of radius 2, both cylinders concentric with the z axis).

7.   The region D consisting of all points (x,y,z) for which $1 < x < 2$ (i.e., all points between the planes $x = 1$ and $x = 2$).

8.   The region D consisting of all points (x,y,z) for which $z \neq 0$.

4.3 : Conservative Fields

In this section we let $\mathbf{F}$ denote a vector field that is defined throughout a domain D.   We say that $\mathbf{F}$ is *continuous* in D if it can be written in the form

(1) $$\mathbf{F} = F_1\mathbf{i} + F_2\mathbf{j} + F_3\mathbf{k}$$

where F_1, F_2, and F_3 are scalar-valued functions each of which is continuous throughout D.   If these three functions have partial derivatives all of which (there will be nine such derivatives, $\partial F_1/\partial x$, $\partial F_1/\partial y, \ldots, \partial F_3/\partial z$) are continuous throughout D, then $\mathbf{F}$ is said to be *continuously differentiable* in D.   It follows from these definitions that, if $\mathbf{F}$ is continuously differentiable in D, then **curl** $\mathbf{F}$ is a vector field that is continuous in D, and div $\mathbf{F}$ is a scalar field that is continuous in D.

A more fundamental definition of continuity can be given, based on the notion of ε-neighborhood introduced in the preceding section.

see notes

19.a

A vector field **F** is *continuous* at a point P if, given an arbitrary
ε-neighborhood S of the point with position vector $\mathbf{F}(P)$, there exists
a δ-neighborhood R of P such that $\mathbf{F}(Q)$ is the position vector of a
point in S, for every point Q in R.   A more fundamental definition
of differentiability will be given in the last chapter.

A vector field **F** is said to be *conservative* in a domain D if there
can be found some scalar field ϕ defined in D such that $\mathbf{F} = \mathbf{grad}\ \phi$.
If this is possible, then ϕ is called a *potential function* or simply a
potential for **F**.

important statement

There is nothing unique about the potential function for a conservative field, since one can always add an arbitrary constant to ϕ
to obtain a new potential whose gradient is also **F**.   (Physicists
conventionally choose potentials to satisfy certain natural boundary
conditions; for instance, they may choose the constant so that the
potential function for a gravitational field is zero along the laboratory
floor, or so that the potential function for an electric field "tends to
zero at infinity.")

In some textbooks a different definition of potential is used,
and relative to that definition one has $\mathbf{F} = -\mathbf{grad}\ \phi$ instead of
$\mathbf{F} = \mathbf{grad}\ \phi$.   The only difference is one of sign, and this will give
the student no difficulty when he is thoroughly familiar with the
basic ideas involved.

The following theorem may indicate why conservative fields are
so important: *A vector field* **F** *continuous in a domain D is conservative
if and only if the line integral of the tangential component of* **F** *along
every regular curve in D depends only on the endpoints of the curve.
In that case, the line integral is simply the difference in potential of the
endpoints.*   That is, we have

theorem (a)

$$\int_C \mathbf{F}\cdot d\mathbf{R} = \int_P^Q F_1\,dx + F_2\,dy + F_3\,dz = \phi(Q) - \phi(P)$$

Before we continue, let us be sure we understand this theorem.
We are given a vector field **F** defined and continuous in a domain D.
The theorem says this field is conservative if and only if the following
condition holds: that if we are given any two points P and Q in D,
and any regular curve C within the domain extending from P to Q,
then

$$\int_P^Q \mathbf{F}\cdot d\mathbf{R}$$

depends only on the location of the endpoints P and Q and not in any way on the choice of the curve C that joins them.   (We summarize this condition by saying "the line integral is independent of path.") Moreover, if this condition holds, then we can evaluate this line integral by first finding a function ϕ such that $\mathbf{F} = \mathbf{grad}\ \phi$, and then subtracting the value of ϕ at P from its value at Q.

This is the first theorem of any depth that has been stated in this book.   We strongly urge the student to read carefully the following outline of the proof.   We have already (in Section 3.7) omitted the proofs of some theorems because we felt that going through them would not be of much value to the reader.   Later on we shall be forced to omit some proofs because they are too technical.   The proof of this theorem does not fall into either category.   *Engineering students: resist that temptation to avoid proofs.*

The proof is in four steps.   First, we assume that $\mathbf{F}$ satisfies the conditions of the theorem, and (i) define a function ϕ in a certain manner, (ii) show that ϕ is a potential for $\mathbf{F}$, and (iii) show that

$$\int_P^Q \mathbf{F} \cdot d\mathbf{R} = \phi(Q) - \phi(P)$$

Then (iv) we prove the converse: assuming that $\mathbf{F}$ is conservative we show that the line integral is given by $\phi(Q) - \phi(P)$ and hence is independent of path.   Here we go:

(i) We choose, once and for all, an arbitrary point (x_0, y_0, z_0) in D, which we call the "point of zero potential."   Given any other point (x, y, z) in D, we choose arbitrarily some smooth arc C_1 in D extending from (x_0, y_0, z_0) to (x, y, z); this is possible since we assume D is a domain. We define $\phi(x, y, z)$ to be

$$\int_{(x_0, y_0, z_0)}^{(x, y, z)} \mathbf{F} \cdot d\mathbf{R}$$

where we integrate along C_1.   Since C_1 is smooth and $\mathbf{F}$ is continuous, there is no difficulty justifying the existence of this integral (here we omit some details, which is why this is only an "outline" of the proof). By hypothesis, this integral is independent of path, and so this definition of $\phi(x, y, z)$ does not depend on the particular arc C_1 that we choose.   In other words, we have defined ϕ in an unambiguous manner.   Another choice of the point of zero potential would lead to another potential function differing from this one by a constant, but that is irrelevant here.

(ii) For reasons that will soon become clear, we now wish to compute $\partial \phi / \partial x$ at (x, y, z).   By definition this equals

(2) $$\lim_{\Delta x \to 0} \frac{\phi(x + \Delta x, y, z) - \phi(x,y,z)}{\Delta x}$$

Since D is open (every domain is!) there is some ε-neighborhood of (x,y,z) that is within D. Let us consider a line segment, parallel to the x axis and passing through (x,y,z), that is within this ε-neighborhood. For a point $(x + \Delta x, y, z)$ along this line segment, let C_2 denote that part of the segment extending from (x,y,z) to $(x + \Delta x, y, z)$. Then C_2, being a line segment, is *a fortiori* a smooth arc, and the path from (x_0,y_0,z_0) to $(x + \Delta x, y, z)$ obtained by joining C_2 to C_1 consists of two smooth arcs and is therefore a regular curve (Fig. 59). We

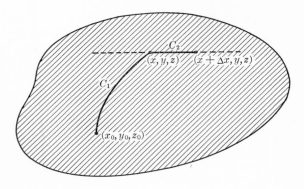

Figure 59

integrate along this curve to find $\phi(x + \Delta x, y, z)$ by first integrating along C_1 and then along C_2: since the first integral gives $\phi(x,y,z)$, we have

$$\phi(x + \Delta x, y, z) = \phi(x,y,z) + \int_{(x,y,z)}^{(x+\Delta x,y,z)} \mathbf{F} \cdot d\mathbf{R}$$

from which it follows that the numerator of (2) is simply the integral

$$\int_{(x,y,z)}^{(x+\Delta x,y,z)} \mathbf{F} \cdot d\mathbf{R}$$

taken along C_2. Since y and z are constant along this line segment, we have $d\mathbf{R} = dx\, \mathbf{i}$, and hence $\mathbf{F} \cdot d\mathbf{R} = F_1\, dx$. Thus (2) becomes

(3) $$\lim_{\Delta x \to 0} \frac{\int_{(x,y,z)}^{(x+\Delta x,y,z)} F_1\, dx}{\Delta x}$$

Only one variable is involved in (3) since y and z are constant along C_2; in other words, one can treat the numerator just like any integral one meets in elementary calculus. The reader will recognize this integral, divided by Δx, as simply the average value of F_1 along the line segment C_2. Since F_1 is continuous, this average value tends to $F_1(x,y,z)$ as Δx tends to zero. (This is proved by a simple application of the fundamental theorem of calculus.) It follows that, at any point (x,y,z), we have $\partial\phi/\partial x = F_1$.

Similarly, we can show (taking line segments parallel to the y and z axes respectively) that $\partial\phi/\partial y = F_2$ and $\partial\phi/\partial z = F_3$. Therefore

$$\mathbf{grad}\ \phi = \frac{\partial\phi}{\partial x}\mathbf{i} + \frac{\partial\phi}{\partial y}\mathbf{j} + \frac{\partial\phi}{\partial z}\mathbf{k} = F_1\mathbf{i} + F_2\mathbf{j} + F_3\mathbf{k} = \mathbf{F}$$

proving that ϕ is a potential function for $\mathbf{F}$.

(iii) Let P and Q be two distinct points in D, and let C denote any regular curve extending from P to Q. Let C_1 be a smooth arc extending from (x_0,y_0,z_0) to P. Since the integral is independent of path, $\phi(Q)$ must equal the integral taken along the regular curve obtained by attaching C_1 and C together. Thus

$$\phi(Q) = \int_{C_1} \mathbf{F}\cdot d\mathbf{R} + \int_C \mathbf{F}\cdot d\mathbf{R}$$

$$= \phi(P) + \int_C \mathbf{F}\cdot d\mathbf{R}$$

from which it follows that

$$\int_C \mathbf{F}\cdot d\mathbf{R} = \phi(Q) - \phi(P)$$

(iv) To prove the converse, we *assume* $\mathbf{F}$ to be conservative, i.e., that there exists ϕ such that $\mathbf{F} = \mathbf{grad}\ \phi$. Then along any smooth arc we have $\mathbf{F}\cdot d\mathbf{R} = d\phi$, where we are thinking of $\mathbf{F}$ and $d\mathbf{R}$ as expressed in terms of some parameter t and its differential dt.

$$\int_P^Q \mathbf{F}\cdot d\mathbf{R} = \int_P^Q \frac{\partial\phi}{\partial x}\,dx + \frac{\partial\phi}{\partial y}\,dy + \frac{\partial\phi}{\partial z}\,dz$$

$$= \int_P^Q \left(\frac{\partial\phi}{\partial x}\frac{dx}{dt} + \frac{\partial\phi}{\partial y}\frac{dy}{dt} + \frac{\partial\phi}{\partial z}\frac{dz}{dt}\right) dt$$

$$= \int_P^Q \frac{d\phi}{dt}\,dt = \phi(Q) - \phi(P)$$

Here we made use of the fact that, if ϕ is a function having continuous partial derivatives with respect to x, y, and z, where x, y, and z are differentiable functions of a single parameter t, then

$$\frac{d\phi}{dt} = \frac{\partial\phi}{\partial x}\frac{dx}{dt} + \frac{\partial\phi}{\partial y}\frac{dy}{dt} + \frac{\partial\phi}{\partial z}\frac{dz}{dt}$$

The above equations may be written in simplified notation:

$$\int_P^Q \mathbf{F}\cdot d\mathbf{R} = \int_P^Q d\phi = \phi(Q) - \phi(P)$$

where

$$\mathbf{F}\cdot d\mathbf{R} = d\phi = \frac{\partial\phi}{\partial x}\,dx + \frac{\partial\phi}{\partial y}\,dy + \frac{\partial\phi}{\partial z}\,dz$$

is the total differential of ϕ.

This completes the outline of the proof. It will be noticed that if the path C is *closed*, i.e., if P and Q coincide, then

$$\oint_C \mathbf{F}\cdot d\mathbf{R} = 0$$

since $\phi(P) - \phi(P) = 0$. Conversely, if

$$\oint_C \mathbf{F}\cdot d\mathbf{R} = 0$$

around every regular closed curve in the domain, then $\mathbf{F}$ must be conservative (see Exercise 1). *A vector field* $\mathbf{F}$ *continuous in a domain D is conservative if and only if around every regular closed curve in D the line integral of the tangential component of* $\mathbf{F}$ *is zero.*

EXAMPLE 1: Show that $\mathbf{F} = xy^2\mathbf{i} + x^3y\mathbf{j}$ is not conservative.

Solution: A routine way of solving such problems will be given later. However, we can prove that a field is not conservative by showing that a line integral depends on the path. In this case, for instance, let us compute the integral along two paths joining $(0,0)$ to $(1,1)$ in the xy plane (Fig. 60). Along the line $y = x$ we have

$$\int_{(0,0)}^{(1,1)} xy^2\,dx + x^3y\,dy = \int_{x=0}^{x=1} (x^3 + x^4)\,dx = \tfrac{9}{20}$$

Now let us move along the regular path consisting of two line segments, the first joining $(0,0)$ to $(1,0)$ and the second joining $(1,0)$ to $(1,1)$. Along the first line segment $y = 0$, so that the line integral is zero. Along the second line segment $x = 1$, so that $dx = 0$ and the integral becomes

$$\int_{y=0}^{y=1} y\,dy = \tfrac{1}{2}$$

The total of the two integrals is thus $\frac{1}{2}$, differing from $\frac{9}{20}$.   Hence the field is not conservative.

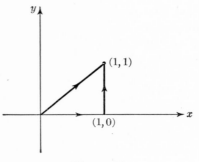

Figure 60

It is important to notice that if these two line integrals had turned out to be equal, we would not have been able to draw any conclusions from that alone.   Such a result could have happened by coincidence even though the field **F** was not conservative.   Since it is obviously impossible to compute $\int \mathbf{F} \cdot d\mathbf{R}$ along every conceivable regular curve, the theorem does not provide a practical way of showing that a given field *is* conservative.

EXAMPLE 2:   Show that $\mathbf{F} = xy^2\mathbf{i} + x^3y\mathbf{j}$ is not conservative, without computing any integrals.

Solution: This can be done by contradiction.   Suppose **F** were conservative.   Then $\mathbf{F} = \mathbf{grad}\ \phi$ for some function ϕ.   Since

$$\mathbf{grad}\ \phi = \frac{\partial \phi}{\partial x}\mathbf{i} + \frac{\partial \phi}{\partial y}\mathbf{j} + \frac{\partial \phi}{\partial z}\mathbf{k}$$

we must have $\partial\phi/\partial x = xy^2$ and $\partial\phi/\partial y = x^3y$.   But this is impossible, since the mixed derivatives $\partial^2\phi/\partial y\,\partial x$ and $\partial^2\phi/\partial x\,\partial y$ would be $2xy$ and $3x^2y$ respectively, whereas the theory of partial differentiation requires these derivatives (when all relevant derivatives are continuous, which they certainly are here) to be equal.   This contradiction shows that such a function ϕ cannot exist, and so **F** is not conservative.

EXAMPLE 3: Show that $\mathbf{F} = 2xy\mathbf{i} + (x^2 + 1)\mathbf{j} + 6z^2\mathbf{k}$ is conservative.

Solution: A routine way of solving such problems will be given later. At this point, we have no alternative but to actually find a function ϕ such that $\mathbf{F} = \mathbf{grad}\ \phi$. As we have already remarked, the theorems of this section are not useful in proving that a field *is* conservative since we would have to compute an infinite number of integrals. (If we were to take two points and compute line integrals along a dozen or so paths joining these points, the equality of these numbers might lead us to suspect the field to be conservative, but the experiment would not provide a rigorous proof.)

If $\mathbf{F} = \mathbf{grad}\ \phi$, then $\partial\phi/\partial x = 2xy$, $\partial\phi/\partial y = x^2 + 1$, and $\partial\phi/\partial z = 6z^2$. In computing $\partial\phi/\partial x$ one differentiates, holding y and z constant, and so evidently $\phi = x^2y +$ (either a constant term or a term involving only y and z). Let us write this as $\phi = x^2y + g(y,z)$, where g is a function not yet determined. Differentiating, we have $\partial\phi/\partial y = x^2 + (\partial g/\partial y)$. Comparing this with $\partial\phi/\partial y$ above, we see that $\partial g/\partial y = 1$. Since g is a function of y and z, evidently $g(y,z) = y +$ (either a constant term or a term involving z alone). Therefore we have $\phi = x^2y + y + h(z)$, where h depends only on z (or may possibly be a constant). Differentiating, this time with respect to z, we have $\partial\phi/\partial z = h'(z)$, and comparison with the above gives $h'(z) = 6z^2$. It follows that $h(z) = 2z^3 + C$, where C is a constant that may be chosen arbitrarily. Now we have $\phi = x^2y + y + 2z^3 + C$, and it is easy to check this to see that $\mathbf{grad}\ \phi = \mathbf{F}$. Hence $\mathbf{F}$ is conservative.

Remark: Mortimer McSnoyd solved this problem by integrating separately: Since $\partial\phi/\partial x = 2xy$, $\phi = x^2y$. Since $\partial\phi/\partial y = x^2 + 1$, $\phi = x^2y + y$. Since $\partial\phi/\partial z = 6z^2$, $\phi = 2z^3$. Adding these three candidates for ϕ he obtained $\phi = 2x^2y + y + 2z^3$. Needless to say, he got a goose egg for his efforts. On the other hand, Horace McSlide just sat back and looked at the partial derivatives, guessed that $\phi = x^2y + y + 2z^3$ would be an acceptable potential for this field, and then verified that $\mathbf{F} = \mathbf{grad}\ \phi$, saving himself a lot of work and earning full credit for this problem. The moral is that nonsense will get you nowhere, but if intelligent guessing yields an answer you can prove is correct, so much the better for you. (Horace also observed that $\mathbf{F}$ is conservative if and only if $\mathbf{F} \cdot d\mathbf{R}$ is an *exact differential,* i.e., equals $d\phi$ for some single-valued function ϕ.)

EXERCISES

1. Show that, if $\oint_C \mathbf{F} \cdot d\mathbf{R} = 0$ for every regular closed curve C, then for two points P and Q,

$$\int_P^Q \mathbf{F} \cdot d\mathbf{R}$$

is independent of path. [Hint: Let C_1 and C_2 be two paths extending from P to Q, and let C be the closed curve obtained by joining these two paths.]

2. Using the method of Example 1, or some similar method, show that the following fields are not conservative:
    (a) $\mathbf{F} = -y\mathbf{i} + x\mathbf{j}$
    (b) $\mathbf{F} = y\mathbf{i} + y(x - 1)\mathbf{j}$
    (c) $\mathbf{F} = y\mathbf{i} + x\mathbf{j} + x^2\mathbf{k}$ [Suggestion: Consider two different paths extending from $(0,0,0)$ to $(1,1,1)$.]
    (d) $\mathbf{F} = z\mathbf{i} + z\mathbf{j} + (y - 1)\mathbf{k}$

    (e) $\mathbf{F} = \dfrac{x\mathbf{i} + x\mathbf{j}}{x^2 + x^2}$ (not defined at the origin)

3. Using methods similar to that of Example 2, show that the fields of Problem 2 are not conservative.

4. Compute $\oint \mathbf{F} \cdot d\mathbf{R}$ around the closed path consisting of a circle of radius r, centered at the origin, in the xy plane, taking $\mathbf{F} = (-y\mathbf{i} + x\mathbf{j})/(x^2 + y^2)$. [Hint: Change to polar coordinates.]

5. If you worked correctly, you obtained a nonzero answer to Problem 4. Yet it appears that $\mathbf{F} = \mathbf{grad}\,\phi$ where $\phi = \tan^{-1}(y/x)$, and this would contradict the second theorem in this section. Investigate this mystery.

6. Find a potential for the force field

$$\mathbf{F} = (y + z \cos xz)\mathbf{i} + x\mathbf{j} + (x \cos xz)\mathbf{k}$$

7. Show that the field $\mathbf{F} = 2xy\mathbf{i} + (x^2 + z)\mathbf{j} + y\mathbf{k}$ is conservative.

4.4 : Conservative Fields (continued)

In the preceding section, we saw that a continuously differentiable vector field $\mathbf{F}$ defined in a domain D is conservative if and only if it possesses any one (and hence all) of the following properties:

(1) It is the gradient of a scalar function.

(2) Its integral around any regular closed curve is zero.

(3) Its integral along any regular curve extending from a point P to a point Q is independent of the path.

Note that we are using slightly sloppy language here.   When we say "its integral" we mean "the line integral of the tangential component," and when we say "any regular closed curve" or "any regular curve" we really do not mean *any* such curve, since we require the curve to lie completely within the domain D.

If the domain D in which $\mathbf{F}$ is defined is *simply connected* we can add a fourth property, equivalent to any one of the other three:

(4) $$\mathbf{curl\ F} = 0$$

This is of practical usefulness, since if we are given a vector field $\mathbf{F}$, defined in a simply-connected domain D, we can test quickly to determine whether it is conservative by computing its curl.   In terms of components, the test to determine whether

$$\mathbf{F} = F_1\mathbf{i} + F_2\mathbf{j} + F_3\mathbf{k}$$

is conservative consists of checking to see whether *all* the following equations are valid:

(5) $$\frac{\partial F_1}{\partial y} = \frac{\partial F_2}{\partial x}, \quad \frac{\partial F_2}{\partial z} = \frac{\partial F_3}{\partial y}, \quad \frac{\partial F_1}{\partial z} = \frac{\partial F_3}{\partial x}.$$

Equations (5) will be valid if and only if $\mathbf{curl\ F} = 0$, as one sees easily from the definition of $\mathbf{curl\ F}$.

Some of the problems of the preceding section may be solved quite easily by using this test.   For instance, consider the vector field $\mathbf{F} = y\mathbf{i} + x\mathbf{j} + x^2\mathbf{k}$.   Equations (5) written out are

$$\frac{\partial}{\partial y}\,(y) = \frac{\partial}{\partial x}\,(x), \quad \frac{\partial}{\partial z}\,(x) = \frac{\partial}{\partial y}\,(x^2), \quad \frac{\partial}{\partial z}\,(y) = \frac{\partial}{\partial x}\,(x^2)$$

The first two of these equations are valid but the third is not, and so the vector field is not conservative.

In Problem 4, Section 4.3, we considered the vector field

$$\mathbf{F} = \frac{-y\mathbf{i} + x\mathbf{j}}{x^2 + y^2}$$

This vector field is defined everywhere except on the z axis, where the denominator $x^2 + y^2 = 0$ and hence the expression for $\mathbf{F}$ is meaningless. Despite the fact that **curl F** $= \mathbf{0}$ in this case (as an exercise, verify this!), the field is not conservative (as shown in Exercise 4 of the preceding section) since it lacks the property (2). This does not contradict the statements made above, since this domain is *not simply-connected*. The test does not apply unless the domain of definition is simply-connected.

In the succeeding problem, Exercise 5, we tried to confuse the reader a little by suggesting that $\mathbf{F} = \mathbf{grad}\ \phi$ where $\phi = \tan^{-1}(y/x)$. This suggests that (1) is valid but (2) is not, contradicting the statements made above. This mystery vanishes when we recall that the function $\tan^{-1}(y/x)$ is ambiguous. For even when y/x makes sense, there are infinitely many angles with tangent equal to y/x. To be sure, this difficulty can be resolved by restricting the values of ϕ to the so-called "principal values" which lie in the range $-\pi/2 < \phi < \pi/2$, but in that case we obtain discontinuities on the y axis, along which x equals 0 and y/x is not defined. Alternatively, we may consider that we have $\mathbf{F} = \mathbf{grad}\ \theta$ where θ is the usual polar coordinate angle whose tangent is y/x. Along the positive x axis we have $\theta = 0$, and as we move counterclockwise around the origin, θ increases. As we return to the positive x axis through the fourth quadrant, θ tends to 2π. According to this viewpoint, θ has discontinuities of magnitude 2π along the positive x axis. (As a third alternative we can restrict θ to the range $-\pi < \theta < \pi$, but we still have discontinuities, this time along the negative x axis.) No matter how we look at it, $\mathbf{F}$ is defined except when x and y are both zero, but there is no scalar field ϕ for which $\mathbf{F} = \mathbf{grad}\ \phi$ throughout the same domain.

We shall now proceed to outline a *proof* that condition (4) is equivalent to condition (1). Actually, this will be a special case of a more general theorem (Stokes' theorem) to be discussed later, and so the reader may omit this and proceed directly to the exercises if he so desires. However, the student who intends to go further into pure mathematics will find this proof rather interesting because it is probably more sophisticated than any he has encountered before. (The more advanced reader should compare the proof with the process of *analytic continuation* that arises in the theory of functions of a complex variable.)

First of all, suppose that $\mathbf{F} = \mathbf{grad}\ \phi$ for some scalar field ϕ. Then by (6), Section 3.7, we have $\mathbf{curl}\ \mathbf{F} = \mathbf{0}$. In other words, condition (1) implies condition (4). To prove that the conditions are equivalent, it remains to show that condition (4) implies condition (1).

To do this, we will show that if a continuously differentiable vector field $\mathbf{F}$ is defined in a simply-connected domain D, and $\mathbf{curl}\ \mathbf{F} = \mathbf{0}$ throughout this domain, then there exists a scalar field ϕ defined throughout D such that $\mathbf{F} = \mathbf{grad}\ \phi$. Our problem is to define such a scalar field ϕ and prove that $\mathbf{F}$ is the gradient of this field.

It is important to keep in mind that a scalar field defined in a domain D is a rule that associates with each point (x,y,z) in D a number $\phi(x,y,z)$. There must be no ambiguity in the definition of this number at a given point. If we were to permit "multiple-valued functions" such as $\tan^{-1}(y/x)$, then, as we have seen in Exercises 4 and 5 of the preceding section, the statements we have made would not be valid.

We must also keep in mind that the scalar field ϕ is not unique; if we were to add a constant scalar to ϕ its gradient would still be the same as before. However, as we shall see, if we select a particular point (x_0,y_0,z_0) in D, and decree that $\phi(x_0,y_0,z_0) = 0$, then ϕ will be uniquely determined. In other words, we will arbitrarily choose the "point of zero potential."

But we need not choose $\phi(x_0,y_0,z_0)$ to be equal to zero. We can choose it to be some other arbitrary number C, and this also will give us a unique determination of the function ϕ. It will differ by the constant C from the potential we would obtain by taking ϕ to be zero at (x_0,y_0,z_0).

Let us therefore begin by selecting, arbitrarily, some point (x_0,y_0,z_0) in the domain D. Since by definition every domain D is open, there will exist some sphere S_0 whose interior is entirely contained in the domain D. We begin by defining $\phi(x,y,z)$ for points (x,y,z) in this sphere S_0.

For such a point (x,y,z), we select as a particular path joining (x_0,y_0,z_0) to (x,y,z) the straight line segments from (x_0,y_0,z_0) to (x,y_0,z_0) to (x,y,z_0) to (x,y,z), and we define $\phi(x,y,z)$ to be $\phi(x_0,y_0,z_0)$ plus the integral of $\mathbf{F}$ along this path. [We select $\phi(x_0,y_0,z_0)$ arbitrarily to be any number we desire, zero if we like.] Physically, thinking of $\mathbf{F}$ as a force field, this is the sum of the potential at (x_0,y_0,z_0) plus the work done in moving a particle along this particular path to (x,y,z). Letting $\mathbf{F} = F_1\mathbf{i} + F_2\mathbf{j} + F_3\mathbf{k}$, we have

(6) $\quad \phi(x,y,z) = \phi(x_0,y_0,z_0) + \displaystyle\int_{x_0}^{x} F_1(x,y_0,z_0) \, dx$

$$+ \int_{y_0}^{y} F_2(x,y,z_0) \, dy + \int_{z_0}^{z} F_3(x,y,z) \, dz$$

Since (x_0,y_0,z_0) is a fixed point, the first of these integrals yields a function of x alone, the second yields a function of x and y only, and the third integral yields a function of x, y, and z. It follows from the Fundamental Theorem of Calculus that

(7) $$\frac{\partial \phi}{\partial z} = F_3(x,y,z)$$

Also, we have

(8) $$\frac{\partial \phi}{\partial y} = F_2(x,y,z_0) + \frac{\partial}{\partial y} \int_{z_0}^{z} F_3(x,y,z) \, dz$$

Since F_3 is continuous and has a continuous derivative $\partial F_3/\partial y$ in the sphere, we can interchange the order of differentiation and integration. (We omit the proof; this is a special case of "Leibnitz's rule" which the interested reader can look up elsewhere.)

(8') $$\frac{\partial \phi}{\partial y} = F_2(x,y,z_0) + \int_{z_0}^{z} \frac{\partial F_3(x,y,z)}{\partial y} \, dz$$

Since we assume that **curl F** $= 0$, we have by (5)

(9) $$\frac{\partial \phi}{\partial y} = F_2(x,y,z_0) + \int_{z_0}^{z} \frac{\partial F_2(x,y,z)}{\partial z} \, dz$$

$$= F_2(x,y,z_0) + F_2(x,y,z)\Big|_{z_0}^{z} = F_2(x,y,z)$$

In a similar manner, we see that

(10) $\quad \dfrac{\partial \phi}{\partial x} = F_1(x,y_0,z_0) + \displaystyle\int_{y_0}^{y} \frac{\partial F_2(x,y,z_0)}{\partial x} \, dy + \int_{z_0}^{z} \frac{\partial F_3(x,y,z)}{\partial x} \, dz$

$$= F_1(x,y_0,z_0) + \int_{y_0}^{y} \frac{\partial F_1(x,y,z_0)}{\partial y} \, dy + \int_{z_0}^{z} \frac{\partial F_1(x,y,z)}{\partial z} \, dz$$

$$= F_1(x,y_0,z_0) + F_1(x,y,z_0)\Big|_{y_0}^{y} + F_1(x,y,z)\Big|_{z_0}^{z}$$

$$= F_1(x,y,z)$$

Hence

(11) $$\mathbf{grad}\ \phi = \frac{\partial \phi}{\partial x}\mathbf{i} + \frac{\partial \phi}{\partial y}\mathbf{j} + \frac{\partial \phi}{\partial z}\mathbf{k} = F_1\mathbf{i} + F_2\mathbf{j} + F_3\mathbf{k}$$

at points (x,y,z) within the sphere S_0.

As far as points within the sphere S_0 are concerned, our proof is complete. We have defined a scalar field ϕ and shown that $\mathbf{grad}\ \phi = \mathbf{F}$. The reader may well ask: Why restrict ourselves to a sphere S_0; why not define $\phi(x,y,z)$ in the same manner for every point (x,y,z) in the domain D? The answer is that the particular path we chose, consisting of three line segments, might pass outside of D where $\mathbf{F}$ is not defined, and then the integrals above would not make sense.

Now let us suppose we are given another sphere S_1 within D, that intersects S_0. Let (x_1,y_1,z_1) be any point within both of these spheres. Since (x_1,y_1,z_1) is within S_0 we have already determined $\phi(x_1,y_1,z_1)$, and we define $\phi(x,y,z)$ for any point (x,y,z) in S_1 to be $\phi(x_1,y_1,z_1)$ plus the integral of $\mathbf{F}$ along the path consisting of the straight line segments from (x_1,y_1,z_1) to (x,y_1,z_1) to (x,y,z_1) to (x,y,z). Since this path is within S_1 and hence within D, $\mathbf{F}$ is defined along this path and the integrals make sense. In this way we *extend* the definition of ϕ to points in S_1, and in the same manner as before we show that $\mathbf{grad}\ \phi = \mathbf{F}$ for points in S_1.

Let us consider briefly other points common to both S_0 and S_1. For such points (x,y,z) we have two ways of finding $\phi(x,y,z)$. We have already defined ϕ within S_0, which gives us one value for $\phi(x,y,z)$; let's call this $\phi_0(x,y,z)$ for the moment. Also, we have just defined ϕ for points in S_1 by starting with the potential at (x_1,y_1,z_1) and moving to (x,y,z), and this might possibly give us another value for $\phi(x,y,z)$, say $\phi_1(x,y,z)$. However, it turns out that we get the same value either way, since in the overlapping region we have $\mathbf{grad}\ \phi_0 = \mathbf{F}$ and $\mathbf{grad}\ \phi_1 = \mathbf{F}$, whence $\mathbf{grad}\ (\phi_0 - \phi_1)$ is identically zero throughout this region, implying that $\phi_0 - \phi_1$ is a constant scalar field. But by the way we defined ϕ_1 we have $\phi_1(x_1,y_1,z_1) = \phi_0(x_1,y_1,z_1)$; hence $\phi_0 - \phi_1$ is zero at (x_1,y_1,z_1) and therefore it is zero throughout this overlapping region. It follows that there is no need to distinguish between ϕ_0 and ϕ_1; in other words, there is no ambiguity in the value of ϕ at points where S_0 and S_1 overlap. We therefore drop the subscripts. Note that this argument also shows that it makes no difference what point (x_1,y_1,z_1) we chose in extending the definition of ϕ to S_1, provided only that it is a point in the region of overlapping of the two spheres.

If now we are given another sphere S_2 in D that overlaps S_1, we can extend the definition of ϕ to points within this sphere also. Similarly, we can proceed from there to extend the definition of ϕ to another sphere S_3 within D that overlaps S_2, and so on to a chain of spheres $S_0, S_1, S_2, \ldots, S_n$, each one of which overlaps the preceding one.

We now make use of the following theorem which, although its proof is beyond the scope of this book, is not "hard to swallow": Given any two points (x_0,y_0,z_0) and (x,y,z) in a domain D, there exists a chain of a finite number of spheres $S_0, S_1, S_2, \ldots, S_n$, each one overlapping the preceding one and all lying completely within the domain D, such that (x_0,y_0,z_0) is within S_0 and (x,y,z) is within S_n. The proof of this theorem makes strong use of the fact that D is both open and connected; the theorem is false for some regions that are not domains. (A region that is not open may have points that are not interior points and therefore are not contained in any spheres that are completely within the region. The theorem is obviously false if the region is not connected.)

It follows that by proceeding along such a chain we can define $\phi(x,y,z)$ for any point (x,y,z) in the domain.   Step by step we extend the definition of ϕ from one sphere to the next.   In every sphere we

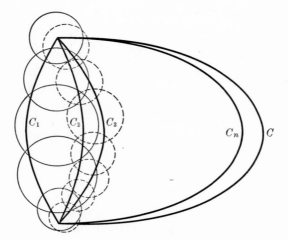

Figure 61

have **grad** ϕ = **F**.   Wherever one sphere overlaps the next sphere in the chain there is no ambiguity in the definition of ϕ.

For any regular curve C_1 extending from (x_0,y_0,z_0) to (x,y,z), within this chain of spheres, we have

$$\int_{C_1} \mathbf{F} \cdot d\mathbf{R} \;=\; \int_{C_1} \mathbf{grad}\ \phi \cdot d\mathbf{R} \;=\; \int_{C_1} d\phi \;=\; \phi(x,y,z) \;-\; \phi(x_0,y_0,z_0)$$

from which

(12) $$\phi(x,y,z) \;=\; \phi(x_0,y_0,z_0) + \int_{C_1} \mathbf{F} \cdot d\mathbf{R}$$

Unfortunately, we still cannot say that $\phi(x,y,z)$ is defined unambiguously; how do we know that another chain of spheres extending from (x_0,y_0,z_0) to (x,y,z) might not yield another value for $\phi(x,y,z)$?

Let us therefore consider two chains of spheres, each extending from (x_0,y_0,z_0) to (x,y,z).   Let the functions obtained by the above processes be denoted ϕ_1 and ϕ_2 respectively.   Let us suppose that these two chains are sufficiently "close together" that we can find a single regular curve C_2 extending from (x_0,y_0,z_0) that is within *both* chains.   (See Figure 61, where the spheres are represented as circles.) Then applying (12) separately, we have

$$\phi_1(x,y,z) \;=\; \phi(x_0,y_0,z_0) + \int_{C_2} \mathbf{F} \cdot d\mathbf{R}$$

and also

$$\phi_2(x,y,z) \;=\; \phi(x_0,y_0,z_0) + \int_{C_2} \mathbf{F} \cdot d\mathbf{R}$$

It follows that $\phi_1(x,y,z) = \phi_2(x,y,z)$.

Now let us consider another such regular curve C_3 lying within the chain defining ϕ_2 but not necessarily within the other chain. Then we have, by (12), that

$$\phi_2(x,y,z) \;=\; \phi(x_0,y_0,z_0) + \int_{C_3} \mathbf{F} \cdot d\mathbf{R}$$

Since

$$\phi_2(x,y,z) \;=\; \phi_1(x,y,z) \;=\; \phi(x_0,y_0,z_0) + \int_{C_1} \mathbf{F} \cdot d\mathbf{R}$$

it follows that

$$\int_{C_3} \mathbf{F} \cdot d\mathbf{R} \;=\; \int_{C_1} \mathbf{F} \cdot d\mathbf{R}$$

that is, the line integrals of **F** along these two paths are identical.

From this we see that the line integrals of **F** along two paths C_1 and C_3 will be equal provided that the paths are sufficiently "close" in the following sense: There exist chains containing C_1 and C_3 overlapping enough that some intermediate curve C_2 is within both chains (Fig. 61).

Now suppose there exists a chain of spheres that is not close to the chains C_1 and C_3. We let C denote a regular curve in this chain extending from (x_0,y_0,z_0) to (x,y,z).

The curve obtained by first traversing C and then moving backwards along C_1 is a closed curve, and since D is simply-connected, this closed curve can be shrunk to a point without leaving the domain D. In the process of shrinking, we generate a surface within D. On this surface we can find a succession of curves C_1, C_2, . . . , C_n, each close to the preceding one in the above-defined sense and with C_n close to C. It follows that

$$\int_C \mathbf{F} \cdot d\mathbf{R} = \int_{C_n} \mathbf{F} \cdot d\mathbf{R} = \ldots = \int_{C_2} \mathbf{F} \cdot d\mathbf{R} = \int_{C_1} \mathbf{F} \cdot d\mathbf{R}$$

Once again applying (12), this time to ϕ as it is defined along the chain containing C, we see that $\phi(x,y,z)$ defined via this chain is the same as that defined along the chain we started with.

This proof is not rigorous, since we leave to the imagination the rigorous proof that the required succession of curves exists. We cannot give a rigorous proof in any event, since we have not defined with sufficient precision the term "simply-connected." However, in any of the specific examples we consider here, it is quite easy to see the validity of this argument.

The above proof is not intended to provide a practical way of finding ϕ. In practice, much simpler methods can usually be found.

EXAMPLE 1: Show that $\mathbf{F} = 2xy\mathbf{i} + (x^2 + 1)\mathbf{j} + 6z^2\mathbf{k}$ is conservative, and find a scalar potential ϕ.

Solution: We use the test (5), which is acceptable since this field $\mathbf{F}$ is defined and continuously differentiable throughout space (the set of *all* points in space is obviously a simply-connected domain):

$$\partial F_1/\partial y = \partial F_2/\partial x = 2x$$

$$\partial F_2/\partial z = \partial F_3/\partial y = 0$$

and

$$\partial F_1/\partial z = \partial F_3/\partial x = 0$$

The test is positive, hence the field is conservative. The potential may be found by the methods of the preceding section, or we may use (6) of this section:

Taking (x_0, y_0, z_0) to be the origin, and letting $\phi(x_0, y_0, z_0) = 0$, we have

$$\phi(x,y,z) = \int_{x_0}^{x} 2xy_0 \, dx + \int_{y_0}^{y} (x^2 + 1) \, dy + \int_{z_0}^{z} 6z^2 \, dz$$

where $x_0 = 0$, $y_0 = 0$, and $z_0 = 0$. The first integral vanishes and we obtain

$$\phi(x,y,z) = (x^2 y + y)\Big|_0^y + 3z^3 \Big|_0^z = x^2 y + y + 3z^3$$

The reader is advised to use the test given in this section to determine whether a given field $\mathbf{F}$ is conservative, but to use the methods of Section 4.3 to actually construct the potential ϕ. The reason we do not advise using (6) of this section is that it may be a little tricky for most students to use correctly, as will be demonstrated in the following example.

EXAMPLE 2:   Use (6) to find a potential for

$$\mathbf{F} = (3x^2 yz + y + 5)\mathbf{i} + (x^3 z + x - z)\mathbf{j} + (x^3 y - y + 7)\mathbf{k}$$

which has the value 10 at the origin.
   Solution: By (6) we have

$$\phi(x,y,z) = 10 + \int_{x_0}^{x} (3x^2 y_0 z_0 + y_0 + 5) \, dx$$
$$+ \int_{y_0}^{y} (x^3 z_0 + x - z_0) \, dy + \int_{z_0}^{z} (x^3 y - y + 7) \, d$$

Since $x_0 = 0$, $y_0 = 0$, and $z_0 = 0$, we have

$$\phi(x,y,z) = 10 + \int_{0}^{x} 5 \, dx + \int_{0}^{y} x \, dy + \int_{0}^{z} (x^3 y - y + 7) \, dz$$

$$= 10 + 5x \Big|_0^x + xy \Big|_0^y + (x^3 yz - yz + 7z) \Big|_0^z$$

$$= 10 + 5x + xy + x^3 yz - yz + 7z$$

EXERCISES

1.   Test the following fields to determine whether they are conservative.
   (a) $\mathbf{F} = (12xy + yz)\mathbf{i} + (6x^2 + xz)\mathbf{j} + xy\mathbf{k}$

(b) $\mathbf{F} = ze^{xz}\mathbf{i} + xe^{xz}\mathbf{k}$

(c) $\mathbf{F} = \sin x\,\mathbf{i} + y^2\mathbf{j} + e^z\mathbf{k}$

(d) $\mathbf{F} = 3x^2yz^2\mathbf{i} + x^3z^2\mathbf{j} + x^3yz\mathbf{k}$

(e) $\mathbf{F} = \dfrac{2x}{x^2 + y^2}\,\mathbf{i} + \dfrac{2y}{x^2 + y^2}\,\mathbf{j} + 2z\mathbf{k}$

2. For which one of the fields in Exercise 1 is the test given in this section not applicable? How, then, can you test this field to determine whether it is conservative in its domain of definition?

3. Let $\mathbf{F}$ and $\mathbf{G}$ be conservative vector fields with potentials ϕ and ψ respectively. Is the vector field $\mathbf{F} + \mathbf{G}$ conservative? If so, determine a potential for it.

4. Suppose that, in the discussion of this section, we had taken as a particular path joining (x_0, y_0, z_0) to (x, y, z) the straight line segments from (x_0, y_0, z_0) to (x_0, y_0, z) to (x_0, y, z) to (x, y, z). What does (6) become in this case?

5. Show that the scalar field

$$\phi = -\frac{1}{|\mathbf{R}|}$$

which is defined except at the origin, is a potential function for the vector field $\mathbf{R}/|\mathbf{R}|^3$, where $\mathbf{R} = x\mathbf{i} + y\mathbf{j} + z\mathbf{k}$,

(a) by writing ϕ in terms of x, y, and z and computing its gradient;

(b) by inspection, using the second and third fundamental properties of the gradient listed in Section 3.1.

6. A force field is defined by

$$\mathbf{F} = \frac{x\mathbf{i} + y\mathbf{j} + z\mathbf{k}}{(x^2 + y^2 + z^2)^{3/2}}$$

at all points in space except the origin. A particle is moved along the straight line segment from the point $(1,2,3)$ to the point $(2,3,5)$. What is the work done by the force on the particle? [Hint: Avoid a lot of work by making use of the statement of Exercise 5.]

7. Would your answer to Exercise 6 be any different if the path extending from $(1,2,3)$ to $(2,3,5)$ were not straight?

4.5 : Oriented Surfaces

A surface S is said to be *smooth* if it is possible to choose a unit normal vector **n** at every point of S in such a way that **n** varies continuously on S. It is said to be *piecewise smooth* if it consists of a finite number of smooth parts joined together. Thus, the surface of a sphere is smooth, whereas the surface of a cube is piecewise smooth (consisting of six smooth surfaces joined together).

At every point of a smooth surface there will, of course, be two choices for the unit normal **n**. There will therefore be two ways in which we can define a field of unit normal vectors continuous on S. [If, for instance, the surface is given by an equation of the form $f(x,y,z) = C$, then the two fields are

$$\frac{\mathbf{grad}\,f}{|\mathbf{grad}\,f|} \quad \text{and} \quad \frac{-\mathbf{grad}\,f}{|\mathbf{grad}\,f|}$$

(Section 3.1).] In choosing one of these two possibilities we *orient* the surface. Thus, there are always two possible orientations of a smooth surface. We have already discussed orientation for the special case of a plane (Section 1.12). The situation is somewhat the

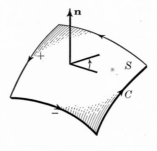

Figure 62

same for more general surfaces. When a smooth surface has been oriented by choosing a particular unit normal field **n**, then a positive direction for angles is determined at each point of the surface (Fig. 62). If the surface is bounded by a regular closed curve C, the orien-

tation also determines what we mean by the *positive direction* along C.
This is determined by the requirement that an observer on the positive side of the surface (i.e., the side on which **n** emerges), walking
in the positive direction along the boundary, always has the surface
at his left.

A piecewise-smooth surface is oriented by choosing **n** at every
point (except along certain edges, perhaps) in such a manner that
along every edge that is the common boundary of two smooth surfaces
the positive direction relative to one of the surfaces is opposite to the
positive direction relative to the other.   This is shown for the surfaces
of a cube and a cylinder in Figures 63 and 64.

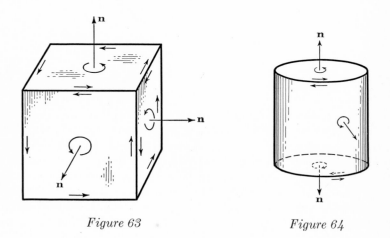

Figure 63   Figure 64

A *closed surface* is one that has no boundary.   Thus the surfaces
of Figures 63 and 64 are closed, whereas the surface in Figure 62 has
a boundary and is not closed.   It is conventional to take the orientation of a closed surface, which encloses a region of space, to be such
that the unit normal **n** always points *away* from the enclosed region,
as illustrated in Figures 63 and 64.

A surface can be oriented only if it has two sides; the process of
orientation consists essentially in choosing which side we will call
"positive" and which "negative."   (If the surface is closed, it is more
natural to speak of the "outside" and the "inside.")

Not all surfaces can be oriented.   The reader may be familiar with the *Möbius strip*, obtained by twisting and pasting together the ends of a strip of paper (Fig. 65).   This surface is nonorientable because it has only one side.   If **n** is a unit vector normal to the surface at a point P, then as it moves around the strip its direction is reversed by the time it reaches P again, which contradicts the requirement that **n** be unambiguous at every point and still vary continuously.

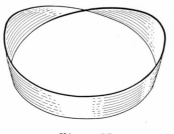

Figure 65

The reader may amuse himself by taking two strips of paper (adding-machine tape is especially convenient) and preparing two strips, one with a twist and one without.   If the strips are long enough to dangle on the floor, no one will notice the difference between them. Have someone cut along a central line of the cylindrical band at the same time that you cut the Möbius strip.   The cylindrical band will separate into two cylindrical bands, but the Möbius strip will not separate into distinct portions.   This trick astonishes most children and those few adults who have never seen it before.

Nonorientable surfaces have other mathematical properties that are rather amazing, so amazing in fact that we must exclude them from further consideration.   Henceforth, whenever we say "surface" we mean an orientable surface.

Just as it is possible to write the equations of a space curve in parametric form, giving x, y, and z as functions of a single parameter t, so also it is possible to represent certain surfaces parametrically by giving x, y, and z as functions of *two* parameters u and v:

$$(1) \qquad x = x(u,v), \quad y = y(u,v), \quad z = z(u,v)$$

This can also be written in vector notation:

$$(1') \qquad \mathbf{R} = \mathbf{R}(u,v)$$

If we hold one of these parameters fixed and vary the other, the point (x,y,z) will trace out a curve on the surface. Thus we obtain a family of curves along each of which u has a different constant value, and another family of curves for different constant values of v (Fig. 66).

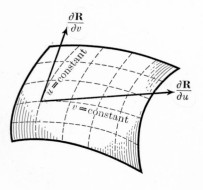

Figure 66

Along any one of these curves, the theory developed in Section 2.2 is applicable. It follows that at any point the vector

(2) $$\frac{\partial \mathbf{R}}{\partial v} = \frac{\partial x}{\partial v}\mathbf{i} + \frac{\partial y}{\partial v}\mathbf{j} + \frac{\partial z}{\partial v}\mathbf{k}$$

is tangent to a curve u = constant passing through that point, and similarly

(3) $$\frac{\partial \mathbf{R}}{\partial u} = \frac{\partial x}{\partial u}\mathbf{i} + \frac{\partial y}{\partial u}\mathbf{j} + \frac{\partial z}{\partial u}\mathbf{k}$$

is tangent to a curve with equation v = constant. We assume here that all the relevant derivatives exist, that $\partial \mathbf{R}/\partial v$ and $\partial \mathbf{R}/\partial u$ are nonzero and not parallel at every point, and that these derivatives are continuous on the surface. It follows that at any point P the vector

(4) $$\frac{\partial \mathbf{R}}{\partial u} \times \frac{\partial \mathbf{R}}{\partial v}$$

is normal to the surface at P. Dividing this vector by its own length we obtain at each point a unit vector $\mathbf{n}$. The opposite orientation is given by dividing $(\partial \mathbf{R}/\partial v) \times (\partial \mathbf{R}/\partial u)$ by its length.

Any portion of a surface that can be represented by equations of the form (1) in such a manner that to distinct ordered pairs (u,v) there correspond distinct points (x,y,z) on the surface, and satisfying the above differentiability and continuity requirements, is called a *regular surface element*. The surface area of such a surface element is defined by the double integral

(5)
$$\iint \left| \frac{\partial \mathbf{R}}{\partial u} \times \frac{\partial \mathbf{R}}{\partial v} \right| du \, dv$$

vector normal to surface

differential area

where appropriate limits of integration must be supplied. We assume here that the boundary of the surface element is such that the integral (5) exists.

As motivation for (5), we note that the integrand is the magnitude of the vector cross product of the vectors $(\partial \mathbf{R}/\partial u) \, du$ and $(\partial \mathbf{R}/\partial v) \, dv$, and therefore represents the area of the parallelogram determined by these two vectors. This is approximately the area ΔS bounded by four curves on the surface (Fig. 67).

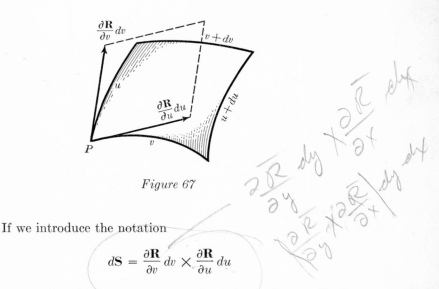

Figure 67

If we introduce the notation

$$d\mathbf{S} = \frac{\partial \mathbf{R}}{\partial v} \, dv \times \frac{\partial \mathbf{R}}{\partial u} \, du$$

then we see that $d\mathbf{S}$ is a vector normal to the surface at P whose magnitude $dS = |d\mathbf{S}|$ is approximately equal to ΔS. The integral (5) may be written in the alternative forms

$$\iint |d\mathbf{S}|$$

or

$$\iint d\mathbf{S}$$

or even

$$\iint \mathbf{n} \cdot d\mathbf{S}$$

where $\mathbf{n}$ is a unit normal in the same direction as $d\mathbf{S}$.

We now consider a *special case* of (5) that will illustrate further its geometrical significance.   Let us suppose that the surface we consider is given in the form $z = f(x,y)$.   In other words, we are told

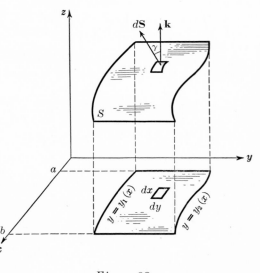

Figure 68

how far above the xy plane the surface is for each point (x,y) in the xy plane.   Then it is convenient to use x and y instead of u and v as the parameters.   Let us suppose that the projection of the surface element on the xy plane is bounded by the curves

$$y = y_1(x), \quad y = y_2(x), \quad x = a, \quad x = b$$

as shown in Figure 68.

We can write $x = u$, $y = v$, and $z = f(u,v)$, in order to make use of the preceding formulas.   From (2) we have

$$\partial \mathbf{R}/\partial v = \partial \mathbf{R}/\partial y = \mathbf{j} + (\partial f/\partial y)\mathbf{k}$$

and by (3)

$$\partial \mathbf{R}/\partial u = \partial \mathbf{R}/\partial x = \mathbf{i} + (\partial f/\partial x)\mathbf{k}$$

Taking the vector cross product,

$$\frac{\partial \mathbf{R}}{\partial u} \times \frac{\partial \mathbf{R}}{\partial v} = \begin{vmatrix} \mathbf{i} & \mathbf{j} & \mathbf{k} \\ 1 & 0 & \partial f/\partial x \\ 0 & 1 & \partial f/\partial y \end{vmatrix} = \mathbf{k} - \frac{\partial f}{\partial x}\mathbf{i} - \frac{\partial f}{\partial y}\mathbf{j}$$

The magnitude of this vector is $\sqrt{1 + (\partial f/\partial x)^2 + (\partial f/\partial y)^2}$, so that the integral (5) is

(6)
$$\int_a^b \int_{y_1(x)}^{y_2(x)} \sqrt{1 + \left(\frac{\partial f}{\partial x}\right)^2 + \left(\frac{\partial f}{\partial y}\right)^2} \, dy \, dx$$

The geometrical significance of this is seen by considering the angle γ between dS and $\mathbf{k}$.   By a simple calculation using scalar products we see that

$$|\cos \gamma| = \frac{|d\mathbf{S} \cdot \mathbf{k}|}{|d\mathbf{S}|} = \left[1 + \left(\frac{\partial f}{\partial x}\right)^2 + \left(\frac{\partial f}{\partial y}\right)^2\right]^{-\frac{1}{2}}$$

so that (6) is simply

(7)
$$\int_a^b \int_{y_1(x)}^{y_2(x)} \frac{dx \, dy}{|\cos \gamma|}$$

This integral could have been obtained heuristically by considering the *area cosine principle* which says that, if we look at a plane area A whose normal makes an acute angle θ with the line of sight,

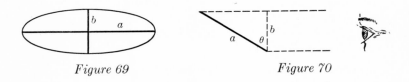

Figure 69   *Figure 70*

the area we appear to see is $A \cos \theta$.   This is because distances in one direction will appear to be shorter by a factor of $\cos \theta$ and distances in a perpendicular direction will not change at all.   Let us digress for a moment to use this law to determine the area of the ellipse shown in Figure 69.

Let us pretend that this ellipse is really a circle of radius a that we are viewing at an angle. In other words, we imagine that this is a circle of radius a (area πa^2) that has been tipped in such a manner that vertical distances are shortened by a factor b/a. The area we see will be $A \cos \theta = (\pi a^2)(b/a) = \pi ab$. Thus we find the area of this ellipse to be πab, by a method that is much easier than using integral calculus.

Returning to Figure 68, we can consider an element of area in S whose projection on the xy plane has area $dx\, dy$. The angle between the normal to this area and the "line of sight" (imagine that you are below the xy plane looking up at the surface) is γ. By the area cosine principle, the area $dx\, dy$ that we see equals $dS\,|\cos \gamma|$. It follows that

$$dS = \frac{dx\, dy}{|\cos \gamma|}$$

The absolute value is unnecessary if γ is acute.

Frequently, a judicious use of the area cosine principle makes it unnecessary to use (5). The cosine of the relevant angle, in this case γ, is easily computed since we can find a normal to the surface by methods we have already learned and then use scalar products to find the desired cosine. For instance, the surface $z = f(x,y)$ can be represented by the equation $z - f(x,y) = 0$, and the gradient of the function $z - f(x,y)$ is $\mathbf{k} - (\partial f/\partial x)\mathbf{i} - (\partial f/\partial y)\mathbf{j}$. This is easier than computing the vector cross product given above. *Caution:* Using gradients to give a normal vector $\mathbf{N}$ may give a vector $\mathbf{N}\, du\, dv$ that does not equal $d\mathbf{S}$ but is only a scalar multiple of it. However, this makes no difference since we are only interested in computing $\cos \gamma = \mathbf{N} \cdot \mathbf{k}/|\mathbf{N}|$ when using (7).

In practice it is frequently unnecessary to use (5) at all, or even expressions derived from it, such as (7). For example, suppose S is part of the sphere $x^2 + y^2 + z^2 = a^2$. Using spherical coordinates (Fig. 71) we have

$$x = a \sin \phi \cos \theta \qquad y = a \sin \phi \sin \theta$$

$$z = a \cos \phi$$

Using the two parameters ϕ and θ instead of u and v, we obtain

(8) $\partial \mathbf{R}/\partial \phi = a \cos \phi \cos \theta\, \mathbf{i} + a \cos \phi \sin \theta\, \mathbf{j} - a \sin \phi\, \mathbf{k}$

(9) $\partial \mathbf{R}/\partial \theta = -a \sin \phi \sin \theta\, \mathbf{i} + a \sin \phi \cos \theta\, \mathbf{j}$

whereupon we compute to show that

(10) $\qquad \dfrac{\partial \mathbf{R}}{\partial \phi} \times \dfrac{\partial \mathbf{R}}{\partial \theta} = a^2 \sin^2 \phi \cos \theta\, \mathbf{i} - a^2 \sin^2 \phi \sin \theta\, \mathbf{j} - a^2 \sin \phi \cos \phi\, \mathbf{k}$

The magnitude of this vector is $a^2 \sin \phi$, so it follows that

(11) $\qquad\qquad\qquad\qquad dS = a^2 \sin \phi\, d\phi\, d\theta$

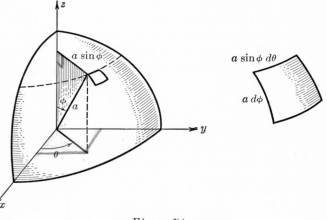

Figure 71

However, a practical engineer would guffaw to see someone go to all this work to obtain a result that can easily be "seen" just by looking at Figure 71. Holding θ fixed and varying ϕ by an amount $d\phi$ we trace out an arc of length $a\, d\phi$. Holding ϕ fixed and varying θ we trace out an arc of a circle of radius $a \sin \phi$, the length of this arc being $a \sin \phi\, d\theta$. For small $d\phi$ and $d\theta$ this gives us very nearly a rectangle with area $a^2 \sin \phi\, d\phi\, d\theta$.

EXERCISES

1.   Draw a diagram similar to those of Figures 63 and 64 for the surface of a tetrahedron.

2.   Consider the triangle with vertices (1,0,0), (0,1,0), and (0,0,1).
   (a) Find a unit vector **n** normal to this triangle, pointing away from the origin.

(b) Determine $\cos \gamma$ for this vector.

(c) Supply the appropriate limits for the integral

$$\iint \frac{dx\,dy}{|\cos \gamma|}$$

if it is to represent the area of this triangle.

(d) Evaluate the integral.

(e) Obtain the same answer by applying the area cosine principle to the projection of this triangle on the xy plane.

3. (a) Derive (10) from (8) and (9).

    (b) Show that the magnitude of this vector is $a^2 \sin \phi$.

4. Determine the element of surface area dS in the special case of the surface $z = x^2 + y^2$.

4.6 : Surface Integrals

Let S denote a smooth surface and let $f(x,y,z)$ be a function defined and continuous on S. The surface integral of f over S is denoted

$$\iint_S f(x,y,z)\,dS$$

and is defined to be the limit of sums obtained in the following manner. We imagine the surface cut up into n pieces having area $\delta S_1, \delta S_2, \ldots, \delta S_n$. In each piece we choose a point (x_i, y_i, z_i), evaluate $f(x_i, y_i, z_i)$, and form $f(x_i, y_i, z_i)\,\delta S_i$. We sum these numbers:

(1) $$\sum_{i=1}^{n} f(x_i, y_i, z_i)\,\delta S_i$$

In this way we obtain a single number. Now we let n tend to infinity, at the same time letting the pieces grow smaller so that the maximum value of the areas $\delta S_1, \delta S_2, \ldots, \delta S_n$ tends to zero. In other words, we are dividing the surface up into smaller and smaller elements of area, each time forming a sum of form (1). If these sums tend to a limit, independent of the way we form the repeated subdivisions, that limit is called the surface integral of f over S:

(2) $$\iint_S f(x,y,z)\,dS = \lim_{\substack{\max \delta S_i \to 0 \\ n \to \infty}} \sum_{i=1}^{n} f(x_i, y_i, z_i)\,\delta S_i$$

We omit a theoretical discussion of surface integrals in favor of the following discussion which serves to motivate the definition and show how important surface integrals are in applications. It is important for the reader to know at the outset that only very seldom will he be called upon to actually evaluate a surface integral. It is the *concept* that is important, for surface integrals provide a convenient language for expressing certain fundamental ideas in mathematics and physics. The actual computation of a surface integral may be very difficult. They are rarely computed directly from the definition we have just given!

Suppose, for instance, that at any point (x,y,z) on a surface S, $f(x,y,z)$ gives the rate of flow of heat per unit area at that point, in units (say) of calories per second per square centimeter. Then $f(x_i,y_i,z_i)\,\delta S_i$ gives, approximately, the number of calories per second flowing across the element of area δS_i. The sum (1) then gives approximately the total number of calories per second flowing across the entire surface S. If $f(x,y,z)$ varies from point to point on the surface, this sum will generally be only an approximation, but one that can be improved by taking smaller elements of area (and hence more such elements). The limit

$$\iint_S f(x,y,z)\,dS$$

gives exactly the number of calories per second flowing across the surface.

If we assume a steady-state temperature distribution, where $T(x,y,z)$ denotes the temperature at each point in space, and if the region we consider is filled with a homogeneous material having coefficient of thermal conductivity k, then the vector

(3) $$\mathbf{Q} = -k\nabla T$$

gives, at each point in space, the direction in which the heat is flowing. The magnitude of $\mathbf{Q}$ gives the rate of heat flow per unit area across an area perpendicular to $\mathbf{Q}$. More generally, we can say that the scalar component of $\mathbf{Q}$ in the direction of a unit vector $\mathbf{n}$ (equal to $\mathbf{Q}\cdot\mathbf{n}$) gives the number of calories per unit time and per unit area across an element of area perpendicular to $\mathbf{n}$. It follows that, to find the total number of calories per second flowing across a surface S, we form the surface integral

(4) $$\iint_S (-k\nabla T)\cdot\mathbf{n}\,dS$$

The reason for the negative sign in (3) and (4) is that the temperature gradient ∇T points in the direction of maximum rate of increase of the temperature, whereas of course heat flows in the opposite direction, from hot to cold.

More generally, if we are given any vector field $\mathbf{F}$, continuous in a region containing an oriented smooth surface S, we can form the surface integral

(5)
$$\iint_S \mathbf{F} \cdot \mathbf{n} \, dS \qquad {(-k\nabla T)}$$

where, at any point on the oriented surface, $\mathbf{n}$ is the unit normal to S. The physical meaning of the integral depends on the nature of the physical quantity represented by $\mathbf{F}$.

Let us consider another situation in physics in which surface integrals arise. Let $\mathbf{V}$ denote the velocity field of a fluid and let ρ denote the density of the fluid. The flux density is the vector field $\mathbf{D} = \rho \mathbf{V}$, already briefly mentioned in Section 3.3. Let us consider a surface element δS (Fig. 72). During a small interval of time Δt a body of fluid will move across this area in the direction of the velocity $\mathbf{V}$.

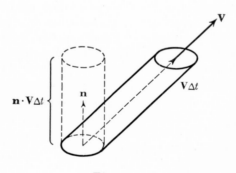

Figure 72

This body of fluid can be thought of roughly as forming a slant cylinder with base area δS and central axis along the vector $\mathbf{V} \Delta t$. The volume of this cylinder is its base times its altitude, $(\delta S)(\mathbf{n} \cdot \mathbf{V} \Delta t)$. The mass of fluid will then be $\rho(\delta S)(\mathbf{n} \cdot \mathbf{V} \Delta t)$. It follows that the mass of fluid per unit time and per unit area flowing across the element is $\mathbf{n} \cdot \rho \mathbf{V} = \mathbf{n} \cdot \mathbf{D}$. This heuristic argument suggests that the surface integral

(6) $$\iint_S \mathbf{n} \cdot \mathbf{D}\, dS$$

gives the rate of flow of liquid across a surface S, expressed as mass per unit time.

As yet another example, consider an electrostatic field $\mathbf{E}$ defined in a region of space. One can form

$$\iint_S \mathbf{n} \cdot \mathbf{E}\, dS$$

which is the surface integral of the normal component of $\mathbf{E}$ over the surface S. This integral arises in connection with Gauss's law of electrostatics which states that if S is a closed surface,

(7) $$\iint_S \mathbf{n} \cdot \mathbf{E}\, dS = \frac{q}{\varepsilon_0}$$

where q is the total charge enclosed by the surface and ε_0 is a constant that depends on the system of units. The numerical value of the surface integral in (7) is sometimes called the *flux* across S or the *number of flow lines of the vector field* $\mathbf{F}$ *crossing the surface*. This last phrase is not to be taken literally, since there will usually be a flow line crossing every point of S and therefore there are really an infinite number of flow lines crossing S. However, in drawing diagrams, it is impossible to draw an infinite number of flow lines, so it may be convenient to visualize (7) as giving approximately the number of flow lines we wish to picture crossing the surface. (This number is necessarily approximate since the value of (7) may not be a whole number.)

Returning to (5), we note that in the notation of the preceding section we can use the alternative forms

(5') $$\iint_S \mathbf{F} \cdot d\mathbf{S}$$

and

(5'') $$\iint_S \mathbf{F} \cdot \frac{\partial \mathbf{R}}{\partial u} \times \frac{\partial \mathbf{R}}{\partial v}\, du\, dv$$

and when the surface is specified by giving z as a function of x and y, we can write

(5''') $$\iint \mathbf{F} \cdot \mathbf{n} \frac{dx\, dy}{|\cos \gamma|}$$

where the limits of integration are determined by the projection of S onto the xy plane.

If the surface S is only piecewise smooth, we integrate over each smooth part separately and add the numbers obtained.

EXAMPLE 1: Compute

$$\iint_S \mathbf{F} \cdot d\mathbf{S}$$

where S is the surface of the sphere $x^2 + y^2 + z^2 = 4$ and

$$\mathbf{F} = x\mathbf{i} + y\mathbf{j} + z\mathbf{k}$$

Solution: We recall that at a point (x,y,z) the vector $x\mathbf{i} + y\mathbf{j} + z\mathbf{k}$ points directly away from the origin. The outward normal $\mathbf{n}$ to this sphere also points away from the origin, since the center of the sphere is at the origin. Hence for points on the surface

$$\mathbf{F} \cdot \mathbf{n} = |\mathbf{F}|\, |\mathbf{n}|\, \cos\theta = |\mathbf{F}| = (x^2 + y^2 + z^2)^{\frac{1}{2}} = 2$$

and

$$\iint_S \mathbf{F} \cdot d\mathbf{S} = \iint_S \mathbf{F} \cdot \mathbf{n}\, dS = \iint_S 2\, dS = 2 \text{ (total surface area)}$$
$$= 2(4\pi r^2) = 32\pi$$

since $r = 2$ is the radius of the sphere.

Note that, in the above example, no integration was needed since $\mathbf{F} \cdot \mathbf{n}$ was constant over the entire surface.

EXAMPLE 2: Compute

$$\iint_S \mathbf{F} \cdot d\mathbf{S}$$

where S is the surface of the cube bounded by the planes $x = 0$, $x = 1$, $y = 0$, $y = 1$, $z = 0$, $z = 1$, and $\mathbf{F} = x\mathbf{i} + y\mathbf{j} + z\mathbf{k}$.

Solution: We see from Figure 73 that the unit normal to the front face of the cube is $\mathbf{n} = \mathbf{i}$, so

$$\mathbf{F} \cdot \mathbf{n} = \mathbf{i} \cdot (x\mathbf{i} + y\mathbf{j} + z\mathbf{k}) = x = 1$$

on this face. It follows that the integral over this face is

$$\iint \mathbf{F} \cdot d\mathbf{S} = \iint \mathbf{F} \cdot \mathbf{n}\, dS = \iint dS = 1$$

since the area of this face is unity. On the opposite face (in the yz plane) $\mathbf{n} = -\mathbf{i}$ so that $\mathbf{F} \cdot \mathbf{n} = -x$, but $x = 0$ for all points in this face and hence

$$\iint \mathbf{F} \cdot \mathbf{n}\, dS = 0$$

On the top of the cube we have

$$\iint \mathbf{F} \cdot \mathbf{n} \, dS = \iint \mathbf{F} \cdot \mathbf{k} \, dS = \iint z \, dS = \iint dS = 1$$

and on the bottom we have

$$\iint \mathbf{F} \cdot \mathbf{n} \, dS = \iint (-z) \, dS = 0$$

since $z = 0$ in the xy plane. Along the right side we have $\mathbf{n} = \mathbf{j}$ so that the normal component of $\mathbf{F}$ is unity and the integral over this face is unity; along the left side $\mathbf{n} = -\mathbf{j}$ and $\mathbf{F} \cdot \mathbf{n} = -y = 0$, so that the contribution to the integral is zero. Summing, we find that

$$\iint_S \mathbf{F} \cdot \mathbf{n} \, dS = 3$$

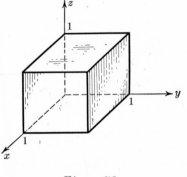

Figure 73

EXAMPLE 3: Compute the surface integral of the normal component of $\mathbf{F} = x^2\mathbf{i} + yx\mathbf{j} + zx\mathbf{k}$ over the triangle with vertices $(1,0,0)$, $(0,2,0)$, $(0,0,3)$. Consider the triangle oriented so that its positive side is that away from the origin (Fig. 74).

Solution: By the methods of Chapter One we find easily that $\mathbf{n} = \frac{6}{7}\mathbf{i} + \frac{3}{7}\mathbf{j} + \frac{2}{7}\mathbf{k}$. Hence $\mathbf{F} \cdot \mathbf{n} = \frac{6}{7}x^2 + \frac{3}{7}yx + \frac{2}{7}zx$ and

$$\cos \gamma = \mathbf{n} \cdot \mathbf{k} = \frac{2}{7}$$

Using (5‴) we have

$$\iint_S \mathbf{F}\cdot\mathbf{n}\,dS = \int_0^1 \int_0^{2-2x} \tfrac{7}{2}\left(\tfrac{6}{7}x^2 + \tfrac{3}{7}yx + \tfrac{2}{7}zx\right)dy\,dx$$

$$= \int_0^1 \int_0^{2-2x}\left(3x^2 + \tfrac{3}{2}yx + zx\right)dy\,dx$$

On S we have $z = 3 - 3x - \tfrac{3}{2}y$ so that $zx = 3x - 3x^2 - \tfrac{3}{2}yx$ and the integral becomes

$$\int_0^1 \int_0^{2-2x} 3x\,dy\,dx = \int_0^1 3x(2-2x)\,dx = 3x^2 - 2x^3\Big|_0^1 = 1$$

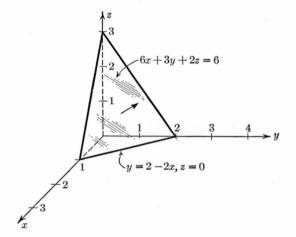

Figure 74

EXAMPLE 4: Compute

$$\iint_S \mathbf{F}\cdot\mathbf{n}\,dS$$

over the surface of the tetrahedron with vertices $(1,0,0)$, $(0,2,0)$, $(0,0,3)$, $(0,0,0)$, where $\mathbf{F} = x^2\mathbf{i} + yx\mathbf{j} + zx\mathbf{k}$ (Fig. 74).

Solution: We have already computed the integral over one surface. Along the bottom face we have $\mathbf{n} = -\mathbf{k}$ and hence $\mathbf{F}\cdot\mathbf{n} = -zx$, but since $z = 0$ the integral over the bottom face is zero. On the face at the left we have $\mathbf{n} = -\mathbf{j}$ and $\mathbf{F}\cdot\mathbf{n} = -yx$, which is also zero since $y = 0$ there. On the rear face, in the yz plane, $\mathbf{n} = -\mathbf{i}$ and $\mathbf{F} \cdot \mathbf{n} = -x^2 = 0$. It follows that

$$\iint_S \mathbf{F} \cdot d\mathbf{S} = 1$$

the only nonzero contribution being the integral already computed in Example 3.

Note that in Examples 1, 2, and 4 we took n to be the *outward* normal, the usual convention for closed surfaces.

EXAMPLE 5: Use Gauss's law (7) to determine the magnitude of the electric field intensity at a point r units away from a point charge of magnitude q.

Solution: Let S be a sphere of radius r with the charge q at its center. Symmetry considerations lead us to believe that $\mathbf{n} \cdot \mathbf{E}$ will be constant over the surface of this sphere, and that $\mathbf{E}$ will be normal to the surface. Hence we can bring $\mathbf{n} \cdot \mathbf{E}$ outside the integral, and we obtain

$$\iint \mathbf{n} \cdot \mathbf{E} \, dS = \mathbf{n} \cdot \mathbf{E} \iint dS = 4\pi r^2 (\mathbf{n} \cdot \mathbf{E})$$

It then follows from (7) that $\mathbf{n} \cdot \mathbf{E} = q/4\pi\varepsilon_0 r^2$. Hence, if the charge is positive, $|\mathbf{E}| = q/4\pi\varepsilon_0 r^2$ and $\mathbf{E}$ is directed away from q. If q is negative, $\mathbf{E}$ will be directed towards the charge q.

EXAMPLE 6: Use Gauss's law (7) to determine the magnitude of the electric field intensity at a point r units away from an infinite plate carrying a charge of density σ (charge per unit area).

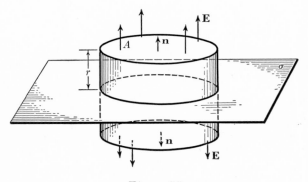

Figure 75

Solution: Let S be the surface of a right circular cylinder of length $2r$ and base area A, bisected by the charged sheet. We take the bases parallel to the sheet, so by symmetry we expect $\mathbf{E}$ to be perpendicular to the bases (Fig. 75).

The charge within S is $q = \sigma A$. On each of the two bases we have (by symmetry, since we assume the charged sheet infinite in extent) $\mathbf{n} \cdot \mathbf{E} = $ constant, and there will be no contribution to the integral around the curved surface of the cylinder because $\mathbf{E}$ is parallel to this surface, therefore

$$\iint_S \mathbf{n} \cdot \mathbf{E} \, dS = \mathbf{n} \cdot \mathbf{E} \iint_S dS = (\mathbf{n} \cdot \mathbf{E})(2A)$$

By (7) we have $(\mathbf{n} \cdot \mathbf{E})(2A) = \sigma A / \varepsilon_0$, so $\mathbf{n} \cdot \mathbf{E} = \sigma / 2\varepsilon_0$. If σ is positive, this shows that $\mathbf{E}$ is in the same direction as $\mathbf{n}$ and $|\mathbf{E}| = \sigma / 2\varepsilon_0$, independent of r.

These last two examples are typical in that they show the role played by symmetry considerations in applying Gauss's law to determine $\mathbf{E}$.

EXAMPLE 7: Consider a cylindrical heat insulator surrounding a steampipe. Let the inner and outer radii of the insulator be $r = a$ and $r = b$ respectively, and let T_a and T_b be the temperatures,

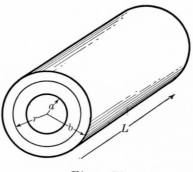

Figure 76

respectively, of the inner and outer surfaces of the insulator. Find the temperature T within the insulator as a function of r (Fig. 76).

Solution: A section of the insulator, of length L, is shown in the figure. By symmetry, we assume that T is a function of r alone, so that $\nabla T = \mathbf{grad}\ T$ is directed radially towards the center of the pipe, with magnitude $-dT/dr$. (On the assumption that the pipe is hotter than the surroundings, dT/dr will be negative.) Let S be a cylindrical surface of radius r and length L within the insulator. By (3) we have

$$\mathbf{Q}\cdot\mathbf{n} = (-k\nabla T)\cdot\mathbf{n} = -k\ dT/dr$$

(as usual, we take $\mathbf{n}$ to be outward, so $\nabla T\cdot\mathbf{n} = |\nabla T|\ |\mathbf{n}|\cos 180° = -|\nabla T| = dT/dr$).

Assuming steady-state heat flow, the number of calories of heat flowing across any such surface S will be the same as that across any other such surface, since otherwise the temperature would also be a function of time. The quantity of heat flow per unit time across any such surface is

$$H = \iint_S \mathbf{Q}\cdot\mathbf{n}\ dS = \iint_S -k\frac{dT}{dr}\ dS = -k\frac{dT}{dr}\iint_S dS$$

$$= -k\frac{dT}{dr}(2\pi Lr)$$

Here again we are using symmetry considerations in assuming that dT/dr is constant along any one surface S (but not necessarily the same as for surfaces with different r), and so dT/dr can be brought outside the integral sign.

Since H is independent of r, we treat it as a constant in solving the differential equation

$$H = -2\pi kLr\ dT/dr$$

Separating variables,

$$H\ dr/r = -2\pi kL\ dT$$

we integrate

$$H\int_a^b \frac{dr}{r} = -2\pi kL\int_{T_a}^{T_b} dT$$

which ultimately yields

$$H = \frac{2\pi Lk(T_a - T_b)}{\ln(b/a)}$$

Substituting this value of H and integrating

$$H\int_a^r \frac{dr}{r} = -2\pi kL\int_{T_a}^{T} dT$$

we finally obtain

$$T = T_a - (T_a - T_b) \frac{\ln (r/a)}{\ln (b/a)}$$

EXERCISES

1. If $\mathbf{F} = z\mathbf{k}$, find the surface integral of the normal component of $\mathbf{F}$ over the closed surface of the right circular cylinder with curved surface $x^2 + y^2 = 9$ and bases in the planes $z = 0$ and $z = 2$. (Mental arithmetic should suffice.)

2. Compute

$$\iint \mathbf{F} \cdot d\mathbf{S}$$

where S is the surface of the cube bounded by the planes $x = \pm 1, y = \pm 1, z = \pm 1$, if
    (a) $\mathbf{F} = x\mathbf{i}$ (e) $\mathbf{F} = y\mathbf{i}$
    (b) $\mathbf{F} = x\mathbf{i} + y\mathbf{j}$ (f) $\mathbf{F} = z\mathbf{i}$
    (c) $\mathbf{F} = x\mathbf{i} + y\mathbf{j} + z\mathbf{k}$ (g) $\mathbf{F} = z^2\mathbf{i}$
    (d) $\mathbf{F} = x^2\mathbf{i} + y^2\mathbf{j} + z^2\mathbf{k}$

3. Compute the surface integral of the normal component of $\mathbf{F} = x\mathbf{i}$ over the triangle with vertices $(1,0,0)$, $(0,2,0)$, $(0,0,3)$, taking the normal on the side away from the origin.

4. Use Gauss's law to determine the magnitude of the electric field intensity at a point r units away from an infinitely long thin wire carrying a charge of λ units per unit length. (Consider a cylinder of length L and radius r concentric with the wire.)

5. Fill in the missing steps in Example 7.

6. Consider a hollow sphere of homogeneous material, with inner radius a and outer radius b, and inner temperature T_a and outer temperature T_b.
    (a) Find the steady-state temperature as a function of the distance r from the center, for values of r between a and b.
    (b) For a value of r halfway between a and b, is T halfway between T_a and T_b?

7. Given $\mathbf{F} = x\mathbf{i} - y\mathbf{j}$, find the value of

$$\iint \mathbf{F} \cdot \mathbf{n}\, dS$$

over the closed surface bounded by the planes $z = 0$, $z = 1$, and the cylinder $x^2 + y^2 = a^2$, where **n** is the unit outward normal, (a) by direct calculation [Hint: the element of area is

$$dS = a \, d\theta \, dz$$

in cylindrical coordinates on the curved surface];
(b) by symmetry considerations, without changing to cylindrical coordinates.

8.   Given $\mathbf{F} = x\mathbf{i} + y\mathbf{j} + (z^2 - 1)\mathbf{k}$, find

$$\iint \mathbf{F} \cdot \mathbf{n} \, dS$$

over the closed surface bounded by the planes $z = 0$, $z = 1$, and the cylinder $x^2 + y^2 = a^2$, where **n** is the unit outward normal.

9.   Given that $\mathbf{F} = y\mathbf{i} + \mathbf{k}$, find the surface integral of the normal component of **F** over the box shown in Figure 77, taking **n** to be the unit outward normal.   Assume this box to have a bottom but no top, i.e., roughly like a shoe.   (Note: Later on you will be asked to do the same problem by mental arithmetic, as a demonstration of the power of the divergence theorem.   Take a furtive peek ahead, at Exercise 7 on page 185.)

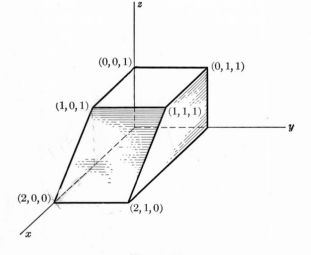

Figure 77

4.7 : Volume Integrals

We consider a function f (i.e., a scalar field) defined within and on the boundary of a domain V. We imagine that V is *bounded*, i.e., that there exists a cube R sufficiently large that every point of V is within R. We imagine the cube R subdivided into rectangular parallelepipeds by planes parallel to the coordinate planes. Ignoring those parallelepipeds that contain no points of V, we let the volumes of the parallelepipeds that do overlap V be denoted $\delta V_1, \delta V_2, \ldots, \delta V_n$, and in each parallelepiped select a point (x_i, y_i, z_i) in V. We form the sum $\sum_{i=1}^{n} f(x_i, y_i, z_i) \, \delta V_i$ and define the volume integral of f over V, if it exists, to be

$$(1) \qquad \iiint_V f(x,y,z) \, dV = \lim \sum_{i=1}^{n} f(x_i, y_i, z_i) \, \delta V_i$$

that is, the limit as the maximum volume δV_i tends to zero (which also makes n tend to infinity). For (1) to make sense in an unambiguous way, we require that the limit exist independently of the particular manner of subdivision. It can be shown that this is the case if f is continuous within and on the boundary of V; we omit the proof.

In general, as the reader has no doubt observed, we omit details of integration theory. The reader who is not familiar already with triple integration will want to study this subject elsewhere; perhaps it will suffice to carefully go over the examples given in this section. In practice one is not often required to compute volume integrals, although they do arise somewhat more often than surface integrals, and are usually easier to compute. Since the volume of a rectangular parallelepiped with edges dx, dy, and dz is $dV = dx \, dy \, dz$, one sometimes writes

$$\iiint_V f(x,y,z) \, dx \, dy \, dz$$

instead of

$$\iiint_V f(x,y,z) \, dV$$

The volume of the domain V is defined by (1), taking $f(x,y,z)$ to be identically equal to unity:

$$(2) \qquad \text{volume of } V = \iiint_V dV = \iiint_V dx \, dy \, dz$$

Since most students have less difficulty with volume integrals than with surface integrals, we shall not pause to give more than a few physical examples. One obvious example is that in which the function to be integrated is the mass density of a material. Let $\rho(x,y,z)$ denote the mass density of a material, say in grams per cubic centimeter, at a point (x,y,z). If ρ is a constant, then the mass of any material occupying a volume δV is precisely $\rho\,\delta V$. If ρ varies from point to point, as may very well be the case for a compressible fluid, then if we take a point (x,y,z) in a small region of volume δV we can say that $\rho(x,y,z)\,\delta V$ gives approximately the mass of the material within this region. We can then interpret the sum $\sum_{i=1}^{n} f(x_i,y_i,z_i)\,\delta V_i$ as giving an approximation to the mass within the entire domain V, an approximation that improves as we take larger n and smaller δV_i. The integral (1) gives, in this case, precisely the mass contained in V.

Similarly, if f represents the charge density (charge per unit volume), then the volume integral of f over V gives the net total charge contained in the region V.

EXAMPLE 1: Find the volume of the region of space above the xy plane and beneath the plane $z = 2 + x + y$, bounded by the planes $y = 0$, $x = 0$, and the surface $y = 1 - x^2$.

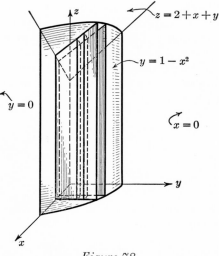

Figure 78

Solution: By (2), the volume is

$$\iiint_V dx\, dy\, dz$$

If we integrate with respect to z first, we obtain* the volume of a strip with cross section $dx\, dy$; then letting y vary, we obtain* the volume of a slice with thickness dx, and finally we integrate to obtain the total volume.   Thus:

$$\int_0^1 \int_0^{1-x^2} \int_0^{2+x+y} dz\, dy\, dx = \int_0^1 \int_0^{1-x^2} (2 + x + y)\, dy\, dx$$

$$= \int_0^1 \left(2y + xy + \frac{y^2}{2} \right) \Big|_0^{1-x^2} dx$$

$$= \int_0^1 \left(\frac{5}{2} + x - 3x^2 - x^3 + \frac{x^4}{2} \right) dx$$

$$= \tfrac{37}{20}$$

Notice especially that in the first integral we give the limits on z as a function of x and y.   This gives the integrand $(2 + x + y)\, dy\, dx$, which is* the volume of a strip erected on the point (x,y) in the xy plane.   Then we integrate letting y vary, the limits of integration depending on x, to obtain* the volume of a slice; the volume of this slice will of course depend on its x coordinate as well as its thickness dx, as we see from Figure 78.   Then we "add up" the slices, beginning with that nearest the yz plane and ending with the slice at $x = 1$.

The volume could also have been computed by means of the integral

$$\int_0^1 \int_0^{(1-y)^{1/2}} \int_0^{2+x+y} dz\, dx\, dy$$

letting x vary before y.   When this procedure is used, the last integration represents the summing up of slices parallel to the xz plane, beginning with the slice nearest the xz plane and ending with the slice at $y = 1$ (not shown in the figure).

EXAMPLE 2:   Find the volume integral of $f(x,y,z) = x + yz$ over the box bounded by the coordinate planes, $x = 1$, $y = 2$, and $z = 1 + x$.

---

* Where the asterisks appear the reader should insert a phrase such as "to a first approximation."   (The integral gives the volume *exactly*.)

Solution: As in the preceding example, we can let z vary first, and then let either x or y vary.   In Figure 79 we let x vary before y, in contrast to the way we proceeded in Figure 78.   We obtain

$$\int_0^2 \int_0^1 \int_0^{1+x} (x + yz) \, dz \, dx \, dy = \int_0^2 \int_0^1 \left(xz + \frac{yz^2}{2} \right)\Big|_0^{1+x} dx \, dy$$

$$= \int_0^2 \int_0^1 \left(x + x^2 + \frac{y}{2} + yx + \frac{yx^2}{2} \right) dx \, dy = \int_0^2 \left(\frac{5}{6} + \frac{7}{6}y \right) dy = 4$$

If we had let y vary before x, we would have had

$$\int_0^1 \int_0^2 \int_0^{1+x} (x + yz) \, dz \, dy \, dx$$

$$= \int_0^1 \int_0^2 \left(x + x^2 + \frac{y}{2} + yx + \frac{yx^2}{2} \right) dy \, dx$$

$$= \int_0^1 \left(xy + x^2y + \frac{y^2}{4} + \frac{y^2x}{2} + \frac{y^2x^2}{2} \right)\Big|_0^2 dx$$

$$= \int_0^1 (1 + 4x + 3x^2) \, dx = 4$$

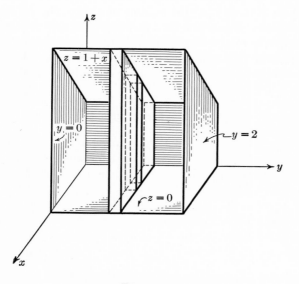

Figure 79

We see from Figure 79 that we could have let y vary first:

$$\int_0^1 \int_0^{1+x} \int_0^2 (x + yz)\, dy\, dz\, dx = \int_0^1 \int_0^{1+x} \left(xy + \frac{y^2z}{2}\right)\Big|_0^2 dz\, dx$$

$$= \int_0^1 \int_0^{1+x} (2x + 2z)\, dz\, dx = \int_0^1 (2xz + z^2)\Big|_0^{1+x} dx$$

$$= \int_0^1 (1 + 4x + 3x^2)\, dx = 4$$

On the other hand, it is inconvenient to let x vary first, since when z is less than 1, x must range from 0 to 1, but when z is between 1 and 2, x ranges from $(z - 1)$ to 1. To let x vary first, we must separate the region into two parts by the plane $z = 1$ and write separate integrals for each part:

$$\int_0^1 \int_0^2 \int_0^1 (x + yz)\, dx\, dy\, dz + \int_1^2 \int_0^2 \int_{z-1}^1 (x + yz)\, dx\, dy\, dz$$

$$= \int_0^1 \int_0^2 \left(\frac{1}{2} + yz\right) dy\, dz + \int_1^2 \int_0^2 \left(2yz - \frac{z^2}{2} + z - yz^2\right) dy\, dz$$

$$= \int_0^1 (1 + 2z)\, dz + \int_1^2 (6z - 3z^2)\, dz = 2 + 2 = 4$$

The reader will notice that, although the volume integral of f over a domain V is defined as the limit of a sum, in practice the process of computing such an integral involves successive integrations. For instance, suppose that the domain V consists of all the points (x,y,z) that satisfy the inequalities $x_1 \leqq x \leqq x_2$, $y_1(x) \leqq y \leqq y_2(x)$, $z_1(x,y) \leqq z \leqq z_2(x,y)$. This means that V consists of all points above the surface $z = z_1(x,y)$ and below the surface $z = z_2(x,y)$, to the right of the surface $y = y_1(x)$ and to the left of the surface $y = y_2(x)$ (compare Fig. 78, where the latter two surfaces were $y = 0$ and $y = 1 - x^2$), and bounded behind by the plane $x = x_1$ and in front by the plane $x = x_2$ (in Fig. 78 the domain is bounded behind by $x = 0$ but no plane $x = x_2$ was specified since the surface $y = 1 - x^2$ bends around to provide the front boundary as well as the boundary on the right). Then the volume integral of f over V is

$$\iiint_V f(x,y,z)\, dx\, dy\, dz = \int_{x_1}^{x_2} \left[\int_{y_1(x)}^{y_2(x)} \left(\int_{z_1(x,y)}^{z_2(x,y)} f(x,y,z)\, dz\right) dy\right] dx$$

In computing the inner integral, y and x are treated as constants and only z is variable. In the next integration, x is treated as a constant

and only y is variable.   The last (outer) integral is an ordinary definite
integral with x varying from x_1 to x_2.   The variables disappear in
steps: after the first integration, z vanishes; after the second, no y
remains; and after the last integration x is gone and we are left with
a numerical value.

EXERCISES

1.   In Example 2, one volume integral was computed in four dif-
     ferent ways.   Repeat all of this yourself, filling in all the missing
     steps in the calculations.

2.   The volume of the region described in Example 2 (Fig. 79)
     obviously equals 3.   Verify this four times by repeating each
     of the integrations given in Example 2, taking $f(x,y,z) = 1$ in-
     stead of $f(x,y,z) = x + yz$.

3.   Sketch the region whose volume is represented by the triple
     integral

     $$\int_0^2 \int_0^3 \int_0^{\sqrt{9-y^2}} dx\ dy\ dz$$

4.   In this exercise you will be asked to make a simple conjecture
     on the basis of what you find on carrying out the following
     requests.
     (a) Let $\mathbf{F}(x,y,z) = x^2\mathbf{i} + y\mathbf{j} + z\mathbf{k}$.   Compute

     $$\iint_S \mathbf{F} \cdot d\mathbf{S}$$

     over the surface of the cube bounded by the planes $x = 0$,
     $x = 1$, $y = 0$, $y = 1$, $z = 0$, $z = 1$ (Fig. 80).

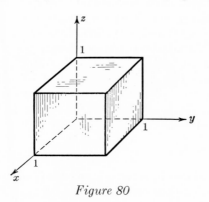

Figure 80

(b) Let $f(x,y,z) = \nabla \cdot \mathbf{F}$, and compute

$$\iiint_V f(x,y,z)\, dV$$

over the cube.   Notice that here limits are no problem; we have simply

$$\int_0^1 \int_0^1 \int_0^1 f(x,y,z)\, dx\, dy\, dz$$

(c) If your answers to (a) and (b) were not equal, check your work until you find the mistake.

(d) Now invent another vector field $\mathbf{F}$ and repeat steps (a) and (b) above.

(e) What do you conjecture from this?

5.   Let V be a domain with volume v.   Let $\mathbf{F} = x\mathbf{i} + y\mathbf{j} + z\mathbf{k}$.

(a) What is

$$\iiint_V \nabla \cdot \mathbf{F}\, dV$$

(b) On the basis of your answer to Exercise 4, what do you conjecture is the value of

$$\iint_S \mathbf{F} \cdot d\mathbf{S}$$

the surface integral of the normal component of $\mathbf{F}$ over the boundary of V?

6.   If $\rho(x,y,z)$ denotes the *charge density* (charge per unit volume) in a region of space, then the total charge in this region V is

$$q = \iiint_V \rho(x,y,z)\, dV$$

By Gauss's law we have

$$\iint_S \mathbf{E} \cdot d\mathbf{S} = \frac{1}{\varepsilon_0} q = \frac{1}{\varepsilon_0} \iiint_V \rho(x,y,z)\, dV$$

Combine this with your conjecture of Exercise 4 concerning

$$\iiint_V \nabla \cdot \mathbf{E}\, dV$$

What might this lead you to guess about the relationship between the divergence of $\mathbf{E}$ and the charge density?

7.   Find the volume of the region bounded by the surface $z = e^{-(x^2+y^2)}$, the cylinder $x^2 + y^2 = 1$, and the plane $z = 0$. [Hint: In cylindrical coordinates, $dV = r\, dr\, d\theta\, dz$.]

4.8 : Introduction to the Divergence Theorem and Stokes' Theorem

With these preliminaries on integration completed, we can now turn to the interesting part of our work.   In this section we introduce two theorems of fundamental importance in vector analysis; most of our work so far has been intended as preliminary to these two theorems.   They will be stated more precisely in later sections; here we intend to state them in crude form, without giving the precise conditions on continuity, differentiability, etc., and we will give proofs for the theorems that are instructive but quite nonrigorous.   In later sections more careful proofs will be given.

The *divergence theorem states that the volume integral of the divergence* of a vector field, taken throughout a bounded domain D, *equals the surface integral of the normal component* of the vector field taken over the boundary of D.   In other words, the total divergence within D equals the net flux emerging from D.

Here is a "simplified proof"; a rigorous proof will be given later. First let us consider a small rectangular parallelepiped, bounded by planes of constant x, $x + dx$, y, $y + dy$, z, $z + dz$.   Let us compute (to a first approximation) the surface integral of $\mathbf{F} \cdot \mathbf{n}$ over the six faces of this parallelepiped, where $\mathbf{F} = F_1\mathbf{i} + F_2\mathbf{j} + F_3\mathbf{k}$.   For the face at x, $\mathbf{n} = -\mathbf{i}$ and $\mathbf{F} \cdot \mathbf{n}$ is approximately $-F_1(x,y,z)$.   For the face at $x + dx$, $\mathbf{n} = \mathbf{i}$ and $\mathbf{F} \cdot \mathbf{n}$ is approximately $F_1(x + dx, y, z)$. Thus the surface integral over these two faces is

$$F_1(x + dx, y, z)\, dy\, dz - F_1(x,y,z)\, dy\, dz$$

Since the rate of change of F_1 in the x direction is $\partial F_1/\partial x$,

$$F_1(x + dx, y, z) - F_1(x,y,z) = \frac{\partial F_1}{\partial x}\, dx$$

and the surface integral over these two faces is $(\partial F_1/\partial x)\, dx\, dy\, dz$. Similarly, for the faces normal to the y and z axes we obtain

$$\frac{\partial F_1}{\partial y}\, dx\, dy\, dz$$

and $(\partial F_2/\partial z)\, dx\, dy\, dz$.   Adding these up we obtain for the total surface integral

$$\frac{\partial F_1}{dx} + \frac{\partial F_2}{dy} + \frac{\partial F_3}{dz}\, dx\, dy\, dz = (\text{div } \mathbf{F})\, dx\, dy\, dz$$

Thus the net outward flux of the vector field $\mathbf{F}$ from the parallelepiped is (div $\mathbf{F}$) δV, where δV is the volume of the parallelepiped. Now let us divide the domain D up into many small parallelepipeds. The net outward flux of $\mathbf{F}$ from D is the sum of the net outward flux over all the little parallelepipeds, since if two such parallelepipeds are adjacent, the flux outward from one over the surface they have in common is exactly equal to the flux inward to the other, so that all we have left is the flux over the exterior surfaces. It follows that the net outward flux of $\mathbf{F}$ from D equals approximately $\sum$ (div $\mathbf{F}$) δV, where we sum over all the parallelepipeds. Passing to the limit by taking repeatedly smaller subdivisions, we see that the net flux emerging from D equals

$$\iiint \text{div } \mathbf{F} \, dV$$

There are two main weaknesses in the above "proof." First of all, when we say (for instance) that $\mathbf{F} \cdot \mathbf{n} = -F_1(x,y,z)$ for the face at x, we ignore the fact that y and z vary over this face; we cannot "cover up" this difficulty by saying x, y, and z are "approximately constant" for a small parallelepiped because, in that case, we would not distinguish between $F_1(x,y,z)$ and $F_1(x + dx, y, z)$. Secondly, it is obviously impossible to divide most domains up into rectangular parallelepipeds by planes parallel to the coordinate planes. Even for a sphere this is impossible; some of the parallelepipeds would need to have surfaces inclined to the coordinate planes.

The first of these difficulties is easily remedied (Exercise 8), but the second is quite fundamental. Incidentally, there is nothing sinful about such "simplified proofs"; often a mathematician constructs such a "proof," even though obviously faulty, as a preliminary to constructing a rigorous proof.

The divergence theorem is sometimes called Gauss's theorem, because of its close relationship to Gauss's law (Section 4.6). To see the connection, it is necessary to know that the divergence of electric field intensity is a scalar multiple of the charge density. Hence the volume integral of the divergence over any domain gives a scalar multiple of the total charge q within the domain. It follows from the divergence theorem that the surface integral of the normal component of the electric intensity, over the boundary of a domain, is a scalar multiple of the charge inside. However, Gauss's law is not just a special case of the divergence theorem, since it can be applied to point charges where the concept of charge per unit volume, in the ordinary sense, is meaningless.

Until some years ago, the divergence theorem was called Green's theorem in three dimensions.

Now let us turn to Stokes' theorem, the other fundamental theorem in vector analysis. This theorem states that *the surface integral of the normal component of the curl* of a vector field, taken over a bounded surface, *equals the line integral of the tangential component* of the field, taken over the closed curve bounding the surface. As with the divergence theorem, we have italicized the colloquial expression for the theorem, which is convenient to memorize.

Here we are considering a closed curve C in space and a surface S that is bounded by the curve. The theorem states that

(1)
$$\iint_S (\mathbf{curl\ F}) \cdot \mathbf{n}\ dS = \int_C \mathbf{F} \cdot \mathbf{T}\ ds$$

where dS refers to the element of *area* and ds refers to *arc length*. We assume that S is a surface oriented by a field of unit normals $\mathbf{n}$, and that the line integral is taken along C in the direction determined positive by the orientation.

The "proof" we give is as follows; a more rigorous proof will be given later. We subdivide the surface S into a set of small surface elements, each approximately rectangular. We first prove the theorem for each of these separate little rectangles. This suffices to prove the theorem in general, since we can sum over the rectangles. The sum of the surface integrals over the separate rectangles equals the surface integral over the whole surface, and the sum of all the line integrals equals the line integral around C since the line integrals over interior boundaries cancel in pairs (Fig. 81).

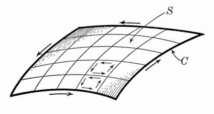

Figure 81

To prove (1) for a small rectangular area, we choose the coordinate axes so that the x and y axes are along the sides of the rectangle and the z axis is in the direction of n. We then have $\mathbf{n} = \mathbf{k}$ and hence

$$(\mathbf{curl\ F}) \cdot \mathbf{n} = (\mathbf{curl\ F}) \cdot \mathbf{k} = \frac{\partial F_2}{\partial x} - \frac{\partial F_1}{\partial y}$$

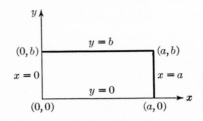

Figure 82

The left side of (1) is therefore

$$\iint \left(\frac{\partial F_2}{\partial x} - \frac{\partial F_1}{\partial y} \right) dx\, dy$$

We split this up into two integrals, choosing the order of integration differently in the two cases:

$$\int_0^b \int_0^a \frac{\partial F_2}{\partial x}\, dx\, dy - \int_0^a \int_0^b \frac{\partial F_1}{\partial y}\, dy\, dx$$

$$= \int_0^b F_2(x,y)\Big|_{x=0}^{x=a}\, dy - \int_0^a F_1(x,y)\Big|_{y=0}^{y=b}\, dx$$

$$= \int_0^b [F_2(a,y) - F_2(0,y)]\, dy - \int_0^a [F_1(x,b) - F_1(x,0)]\, dx$$

$$= \int_0^b F_2(a,y)\, dy + \int_b^0 F_2(0,y)\, dy + \int_a^0 F_1(x,b)\, dx + \int_0^a F_1(x,0)\, dx$$

$$= \int_0^a F_1(x,0)\, dx + \int_0^b F_2(a,y)\, dy + \int_a^0 F_1(x,b)\, dx + \int_b^0 F_2(0,y)\, dy$$

$$= \int_C \mathbf{F} \cdot \mathbf{T}\, ds$$

This is the right side of (1), as we desired to prove.

What mistakes are involved in this "proof"? First of all, it is generally not possible to chop up a surface S into a number of rectangles, and what precisely is meant by the term "approximately rectangular" used above? Even if we could give some precise definition, we would need to pass to a limit in some sense, taking smaller subdivisions, and show that both sides of (1) converge to the actual surface and line integrals, respectively, over S and around C.

This is not the main objection, however; there is a more fundamental one, involved in choosing the coordinate axes so that the x and y axes are along two sides of the rectangle. Let us analyze this more closely.

Suppose, for the sake of argument, that the surface S is a rectangle. Then the first objection above does not apply, we do not need to chop up S at all. If it happens that S is already in the xy plane, lying along the x and y axes as shown in Figure 85, then there is no objection to the proof given above (provided we assume continuity of the relevant partial derivatives, etc., so that the integrals exist). But suppose S is not in the xy plane. The above procedure amounts to choosing a new set of coordinates x',y',z' so that S is in the plane $z' = 0$ and has sides along the x' and y' axes, and the above argument shows that (1) is valid when we compute everything relative to the coordinates x', y', and z'. But how do we know that (1) is valid relative to the original coordinates x, y, and z? This is a serious objection, because we have defined **curl F** in terms of a fixed set of coordinates, and we have not yet studied what happens when we change to another set of coordinates.

Let us be very explicit about this, because it is conceptually very important. Let us suppose we are given a vector field **F** in terms of coordinates x, y, and z. Suppose now we are given new coordinates x', y', and z', which we can express as functions of the old coordinates x, y, and z. Substituting into $\mathbf{F}(x,y,z)$, we can now write **F** in terms of x', y', and z'. Now let us compute **curl F** in terms of x', y', and z', and afterwards change back to x, y, and z, so that we have **curl F** in terms of x, y, and z. The question is, do we get the same thing as we would get computing **curl F** directly, from the very beginning, in terms of x, y, and z?

In other words, does the curl of a vector field depend only on the nature of the field, or does it also depend on our particular choice of coordinate axes?

It turns out that the curl does not depend on the choice of coordinate axes provided (1) that we always choose axes that are mutually perpendicular, (2) that we are consistent in the way we mark off distances on these axes (physically, this means that we select some unit of distance, say centimeters, and mark all axes so that distances come out in centimeters), (3) and that we always take a right-handed coordinate system, i.e., one for which $\mathbf{i} \times \mathbf{j} = \mathbf{k}$.

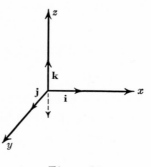

Figure 83

In this connection, it is worth mentioning that some textbooks (not written in English) consistently use left-handed coordinates, as in Figure 83. Then either $\mathbf{i} \times \mathbf{j} = -\mathbf{k}$ or the definition of vector cross product must be modified to give $\mathbf{i} \times \mathbf{j} = \mathbf{k}$, in which case our "right-hand rule" (Section 1.12) becomes a "left-hand rule." (This convention has an obvious advantage for a right-handed student who is pressed for time when taking an examination; he need not put his pencil down when applying the left-hand rule, since his left hand is free.)

We shall return later on to this important matter of coordinate transformations.

Summarizing, we have given rough statements of the divergence theorem and Stokes' theorem, and have given instructive but incorrect proofs of both theorems. Before proceeding to a more careful analysis the reader is strongly urged to study the following examples and work the exercises. These are the most important theorems in this book and they must ultimately be thoroughly understood.

The student who has studied attentively up to this point is "over the hump." *The rest of this book is devoted entirely to the deeper study of concepts already introduced.*

EXERCISES

1. Use the divergence theorem to solve Exercise 1, Section 4.6.

2. Do all seven parts of Exercise 2, Section 4.6, by computing

$$\int_{-1}^{1}\int_{-1}^{1}\int_{-1}^{1} \nabla \cdot \mathbf{F}\, dx\, dy\, dz \qquad \textit{divergence theorem}$$

in each case.

3. Use the divergence theorem to solve
(a) Exercise 7, Section 4.6;
(b) Exercise 8, Section 4.6.

4. Use Stokes' theorem to solve Exercise 8, Section 4.1.

5. Use Stokes' theorem to solve Exercise 10, Section 4.1.

6. Verify Stokes' theorem in the following five special cases. Let C be the square in the xy plane with equation $|x| + |y| = 1$. Let $\mathbf{F}$ be as follows:
(a) $\mathbf{F} = x\mathbf{i}$ (d) $\mathbf{F} = \mathbf{i} + \mathbf{j}$
(b) $\mathbf{F} = y\mathbf{i}$ (e) $\mathbf{F} = y^3\mathbf{i}$
(c) $\mathbf{F} = -y\mathbf{i} + x\mathbf{j}$

7. Despite the fact that the surface of Exercise 9, Section 4.6, is not closed, the divergence theorem can be used to reduce this to a problem in mental arithmetic. Show how to do this.

8. By integration, show that

$$\iiint \frac{\partial F_1}{\partial x}\, dx\, dy\, dz = \iint \mathbf{F} \cdot \mathbf{n}\, dy\, dz,$$

over any parallelepiped bounded by planes parallel to the coordinate planes. Hence, modify the "simplified proof" of the divergence theorem, removing the first objection mentioned in the text.

4.9 : The Divergence Theorem

To fix ideas for the moment, let us consider a vector field

$$\mathbf{F} = F_1\mathbf{i} + F_2\mathbf{j} + F_3\mathbf{k}$$

defined throughout a region, with components F_1, F_2, F_3 having continuous partial derivatives in this region. Let S denote the surface of a sphere, located within the region, and let D denote the set of points within S. Let **n** denote the field of unit vectors normal to S. At each point on S, we take **n** to be the *outward* normal, thus orienting S in the conventional way.

Consider the surface integral

(1) $$\iint_S \mathbf{F} \cdot \mathbf{n}\, dS$$

Written out in terms of its components, this becomes

(2) $$\iint_S (F_1\mathbf{i} + F_2\mathbf{j} + F_3\mathbf{k}) \cdot \mathbf{n}\, dS$$

which equals

(3) $$\iint_S F_1(\mathbf{n}\cdot\mathbf{i})\, dS + \iint_S F_2(\mathbf{n}\cdot\mathbf{j})\, dS + \iint_S F_3(\mathbf{n}\cdot\mathbf{k})\, dS$$

Let us concentrate on only one of these integrals, the one in the middle. Consider the sphere to be cut up into filaments, each parallel to the y axis. A typical filament is shown in Figure 84. It has cross-

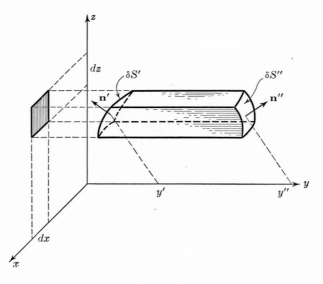

Figure 84

sectional area $dx\,dz$ and cuts out two portions from S, having areas $\delta S'$ and $\delta S''$. The contribution to the middle integral of the two portions is approximately

$$F_2'(\mathbf{n}'\cdot\mathbf{j})\,\delta S' + F_2''(\mathbf{n}''\cdot\mathbf{j})\,\delta S''$$

where F_2' and F_2'' are, respectively, values of F_2 at points on the two portions. By the area cosine principle (Section 4.5), $(\mathbf{n}''\cdot\mathbf{j})\,\delta S'$ and $(\mathbf{n}'\cdot\mathbf{j})\,\delta S''$ are approximately equal to $dx\,dz$ and $-(dx\,dz)$ respectively, since the scalar product of two unit vectors equals the cosine of the angle between them. Therefore the contribution from these two portions is $(F_2'' - F_2')\,dx\,dz$.

Since, by the fundamental theorem of calculus, we have

$$\int_{y'}^{y''} \frac{\partial F_2}{\partial y}\,dy = F_2'' - F_2'$$

it follows from the above discussion that the middle integral in (3) can be written

$$\iint_S \left(\int_{y'}^{y''} \frac{\partial F_2}{\partial y}\,dy\right)dx\,dz$$

where the middle integral is taken with y varying from y' to y'' within the sphere, and the double integral is taken over the projection of S on the xz plane. This equals the volume integral over D; hence we can write

$$\iiint_D \frac{\partial F_2}{\partial y}\,dx\,dy\,dz$$

This shows that the surface integral of $F_2(\mathbf{n}\cdot\mathbf{j})$ over S equals the volume integral of $\partial F_2/\partial y$ throughout the domain enclosed by S.

Similarly, we can show that the surface integral of $F_1(\mathbf{n}\cdot\mathbf{i})$ over S equals the volume integral of $\partial F_1/\partial x$ throughout D; and $F_3(\mathbf{n}\cdot\mathbf{k})$ and $\partial F_3/\partial z$ are similarly related. Therefore (3) becomes

$$\iiint_D \left(\frac{\partial F_1}{\partial x} + \frac{\partial F_2}{\partial y} + \frac{\partial F_3}{\partial z}\right)dx\,dy\,dz$$

This is simply the volume integral, throughout D, of the divergence of the vector field $\mathbf{F}$. Since (1) equals (3) we obtain

(4) $$\iint_S \mathbf{F}\cdot\mathbf{n}\,dS = \iiint_D \operatorname{div}\mathbf{F}\,dV$$

In this way we have proved the divergence theorem, already stated roughly in the preceding section, for the special case of a

spherical domain.   This is about as rigorous a proof as it is possible
to give in a book written on this level.   The use of the term "approximately equal" covers up certain details of integration theory which,
as we have already mentioned, are omitted in this book.

The same proof applies without change to other special cases,
e.g., where S is the surface of an ellipsoid, a cube, or a right circular
cylinder, or even a potato-shaped region of a rather arbitrary nature,
since we made no use of the equation of a sphere or of many of its
special properties.   It is now instructive to ask, just what properties
did we use?

We used, of course, the fact that S is a smooth surface, since
otherwise **n** would not be defined at every point of S.   However, very
little reflection will convince the reader that the proof applies also
to the right circular cylinder, which is only piecewise smooth since
it consists of three smooth surfaces joined together.

We made strong use of the idea of cutting up the sphere by
filaments parallel to a coordinate axis.   We assumed in Figure 84
that any such filament cuts out two portions from the surface.   Thus
the proof does not apply without modification to a domain such as
the dumbbell-shaped one in Figure 85.   Here, such a filament can

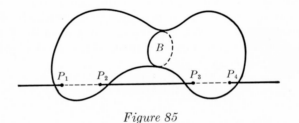

Figure 85

cut out four portions from the surface.   However, it is easy to see
that the theorem still applies to such a domain, since the dumbbell
can be cut in the middle and the theorem applied separately to the
two parts.   The volume integral over the whole domain equals the
sum of the two separate volume integrals, and the corresponding
surface integrals add up to give the surface integral over the dumbbell
(there will be two contributions from the common boundary B, but
they will cancel each other since **n** will have opposite directions in the
two integrals).

We are now ready to state the divergence theorem with greater precision. The reader should now be in a position to understand this theorem, and if he is thoroughly familiar with the theory of multiple integrals he can easily supply any of the details glossed over above.

The Divergence Theorem: Let D be any domain with the property that each straight line through any interior point of the domain cuts the boundary in exactly two points, and such that the boundary S is a piecewise-smooth, closed, oriented surface with unit normal directed outward from the domain. Let $\mathbf{F}$ be a vector field, $\mathbf{F} = F_1\mathbf{i} + F_2\mathbf{j} + F_3\mathbf{k}$, continuous throughout a region containing D and its boundary, and such that the partial derivatives of F_1, F_2, and F_3 are also continuous in this region. Then

$$\iiint_D \operatorname{div} \mathbf{F} \, dV = \iint_S \mathbf{F} \cdot \mathbf{n} \, dS$$

The reader will note that we have not stated this theorem in full generality, for, as already noted, it also holds for domains such as that in Figure 85 that can be suitably decomposed into a finite number of parts for which the theorem holds.

Let us now investigate one interesting consequence of the divergence theorem. Let us suppose that the domain D is a very small one surrounding a point P. If it is sufficiently small, div $\mathbf{F}$ will be approximately constant, and the volume integral of div $\mathbf{F}$ over the volume V will be approximately equal to the product $(\operatorname{div} \mathbf{F})V$. More precisely, we have

$$\lim_{V \to 0} \frac{\iiint \operatorname{div} \mathbf{F} \, dV}{V} = \operatorname{div} \mathbf{F}$$

By the divergence theorem, we can replace the volume integral of div $\mathbf{F}$ by the surface integral of $\mathbf{F}$ over the boundary enclosing the volume, from which it follows that

$$\operatorname{div} \mathbf{F} = \lim_{V \to 0} \frac{\iint_S \mathbf{F} \cdot \mathbf{n} \, dS}{V}$$

This can be used as an alternative definition of divergence; compare the discussion given in Section 3.3. We are now justified in saying that the divergence of a vector field $\mathbf{F}$ gives, at any point P, the flux output per unit volume at point P.

EXERCISES

Note: Computational exercises on the divergence theorem were given at the end of Section 4.8, and more are given at the end of this chapter (Supplementary Exercises 26–31). The following exercises are relatively more theoretical. Throughout these exercises, D and S have the properties stated in the divergence theorem.

1. At what point in the proof of the divergence theorem did we make use of the requirement that the partial derivative $\partial F_2/\partial y$ be a continuous function of y?

2. In the proof, we required that the three partial derivatives be continuous, i.e., that each of them be continuous in all three variables. Why, for example, should we care whether or not the partial derivative $\partial F_2/\partial y$ is a continuous function of x?

3. Show, by a diagram similar to that of Figure 84, that the volume integral of a function, taken over D, can be obtained by first integrating with respect to z and then integrating over the projection of S on the xy plane.

4. Outline a proof of the divergence theorem, taking Exercise 3 as the starting point. Start with

    $$\iiint_D \operatorname{div} \mathbf{F} \, dV$$

    integrating first with respect to z. Your proof will differ only slightly from that given in this section, i.e., you will integrate first with respect to z rather than y. By using the definition of surface integral you can avoid completely any use of such words as "approximately"; for simplicity, assume that S is a smooth surface.

5. Where, in your "proof" (Exercise 4), did you make unconscious use of the fact that the points on S with normals parallel to the xy plane have a projection on the xy plane of zero area? [Hint: Look again at the definition of the area of a surface (Section 4.5). What is $\cos \gamma$ for such points?]

6. Using the divergence theorem, prove that

    $$\iiint_D \nabla^2 \phi \, dV = \iint_S \frac{\partial \phi}{\partial n} \, dS$$

where $\partial\phi/\partial n$, at any point on S, denotes the rate of change of the scalar field in the direction of the outward normal to S at that point. [Hint: Let $\mathbf{F} = \mathbf{grad}\ \phi$.]

7. Let ϕ be a scalar field, and define the *lumpiness* of ϕ at any point to be the scalar

$$\lim_{V \to 0} \frac{\displaystyle\iint_S \frac{\partial\phi}{\partial n}\, dS}{V}$$

with notation as used in this section.

(a) Explain in your own words why the word "lumpiness" is appropriate. [Hint: Think of ϕ as the density of a fluid or, if you prefer, as the concentration of salt at each point in a brine solution.]

(b) How is lumpiness related to the Laplacian?

(c) What can you say about the lumpiness of a harmonic function? (See Section 3.6).

8. Let $\phi(x,y,z)$ be the temperature at (x,y,z). If ϕ represents a steady-state temperature distribution, show that ϕ is a harmonic function. [Hint: This can be done directly, using the fact (Section 4.6) that $\mathbf{Q} = -k\ \mathbf{grad}\ \phi$ gives the rate of heat flow per unit area, by drawing a small parallelepiped. However, it is intended here that you make use of Exercise 6 and the ideas of Exercise 7.]

9. Suppose that ϕ represents a temperature distribution that is not steady-state, so that ϕ is a function of both position and time. Find the relationship between the Laplacian of ϕ and the time rate of change of ϕ at each point. (Let k denote the coefficient of thermal conductivity, let c denote specific heat capacity, and ρ the mass density.)

4.10 : Green's Theorem

This section is relatively elementary and is intended to provide some preparation for the next section.

Let us work entirely in the xy plane.   Let C denote a closed smooth arc in the plane (Fig. 86).   Consider the line integral

$$\int_C y \, dx$$

Since it is conventional to orient closed curves in the xy plane so that $\mathbf{k}$ is the positive normal to the plane, we traverse C in a counter-clockwise direction.   Therefore the line integral can be expressed as the sum of two ordinary integrals,

(1) $$\int_C y \, dx = \int_a^b y'(x) \, dx + \int_b^a y''(x) \, dx$$

where the first integral is along the bottom portion of the curve and the second is along the top portion; the notation should be self-evident from the figure.   (Note that the primes here do *not* denote derivatives.)

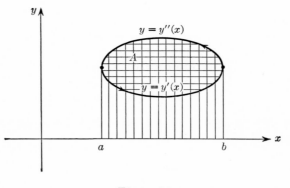

Figure 86

The first integral gives the area beneath the lower curve and above the x axis.   The second integral equals

$$-\int_a^b y''(x) \, dx$$

and gives the negative of the area beneath the upper curve and above the x axis.   Therefore the sum of the two integrals is $-A$, the negative of the area within C,

(2) $$\int_C y \, dx = -A$$

Here we assumed C to be in the upper half-plane, but the reader can easily verify that (2) also holds if C intersects the x axis or if C is beneath the x axis.

A similar argument shows that

$$(3) \qquad \int_C x \, dy = A$$

Here we obtain A rather than $-A$, as is easily seen from Figure 87.

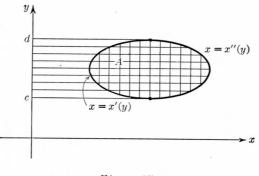

Figure 87

Now let us consider various other simple line integrals about C. For instance, it is easy to verify that

$$(4) \qquad \int_C x \, dx = 0$$

Indeed, $x \, dx$ is the differential of the function $x^2/2$ so that the line integral of $x \, dx$ gives the change in $x^2/2$ as we move from initial point to final point, but for any closed curve these points coincide and hence the line integral is zero. In similar fashion, since $y \, dy$ is an exact differential, we have

$$(5) \qquad \int_C y \, dy = 0$$

Also, we have

$$(6) \qquad \int_C dx = 0$$

$$(7) \qquad \int_C dy = 0$$

It is entertaining, though not particularly instructive, to combine these line integrals in various ways. For instance, if x_0 is a constant, we derive

(8) $$\int_C (x - x_0)\, dy = A$$

by using (3) and (7). Similarly,

(9) $$\int_C (x - x_0)\, dx = 0$$

by (4) and (6).

Somewhat more interesting is

(10) $$\int_C \tfrac{1}{2} (x\, dy - y\, dx) = A$$

which we obtain by combining (2) and (3).

In view of the fact that the line integrals in (2), (3), (8), and (10) may be interpreted in terms of the area A within C, it is natural to ask whether there are any similar interpretations for the other line integrals. More generally, suppose we are given an arbitrary differential $F_1(x,y)\, dx + F_2(x,y)\, dy$, where F_1 and F_2 are continuous functions. Is there any connection between the line integral of this differential about C and the area within?

The answer is both "yes" and "no." In general, there is no connection in the sense that we can draw a picture like that of Figure 87 and interpret the integral in terms of areas. There is, however, a connection between the line integral about C and a double integral taken over the region within C. This relation is given by the formula

(11) $$\int_C F_1\, dx + F_2\, dy = \iint_D \left(\frac{\partial F_2}{\partial x} - \frac{\partial F_1}{\partial y} \right) dx\, dy$$

where D is the domain within C (having area A). In the special case that the integrand in the double integral on the right side of (11) is identically equal to one, the right side of (11) gives precisely A. If the integrand is zero, we get zero for the integral. In general, however, our result may not be related to A in any elementary manner and may be difficult to compute even with the help of (11).

The reader will recognize (11) as a special case of Stokes' theorem, discussed briefly in Section 4.8. To see this, let $F = F_1\mathbf{i} + F_2\mathbf{j}$ and $\mathbf{n} = \mathbf{k}$. The integral on the left is the line integral of the tangential component of $\mathbf{F}$ about C, and that on the right is the surface integral of the normal component of **curl F** over the surface enclosed by C.

This special case of Stokes' theorem is sometimes called *Green's theorem*. (Several other theorems are also called Green's theorem, incidentally.) The precise statement of the theorem is as follows: Let F_1 and F_2 be continuous functions of x and y for which the partial derivatives $\partial F_2/\partial x$ and $\partial F_1/\partial y$ exist and are continuous throughout a domain D in the xy plane. We require that D be bounded by a regular closed curve C, oriented by choosing **k** as the unit normal to the plane. We also require that any line passing through an interior point and parallel to either coordinate axis cuts the boundary in exactly two points. Then equation (11) is valid. More generally, (11) is valid for regions in the plane that can be decomposed into finitely many domains having these properties.

The proof of the theorem is similar to that of the divergence theorem and goes as follows. Let us first look at the right side of (11). The integral can be broken up into two integrals, of which the first is

$$\iint_D \frac{\partial F_2}{\partial x}\, dx\, dy$$

Integrating first with respect to x, we have (with notation as in Figure 87)

$$\int_c^d \int_{x'(y)}^{x''(y)} \frac{\partial F_2}{\partial x}\, dx\, dy = \int_c^d [F_2(x'',y) - F_2(x',y)]\, dy = \int_C F_2\, dy$$

Similarly,

$$-\iint \frac{\partial F_1}{\partial x}\, dx\, dy = -\int_a^b \int_{y'(x)}^{y''(x)} \frac{\partial F_1}{\partial y}\, dy\, dx$$

$$= \int_a^b [F_1(y') - F_1(y'')]\, dy = \int_C F_1\, dy$$

Adding these two gives the desired result. If D is a region that can be decomposed into finitely many domains having the stated properties, we simply sum the integrals involved over all the domains. The double integral must extend over all the parts, and the line integral over the entire boundary. If the boundaries of two parts have arcs in common, these arcs may be neglected, since the integrals will cancel.

EXERCISES

1. Use Green's theorem to derive (2).

2. Use Green's theorem to derive (3).

3. Use Green's theorem to derive (4).

4. Use Green's theorem to derive (10).

5. Let $\mathbf{R} = x\mathbf{i} + y\mathbf{j}$ and $d\mathbf{R} = dx\,\mathbf{i} + dy\,\mathbf{j}$.
   (a) Compute the magnitude of the vector cross product $\mathbf{R} \times (\mathbf{R} + d\mathbf{R})$.
   (b) Thus give a direct geometrical interpretation of the integrand of (10). [Hint: Consider the triangle with vertices $(0,0)$, (x,y), and $(x + dx, y + dy)$.]
   (c) Using Figure 88, give an alternative derivation of (10).

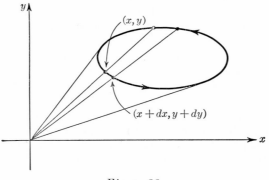

Figure 88

6. Let $\mathbf{F} = x\mathbf{i} + y\mathbf{j}$, and let C be an oriented closed curve enclosing an area A. What is

$$\int_C \mathbf{F} \cdot \mathbf{T} \, ds$$

(As usual, $\mathbf{T}$ denotes the unit tangent to C in the positive direction.)

7. Let C denote the circle $x^2 + y^2 = 9$, and let $\mathbf{F} = y\mathbf{i} - 3x\mathbf{j}$. What is the line integral of the tangential component of $\mathbf{F}$ around C, taken in the usual counterclockwise direction?

8.   Let C denote the ellipse $(x^2/4) + (y^2/9) = 1$, and let

$$\mathbf{F} = (3y^2 - y)\mathbf{i} + (x^2 + 2)\mathbf{j}$$

(a) What is the area enclosed by C? (Don't integrate, for heaven's sake; we have already derived the area of an ellipse by using the area cosine principle.)

(b) Find the line integral of the tangential component of $\mathbf{F}$ around C, in the counterclockwise direction. [Hint: By Green's theorem, this resolves itself to a double integral, but no computation is necessary if you observe that the symmetry enables you to ignore certain terms. Just multiply the area by the average value of $(\partial F_2/\partial x) - (\partial F_1/\partial y)$.]

9.   Compute

$$\int_C 4y^3 \, dx - 2x^2 \, dy$$

around the square bounded by the lines $x = \pm 1$ and $y = \pm 1$,

(a) directly, by performing the line integration;

(b) by using Green's theorem.

(c) By symmetry, it is obvious that one of the terms in the integrand of the above line integral can be ignored. Which term?

10.   Let $\mathbf{F} = 4z\mathbf{i} - 3x\mathbf{k}$. Compute the line integral of the tangential component of $\mathbf{F}$ about the circle $(x - 5)^2 + (z - 7)^2 = 4$ in the xz plane. Orient the plane by taking $\mathbf{j}$ to be unit normal. (Careful: if you just replace y by z in (11) you will get the wrong orientation.)

11.   In (11), the functions F_1 and F_2 are fairly arbitrary functions of x and y (we only require that certain partial derivatives be continuous). It therefore appears that we can interchange F_1 and F_2 and also x and y to obtain the formula

$$\int_C F_2 \, dy + F_1 \, dx = \iint_D \left(\frac{\partial F_1}{\partial y} - \frac{\partial F_2}{\partial x} \right) dy \, dx$$

The left side of this equation is the same as the left side of (11), but the right side has the opposite sign. It follows that this expression is incorrect. Give a clue, *in only one word*, to explain away this paradox.

4.11 : Stokes' Theorem

A rough statement of Stokes' theorem has already been given in Section 4.8. Green's theorem, discussed in the preceding section, is only a special case of Stokes' theorem, as the reader has already observed. In both theorems, we consider a surface S bounded by a closed curve C; in Green's theorem we require C to be a curve in the plane and the surface S to be a portion of the plane, but in Stokes' theorem it may be that C is not contained in a plane and, even if it is, S need not be flat.

Throughout this section we let S denote a portion of a smooth, oriented surface in space, bounded by a piecewise-smooth, closed curve C (Fig. 89) with orientation consistent with that of S.

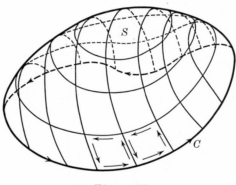

Figure 89

Stokes' theorem states that the surface integral of the normal component of **curl F** over S equals the line integral of the tangential component of **F** about C:

$$(1) \qquad \iint_S (\textbf{curl F}) \cdot \textbf{n} \, dS = \int_C \textbf{F} \cdot d\textbf{R}$$

If $\textbf{F} = F_1\textbf{i} + F_2\textbf{j} + F_3\textbf{k}$, (1) is equivalent to

$$(2) \qquad \iint_S \left[\left(\frac{\partial F_3}{\partial y} - \frac{\partial F_2}{\partial z} \right) \textbf{i} + \left(\frac{\partial F_1}{\partial z} - \frac{\partial F_3}{\partial x} \right) \textbf{j} \right.$$

$$\left. + \left(\frac{\partial F_2}{\partial x} - \frac{\partial F_1}{\partial y} \right) \textbf{k} \right] \cdot \textbf{n} \, dS = \int_C F_1 \, dx + F_2 \, dy + F_3 \, dz$$

By making use of the divergence theorem, it is possible to give a tricky proof of Stokes' theorem; alternatively, several proofs can be given that use Green's theorem. A really rigorous proof must of necessity involve some knowledge of the theory of Jacobian determinants, which we do not require as a prerequisite. The following proof is quite convincing, and more instructive than any other proof known to the author. It actually involves a reexamination of the concept of the curl of a vector field **F**.

Let us assume that **F** is continuously differentiable in a domain D and let $P(x_0, y_0, z_0)$ be a point in D. Let us consider a circle of radius r and center at P; let this circle have area A (of course $A = \pi r^2$, but for reasons that will be apparent later we do not make use of this fact) and let **n** be a unit vector normal to the plane of the circle. Having chosen **n**, we have determined a positive direction about the circumference of the circle; this oriented circumference will be denoted C (Fig. 90).

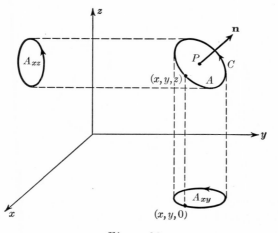

Figure 90

We now proceed to compute

$$\int_C F_1 \, dx + F_2 \, dy + F_3 \, dz$$

We split this up into three integrals. First we compute

$$\int_C F_1 \, dx$$

Since F_1 is a continuously differentiable function, it has a continuous gradient ∇F_1. We recall that the rate of change of a function in any desired direction is the scalar component of the gradient in that direction. Thus, if (x,y,z) is a point on the circumference C, the vector $(x - x_0)\mathbf{i} + (y - y_0)\mathbf{j} + (z - z_0)\mathbf{k}$ is directed from the center of the circle to this point, and the scalar product of this vector with ∇F_1 gives, to a first approximation, the difference between the value of F_1 at (x,y,z) and its value at (x_0,y_0,z_0). Thus we have

$$(3) \qquad F_1(x,y,z) = F_1(x_0,y_0,z_0) + \left(\frac{\partial F_1}{\partial x}\right)_P (x - x_0)$$

$$+ \left(\frac{\partial F_1}{\partial y}\right)_P (y - y_0) + \left(\frac{\partial F_1}{\partial y}\right)_P (z - z_0) + \varepsilon$$

where the partial derivatives are evaluated at $P(x_0,y_0,z_0)$ and ε is an error term depending on (x,y,z), which will be analyzed more carefully later. (If the reader is familiar with Taylor's theorem for functions of three variables, he will recognize (3) immediately.)

Now let us find

$$\int_C F_1 \, dx$$

making use of (3). We have

$$(4) \qquad \int_C F_1(x,y,z) \, dx = \int_C F_1(x_0,y_0,z_0) \, dx + \int_C \left(\frac{\partial F_1}{\partial x}\right)_P (x - x_0) \, dx$$

$$+ \int_C \left(\frac{\partial F_1}{\partial y}\right)_P (y - y_0) \, dx + \int_C \left(\frac{\partial F_1}{\partial z}\right)_P (z - z_0) \, dx + \int_C \varepsilon \, dx$$

Keeping in mind that the value of F_1 and the three partial derivatives at (x_0,y_0,z_0) are simply numbers that can be brought outside the integral sign, we have

$$(5) \qquad \int_C F_1(x,y,z) \, dz = F_1(x_0,y_0,z_0) \int_C dx + \left(\frac{\partial F_1}{\partial x}\right)_P \int_C (x - x_0) \, dx$$

$$+ \left(\frac{\partial F_1}{\partial y}\right)_P \int_C (y - y_0) \, dx + \left(\frac{\partial F_1}{\partial z}\right)_P \int_C (z - z_0) \, dx + \int_C \varepsilon \, dx$$

As (x,y,z) traverses C, its projection $(x,y,0)$ on the xy plane traverses a curve in the xy plane whose area we denote A_{xy}; similarly, the area of the projection of the circle on the xz plane will be denoted A_{xz}. Therefore we have, by the results of the preceding section,

(6) $\quad \displaystyle\int_C F_1(x,y,z)\,dz = 0 + 0 + \left(\dfrac{\partial F_1}{\partial y}\right)_P (-A_{xy}) + \left(\dfrac{\partial F_1}{\partial z}\right)_P (A_{xz}) + \varepsilon'$

where ε' is an error term that will be analyzed more carefully later. In a similar way one shows that

(7) $\quad \displaystyle\int_C F_2(x,y,z)\,dy = \left(\dfrac{\partial F_2}{\partial x}\right)_P A_{xy} + \left(\dfrac{\partial F_2}{\partial z}\right)_P (-A_{yz}) + \varepsilon''$

and

(8) $\quad \displaystyle\int_C F_3(x,y,z)\,dz = \left(\dfrac{\partial F_3}{\partial x}\right)_P (-A_{xz}) + \left(\dfrac{\partial F_3}{\partial y}\right)_P (A_{yz}) + \varepsilon'''$

Adding,

(9) $\quad \displaystyle\int_C \mathbf{F}\cdot d\mathbf{R} = A_{xy}\left(\dfrac{\partial F_2}{\partial x} - \dfrac{\partial F_1}{\partial y}\right)_P + A_{xz}\left(\dfrac{\partial F_1}{\partial z} - \dfrac{\partial F_3}{\partial x}\right)_P$

$$+ A_{yz}\left(\dfrac{\partial F_3}{\partial y} - \dfrac{\partial F_2}{\partial z}\right)_P + E$$

where $E = \varepsilon' + \varepsilon'' + \varepsilon'''$. If we now divide both sides by A, and observe that (by the area cosine principle) $A_{xy}/A = \cos\gamma$, $A_{xz}/A = \cos\beta$, and $A_{yz}/A = \cos\alpha$, where $\cos\alpha$, $\cos\beta$, and $\cos\gamma$ are the components of $\mathbf{n}$ in the x, y, and z directions respectively, we find that

(10) $\qquad \dfrac{\displaystyle\int_C \mathbf{F}\cdot d\mathbf{R}}{A} = (\mathbf{curl\ F})\cdot\mathbf{n} + \dfrac{E}{A}$

Let us now look at the error terms. By the definition of directional derivative, the error in (3) has the property $\varepsilon/r \to 0$ as $r \to 0$. Let ε_m denote the maximum value of $|\varepsilon|$ on C. Then when we integrate over C, the error ε' must have the property $|\varepsilon'| < 2\pi r\varepsilon_m$, from which it follows that $\varepsilon'/r^2 \to 0$ as $r \to 0$. The errors ε'' and ε''' have the same property, hence $E/r^2 \to 0$ as $r \to 0$. Since $A = \pi r^2$, it follows that E/A tends to zero as $A \to 0$.

(11) $\qquad \displaystyle\lim_{A\to 0} \dfrac{\displaystyle\int_C \mathbf{F}\cdot d\mathbf{R}}{A} = (\mathbf{curl\ F})\cdot\mathbf{n}$

Except in the preceding paragraph, we have made no use of the requirement that C be the circumference of a circle. It is easy to see, in fact, that C may be ellipsoidal, triangular, or even an odd shape like that shown in Figure 91.   It is also not essential that C lie in a plane; C could lie on a portion of a smooth surface containing P, since if we let $A \to 0$ (requiring the maximum distance between points on C to tend to zero) we will have (for instance) that A_{xy}/A tends to $\cos \gamma$.

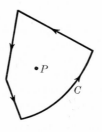

Figure 91

Now let us return to Figure 89.   Imagine the surface S cut up into small portions as shown.   In each portion select a point P_i, let $\mathbf{n}_i$ be the unit normal at P_i, and form $(\mathbf{curl}\ \mathbf{F})_i \cdot \mathbf{n}_i\ \delta S_i$, where δS_i is the area (denoted A above) of the portion.   Adding, we obtain

$$(12) \qquad\qquad \sum_i (\mathbf{curl}\ \mathbf{F})_i \cdot \mathbf{n}_i\ \delta S_i$$

which, by (10), since contributions to the line integral from adjacent interior boundaries cancel out in pairs, equals

$$\int_C \mathbf{F} \cdot d\mathbf{R}$$

taken over the boundary of S, plus an "error."   Now let us pass to the limit as the maximum δS_i tends to zero; (12) tends to

$$\int_S (\mathbf{curl}\ \mathbf{F}) \cdot \mathbf{n}\ dS$$

We must show that the error tends to zero.

Suppose we have cut up the surface into m portions.   Suppose these are all of about the same area A.   Then the total error equals mE where E is as in (10).   Since mA is approximately equal to the total area S, we have $m = S/A$, and the total error is $(S/A)E$.   But we have seen already that $E/A \to 0$ as $A \to 0$, and so this total error tends to zero also.

Thus we have, when we pass to the limit,

$$\int_S (\text{curl } \mathbf{F}) \cdot \mathbf{n} \, dS = \int_C \mathbf{F} \cdot d\mathbf{R}$$

which is what we wanted to prove.

EXERCISES

1. At any point P in space, define the "swirl" of $\mathbf{F}$ at P in a direction $\mathbf{n}$ by the left side of (11). Using the word "swirl," define **curl F**. [Hint: Use the maximum principle of Section 1.9 to define the direction of **curl F**. Imitate the definition of **grad** f as a vector in the direction of maximum rate of increase with magnitude equal to this maximum rate of increase.]

2. Spend at least five minutes comparing your definition of **curl F** (Exercise 1) with the paddle-wheel definition given in Section 3.4. Draw a few appropriate doodles to indicate to your instructor that you did think about it.

3. Look up Ampere's law in an elementary physics text. (If you can't find it in the index, the textbook is too elementary.) Letting $\mathbf{J}$ denote the current density (a vector in the direction of the current, with magnitude in units of current/area) and $\mathbf{B}$ the magnetic intensity, conjecture a relationship between $\mathbf{J}$ and $\mathbf{B}$ that will lead to Ampere's law by virtue of Stokes' theorem.

4. By using Stokes' theorem, give an alternative proof that, if $\mathbf{F}$ is a continuously differentiable vector field defined in a simply-connected domain D, such that **curl F** is identically the zero vector, then the line integral of the tangential component of $\mathbf{F}$ is independent of path. Be sure to indicate where, in your proof, you make use of the property of simple connectedness of the domain.

5. Be a bit fanciful, and imagine that S is the surface of a laundry bag with a draw-string forming the boundary C. Then Stokes' theorem states that the surface integral of the normal component of **curl F** over the laundry bag equals the line integral of its tangential component around the draw-string. Now suppose that we close the bag by pulling the draw-string; the effective length of the draw-string becomes zero and the line integral is therefore zero. S has become a closed surface.

(a) What is the surface integral of the normal component of **curl F** over a closed surface?

We now apply the divergence theorem, which says that the volume integral of the divergence of a vector field through the interior of a closed laundry bag equals the surface integral of the normal component of the field over its surface.   Let the vector field be **curl F**.

(b) What is the volume integral of the divergence of **curl F** over a domain?

If the laundry bag is very, very small, the divergence of **curl F** will be approximately constant throughout, and the volume integral of div(**curl F**) will be approximately div (**curl F**), at a point within the laundry bag, times the volume the bag encloses.

(c) What is div (**curl F**) at any point P?

(d) To which of the identities of Section 3.7 is this related?

6.   This is very similar to Exercise 5, but the point of view is somewhat different.   Let S be the surface of a sphere, and let us imagine the sphere divided into two parts, an upper hemisphere and a lower hemisphere, by a plane parallel to the xy plane passing through its center.   (Draw a diagram.)   Let **F** be a vector field, and consider the surface integral of the normal component of **curl F** over the upper hemisphere.   Relate this mentally to the line integral

$$\int_C \mathbf{F} \cdot d\mathbf{R}$$

where C is the equator, oriented relative to the outward normal of the upper hemisphere (i.e., the positive direction is west to east).   Now do the same thing for the lower hemisphere: the surface integral of (**curl F**) $\cdot$ **n** over the lower hemisphere equals the line integral over the equator with, however, an east-to-west direction of integration.   Add the two.

(a) What is the surface integral of the normal component of **curl F** over a sphere?

(b) What is the volume integral of div (**curl F**) through the interior of a sphere?

(c) Let the sphere shrink to a point; what does this say about div (**curl F**) at a point?

7. Suppose that $\mathbf{F} = \mathbf{grad}\ \phi$, so that the line integral of the tangential component of $\mathbf{F}$ along any curve is equal to the difference in the values of ϕ at the endpoints of the curve. In particular, if C is a closed curve,

$$\int_C \mathbf{F} \cdot d\mathbf{R} = 0$$

Let S be a surface with boundary C.

(a) What is the surface integral of the normal component of **curl** (**grad** ϕ) over a surface S?

If S is a very small element of surface, bounded by a closed curve C, **curl** (**grad** ϕ) will be approximately constant on S, and the surface integral of the normal component of **curl** (**grad** ϕ) will be approximately $\mathbf{n} \cdot \mathbf{curl}$ (**grad** ϕ) times the area of the surface.

(b) For any unit vector $\mathbf{n}$, and any point in space, what is $\mathbf{n} \cdot \mathbf{curl}$ (**grad** ϕ) at this point?

(c) Since this result is independent of the direction of $\mathbf{n}$, what can you say about **curl** (**grad** ϕ)?

(d) To which of the identities of Section 3.7 is this related?

4.12 : Orthogonal Curvilinear Coordinates

In practice, it is common to use coordinate systems other than Cartesian coordinates. For example, one frequently uses spherical or cylindrical coordinates (Figs. 92 and 93). Other coordinate systems are also used, but less frequently. Since the coordinates in such systems (for example, ϕ in spherical coordinates) need not represent lengths, certain complications are introduced. Indeed, these complications are present even with Cartesian coordinates, if one is rash enough to take (say) units of inches along one axis and units of feet along another.

Let us suppose that we have one fixed set of Cartesian coordinates x, y, and z, and that we agree to call

$$\sqrt{(x_1 - x_2)^2 + (y_1 - y_2)^2 + (z_1 - z_2)^2}$$

the distance between the points (x_1, y_1, z_1) and (x_2, y_2, z_2). Physically, this simply means we have agreed on some unit of length, say the centimeter, and that we mark the axes accordingly. Now suppose we let u_1, u_2, and u_3 be another set of coordinates. In other words, we have three functions

(1) $$u_1 = f(x,y,z), \quad u_2 = g(x,y,z), \quad u_3 = h(x,y,z)$$

by which we associate to any point (x,y,z) an ordered triple (u_1,u_2,u_3) that we now call the curvilinear coordinates of (x,y,z).

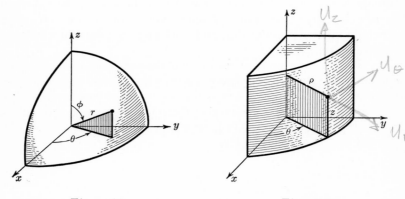

Figure 92   *Figure 93*

For example, the equations

$$r = \sqrt{x^2 + y^2 + z^2}$$

(2) $$\theta = \tan^{-1}(y/x) \qquad\qquad -\pi < \theta \leq \pi$$

$$\phi = \cos^{-1}\frac{z}{\sqrt{x^2 + y^2 + z^2}} \qquad 0 \leq \phi \leq \pi$$

define what we mean by the spherical coordinates (r,θ,ϕ) of a point (x,y,z).

It is not possible to define useful curvilinear coordinates by taking the functions f, g, and h entirely arbitrarily. For example, the curvilinear coordinates $u_1 = x^2$, $u_2 = y - z$, $u_3 = 2y - 2z$ would not be very useful because such pairs of points as $(1,2,3)$ and $(1,3,4)$ would have identical curvilinear coordinates $(1,-1,-2)$.

Therefore we shall assume that the functions f, g, and h possess continuous partial derivatives of all orders in some domain, that they assign different ordered triples to different points, and that at every point P in this domain the gradients of these functions are nonzero and mutually perpendicular. To avoid difficulties with orientation, we assume that **grad** f, **grad** g, and **grad** h, in that order, form a right-handed system. If these conditions are satisfied, we say that (1) defines an *orthogonal coordinate system* in the domain.

Generally, we do not require that the coordinates satisfy these requirements at every point in space. For example, if we pass through the z axis along a line parallel to the x axis, the spherical coordinate θ undergoes a discontinuous jump from 0 to π. We shall generally ignore this difficulty, and work only in a domain where the conditions are satisfied.

The conditions stated ensure that through each point P in the domain, having curvilinear coordinates (c_1,c_2,c_3), there will pass three isotimic surfaces $u_1 = c_1$, $u_2 = c_2$, $u_3 = c_3$. These surfaces intersect at P and intersect in pairs to give three curves passing through P, and the curves have mutually perpendicular tangents at P (Fig. 94). We call these *coordinate curves*.

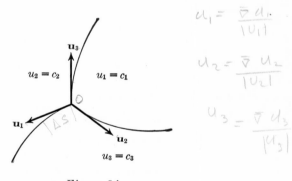

Figure 94

Along each coordinate curve, arc length is a function of only one curvilinear coordinate. Letting s_1, s_2, and s_3 denote the arc lengths measured along the coordinate curves in the direction of increasing u_1, u_2, and u_3, respectively, we define

(3) $$h_1 = \frac{ds_1}{du_1}, \qquad h_2 = \frac{ds_2}{du_2}, \qquad h_3 = \frac{ds_3}{du_3}$$

where the derivatives are evaluated at point P. We call these the *scale factors* at P.

In terms of these scale factors, we shall now give the formulas for arc length, gradient, etc. We omit the derivations of these expressions, but give arguments that tend to make them plausible.

The arc length along a curve C is given by the line integral

$$(4) \qquad \int \sqrt{(h_1 \, du_1)^2 + (h_2 \, du_2)^2 + (h_3 \, du_3)^2}$$

More generally, if $f(u_1, u_2, u_3)$ is a continuous function, the line integral of f along C is obtained by

$$(5) \qquad \int f(u_1, u_2, u_3) \sqrt{(h_1 \, du_1)^2 + (h_2 \, du_2)^2 + (h_3 \, du_3)^2}$$

where in practice one usually has u_1, u_2, and u_3 given in terms of some parameter t so that (5) ultimately becomes an integral involving t and dt.

The volume integral of a function $f(u_1, u_2, u_3)$ is

$$(6) \qquad \iiint f(u_1, u_2, u_3) \, dV = \iiint f(u_1, u_2, u_3)(h_1 h_2 h_3) \, du_1 \, du_2 \, du_3$$

The plausibility of these expressions for ds and dV is enhanced by contemplating a rectangular parallelepiped with edges $ds_1 = h_1 \, du_1$, $ds_2 = h_2 \, du_2$, and $ds_3 = h_3 \, du_3$ (Fig. 95).

Letting $\mathbf{u}_1$, $\mathbf{u}_2$, and $\mathbf{u}_3$ denote unit tangent vectors at P in the directions of increasing u_1, u_2, and u_3 respectively (Fig. 94), we can write the gradient of a scalar field f:

$$(7) \qquad \mathbf{grad}\, f = \frac{1}{h_1}\left(\frac{\partial f}{\partial u_1}\right)\mathbf{u}_1 + \frac{1}{h_2}\left(\frac{\partial f}{\partial u_2}\right)\mathbf{u}_2 + \frac{1}{h_3}\left(\frac{\partial f}{\partial u_3}\right)\mathbf{u}_3$$

This is plausible since, for instance, the rate of change of f with respect to distance in the direction of u_1 is $df/ds_1 = df/(h_1 \, du_1)$, by (3).

The expression for divergence is more complicated. Let

$$\mathbf{F} = F_1\mathbf{u}_1 + F_2\mathbf{u}_2 + F_3\mathbf{u}_3$$

be the vector field, given in terms of the unit vectors $\mathbf{u}_1$, $\mathbf{u}_2$, $\mathbf{u}_3$ along the coordinate curves. Then

$$(8) \qquad \text{div } \mathbf{F} = \frac{1}{h_1 h_2 h_3}\left[\frac{\partial}{\partial u_1}(F_1 h_2 h_3) + \frac{\partial}{\partial u_2}(F_2 h_1 h_3) + \frac{\partial}{\partial u_3}(F_3 h_1 h_2)\right]$$

It is not possible in general to cancel the h's in this expression since they are functions of u_1, u_2, and u_3.   This expression is made plausible by thinking of div $\mathbf{F}$ as the flux output per unit volume.   Consider the parallelepiped of Figure 95.   The flux density normal to the face

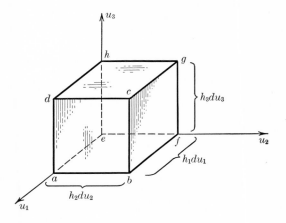

Figure 95

$abcd$ is $\mathbf{F} \cdot \mathbf{u}_1 = F_1$ and the area of this face is $h_2h_3\, du_2\, du_3$.   Therefore the flux outward from that face is $F_1h_2h_3\, du_2\, du_3$.   The unit outward normal to face $efgh$ is $-\mathbf{u}_1$, so that the flux outward from that face is $-F_1h_2h_3\, du_2\, du_3$.   Since F_1, h_2, and h_3 are functions of u_1 as we move along the u_1-coordinate curve, the sum of these two is approximately

$$\left[\frac{\partial}{\partial u_1} (F_1h_2h_3)\, du_1\right] du_2\, du_3$$

From this and similar expressions for the other two pairs of faces we see that the net flux outward from the parallelepiped is approximately

$$\left[\frac{\partial}{\partial u_1} (F_1h_2h_3) + \frac{\partial}{\partial u_2} (F_2h_1h_3) + \frac{\partial}{\partial u_3} (F_3h_1h_2)\right] du_1\, du_2\, du_3$$

and so the flux output per unit volume is this expression divided by the volume $h_1h_2h_3\, du_1\, du_2\, du_3$, giving (8).

The curl is given by

(9) $\quad$ $\mathbf{curl\ F} = \dfrac{1}{h_2 h_3}\left[\dfrac{\partial}{\partial u_2}(F_3 h_3) - \dfrac{\partial}{\partial u_3}(F_2 h_2)\right]\mathbf{u}_1$

$+ \dfrac{1}{h_1 h_3}\left[\dfrac{\partial}{\partial u_3}(F_1 h_1) - \dfrac{\partial}{\partial u_1}(F_3 h_3)\right]\mathbf{u}_2$

$+ \dfrac{1}{h_1 h_2}\left[\dfrac{\partial}{\partial u_1}(F_2 h_2) - \dfrac{\partial}{\partial u_2}(F_1 h_1)\right]\mathbf{u}_3$

$= \dfrac{1}{h_1 h_2 h_3}\begin{vmatrix} h_1\mathbf{u}_1 & h_2\mathbf{u}_2 & h_3\mathbf{u}_3 \\ \dfrac{\partial}{\partial u_1} & \dfrac{\partial}{\partial u_2} & \dfrac{\partial}{\partial u_3} \\ F_1 h_1 & F_2 h_2 & F_3 h_3 \end{vmatrix}$

From these it is easy to see that the Laplacian is

(10) $\quad \nabla^2 f = \operatorname{div} \mathbf{grad} f$

$= \dfrac{1}{h_1 h_2 h_3}\left[\dfrac{\partial}{\partial u_1}\left(\dfrac{h_2 h_3}{h_1}\dfrac{\partial f}{\partial u_1}\right) + \dfrac{\partial}{\partial u_2}\left(\dfrac{h_1 h_3}{h_2}\dfrac{\partial f}{\partial u_2}\right) + \dfrac{\partial}{\partial u_3}\left(\dfrac{h_1 h_2}{h_3}\dfrac{\partial f}{\partial u_3}\right)\right]$

To apply these formulas, it is necessary first to know h_1, h_2, and h_3. This can be accomplished either by drawing a picture or by determining ds^2 and comparing it with the expression

$$h_1{}^2\,du_1{}^2 + h_2{}^2\,du_2{}^2 + h_3{}^2\,du_3{}^2$$

Thus, for spherical coordinates we have

(11) $\quad$ $\begin{aligned} x &= r \sin \phi \cos \theta \\ y &= r \sin \phi \sin \theta \\ z &= r \cos \phi \end{aligned}$

and by a rather tedious operation we compute $dx^2 + dy^2 + dz^2$ to obtain $ds^2 = dr^2 + r^2\,d\phi^2 + r^2 \sin^2 \phi\,d\theta^2$. Hence $h_1 = 1$, $h_2 = r$, $h_3 = r \sin \phi$. Now it is simple enough to substitute into the other formulas to obtain any of these expressions in spherical coordinates. For example, the element of volume is $dV = r^2 \sin \phi\,dr\,d\phi\,d\theta$, and the gradient in spherical coordinates is

$$\mathbf{grad}\,f = \frac{\partial f}{\partial r}\mathbf{u}_r + \frac{1}{r}\frac{\partial f}{\partial \phi}\mathbf{u}_\phi + \frac{1}{r \sin \phi}\frac{\partial f}{\partial \theta}\mathbf{u}_\theta$$

where we denote the unit vectors by $\mathbf{u}_r$, $\mathbf{u}_\phi$, and $\mathbf{u}_\theta$ rather than by $\mathbf{u}_1$, $\mathbf{u}_2$, and $\mathbf{u}_3$.

The reader using this book as a reference should note that the expressions for gradient, divergence, curl, and the Laplacian in cylindrical and spherical coordinates are given on page 337.

EXERCISES

1. By using the "lumpiness" definition of the Laplacian (Exercise 7, Section 4.9) applied to a rectangular parallelepiped, give a direct derivation of (10).

2. Write down the expressions for gradient, divergence, curl, and the Laplacian in spherical coordinates.

3. Write down the expressions for gradient, divergence, curl, and the Laplacian in cylindrical coordinates.

4. In Cartesian coordinates, $dV = dx\,dy\,dz$. Beginning with (11), differentiate to form dx, dy, and dz in terms of dr, $d\phi$, and $d\theta$, and multiply to obtain $dx\,dy\,dz$.
    (a) Does this give dV in spherical coordinates?
    (b) Explain this phenomenon.

5. Let $u_1 = x + y$, $u_2 = x - y$, and $u_3 = 2z$.
    (a) Solve for x, y, and z in terms of u_1, u_2, and u_3.
    (b) Find ds^2 and hence determine h_1, h_2, and h_3 for this coordinate system.
    (c) What is the Laplacian relative to this coordinate system?
    (d) Let $f(u_1,u_2,u_3) = u_1 + u_2 + 2u_3$. Find **grad** f.

6. Let $u_1 = x + y$, $u_2 = x - 2y$, and $u_3 = 2z$.
    (a) Solve for x, y, and z in terms of u_1, u_2, and u_3.
    (b) Attempt to determine the scale factors h_1, h_2, and h_3.
    (c) What is "wrong"?

7. What is the element of volume relative to the coordinate system $u_1 = e^x$, $u_2 = y$, $u_3 = z$?

8. Consider the coordinate system $u_1 = y$, $u_2 = x$, $u_3 = z$. The scale factors are all equal to unity, so that (9) takes an especially simple form.
    (a) Let $\mathbf{F} = -u_2\mathbf{u}_1 + u_1\mathbf{u}_2$. Show that (9) gives

    $$\textbf{curl } \mathbf{F} = 2\mathbf{u}_3$$

    (b) Obviously $\mathbf{u}_1 = \mathbf{j}$, $\mathbf{u}_2 = \mathbf{i}$, and $\mathbf{u}_3 = \mathbf{k}$, so that $\mathbf{F} = y\mathbf{i} - x\mathbf{j}$ and by part (a), **curl** $\mathbf{F} = 2\mathbf{k}$. But direct calculation of

curl F in Cartesian coordinates shows that **curl F** $= -2\mathbf{k}$, not $2\mathbf{k}$. What is "wrong"?

9. Letting $\mathbf{R} = x\mathbf{i} + y\mathbf{j} + z\mathbf{k}$, and $r = |\mathbf{R}|$, write the vector field $\mathbf{F} = \mathbf{R}/r^3$ in terms of r and $\mathbf{u}_r$.
    (a) Show that div **F** is identically zero throughout the domain of definition of **F**.
    (b) Show that the surface integral of the normal component of **F** over the surface of the unit sphere $r = 1$ is 4π.
    (c) Explain why (a) and (b) above do not contradict the divergence theorem.
    (d) What is the surface integral of the normal component of **F** over the surface of a unit sphere with center 4 units away from the origin?

SUPPLEMENTARY EXERCISES

1. Vectors from the origin O to four points A, B, C, D are given as follows:
    $$\mathbf{A} = 2\mathbf{i}, \quad \mathbf{B} = 3\mathbf{j}, \quad \mathbf{C} = 4\mathbf{k}, \quad \mathbf{D} = \mathbf{i} + \mathbf{j} + 2\mathbf{k}$$
    (a) Find the length of the perpendicular drawn from A to the plane BCD.
    (b) Find the length of the common perpendicular to the lines AB and CD.
    (c) Find a vector parallel to this perpendicular.

2. The vertices of a regular tetrahedron are $OABC$. Prove that the vector $OA + OB + OC$ is perpendicular to the plane ABC.

3. Find the angle which the plane OAB makes with the z axis, if A is the point $(1,3,2)$ and B is $(2,1,1)$.

4. Given the points $O(0,0,0)$, $A(1,2,3)$, $B(0,-1,1)$, $C(2,0,2)$.
    (a) Find a vector perpendicular to the plane OAB.
    (b) Find the distance from C to the plane OAB.

5. Determine the shortest distance from the point $(3,4,5)$ to the line through the origin parallel to the vector $2\mathbf{i} - \mathbf{j} + 2\mathbf{k}$.

6. Write the scalar equations of the line parallel to the intersection of the planes $3x + y + z = 5$, $x - 2y + 3z = 1$ and passing through the point $(4,2,1)$.

7. Given the points $P_1(2,-1,4)$, $P_2(-1,0,3)$, $P_3(4,3,1)$, and $P_4(3,-5,0)$, determine
   (a) the volume of the tetrahedron $P_1P_2P_3P_4$;
   (b) the equation of the plane containing the points P_1, P_2, and P_3;
   (c) the cosine of the angle between the line segments P_1P_2 and P_1P_3.

8. Write an expression for a vector 5 units long, parallel to the plane $3x + 4y + 5z = 10$ and perpendicular to the vector $\mathbf{i} + 2\mathbf{j} + 2\mathbf{k}$.

9. Let $\mathbf{A}$, $\mathbf{B}$, $\mathbf{C}$, and $\mathbf{D}$ be position vectors of the points $A(1,3,-2)$, $B(3,5,-3)$, $C(-5,9,-5)$, and $D(4,-1,10)$, respectively. Find
   (a) $|\mathbf{A} - \mathbf{D}|$ (c) $(\mathbf{A} - \mathbf{C})\cdot(\mathbf{A} - \mathbf{B})$
   (b) $\mathbf{A} \times \mathbf{B}$ (d) $\mathbf{A}\cdot\mathbf{B} \times \mathbf{C}$.

10. Given the four points specified in Exercise 9, determine
    (a) the area of the triangle OAB;
    (b) the volume of the tetrahedron $OABC$;
    (c) the angle CAB.

11. Given $f(x,y,z) = 2x^2 + y$ and $\mathbf{R} = x\mathbf{i} + y\mathbf{j} + z\mathbf{k}$, find (a) ∇f, (b) $\nabla \cdot \mathbf{R}$, (c) $\nabla^2 f$, (d) $\nabla \times (f\mathbf{R})$.

12. If $\mathbf{F} = x^2\mathbf{i} + xy\mathbf{j} + z\mathbf{k}$, evaluate each of the following at the point $(-1,2,3)$: (a) $\nabla^2\mathbf{F}$ (b) $\nabla \times \mathbf{F}$ (c) $\nabla \cdot \mathbf{F}$.

13. Evaluate $\nabla^2[(\mathbf{i} + \mathbf{j} + \mathbf{k}) \times \nabla(\mathbf{R}\cdot\mathbf{R})^2]$, where
$$\mathbf{R} = x\mathbf{i} + y\mathbf{j} + z\mathbf{k}$$

14. Evaluate $\nabla \ln (xyz + 5)$ at the point $(-1,2,3)$.

15. Evaluate $\mathbf{A} \cdot \nabla \mathbf{R} + \nabla(\mathbf{A}\cdot\mathbf{R}) + \mathbf{A}\cdot\nabla \times \mathbf{R}$ where $\mathbf{A}$ is a constant vector field and $\mathbf{R} = x\mathbf{i} + y\mathbf{j} + z\mathbf{k}$.

16. If $r^2 = x^2 + y^2 + z^2$, $\mathbf{R} = x\mathbf{i} + y\mathbf{j} + z\mathbf{k}$, and $\mathbf{A}$ is a constant vector field, find
    (a) $\nabla \cdot (r^2\mathbf{A})$ (f) $\mathbf{R} \cdot \nabla(\mathbf{A}\cdot\mathbf{R}\mathbf{A})$
    (b) $\nabla \times (r^2\mathbf{A})$ (g) $\nabla \cdot (\mathbf{A} \times \mathbf{R})$
    (c) $\mathbf{R} \cdot \nabla(r^2\mathbf{A})$ (h) $\nabla \times (\mathbf{A} \times \mathbf{R})$
    (d) $\nabla(\mathbf{A}\cdot\mathbf{R})^4$ (i) $\nabla^2(\mathbf{R}\cdot\mathbf{R})$
    (e) $\nabla \cdot (r\mathbf{A})$

17. Consider the potential $\phi(x,y,z) = xyz$.
     (a) Find a vector normal to the equipotential surface through the point $(1,2,3)$.
     (b) Find $d\phi/ds$ at the same point, if s is measured in the direction of the vector $6\mathbf{i} + 3\mathbf{j} + 2\mathbf{k}$.

18. Given $\phi(x,y,z) = z^2 - x - y$, determine
     (a) an equation of the plane tangent to the surface $\phi = 2$ at the point $(-2,4,2)$;
     (b) equations of the line normal to the surface $\phi = 2$ at the point $(-2,4,2)$;
     (c) the derivative of ϕ at $(-2,4,2)$ in the direction of the vector $3\mathbf{i} - 2\mathbf{j} + 6\mathbf{k}$.

19. What angle does the vector $3\mathbf{i} + 4\mathbf{j} + 5\mathbf{k}$ make with the surface $xy - z^2 = 3$ at the point $(3,4,3)$?

20. If r is the distance from the origin to the point (x,y,z) and $\mathbf{A}$ is a constant vector, evaluate

$$\nabla \left(\mathbf{A} \cdot \nabla \frac{1}{r} \right) + \nabla \times \left(\mathbf{A} \times \nabla \frac{1}{r} \right)$$

21. By changing to cylindrical coordinates, find the divergence and the curl of

$$\mathbf{F} = \frac{x\mathbf{i} + y\mathbf{j}}{x^2 + y^2}$$

22. By means of Stokes' theorem, find

$$\int \mathbf{F} \cdot d\mathbf{R}$$

around the ellipse $x^2 + y^2 = 1$, $z = y$, where
$$\mathbf{F} = x\mathbf{i} + (x + y)\mathbf{j} + (x + y + z)\mathbf{k}$$

23. Let D be the region $x \geq 0$, $y \geq 0$, $z \geq 0$, $x + \frac{y}{2} + \frac{z}{3} \leq 1$.

     (a) Is this region a domain?
     (b) Is this region simply-connected?
     (c) If $\mathbf{F} = 2x\mathbf{i} + y\mathbf{j} + z\mathbf{k}$, find the surface integral of the normal component of $\mathbf{F}$ over the boundary of this region, oriented by selecting the outward normal.

24. Given the vector field $\mathbf{F} = 3y\mathbf{i} + (5 - 2x)\mathbf{j} + (z^2 - 2)\mathbf{k}$, find
     (a) div $\mathbf{F}$, (b) **curl F**, (c) the surface integral of the normal

component of **curl F** over the open hemispherical surface $x^2 + y^2 + z^2 = 4$ above the xy plane. [Hint: By a double application of Stokes' theorem, part (c) can be reduced to a triviality.]

25. Given that **curl F** $= 2y\mathbf{i} - 2z\mathbf{j} + 3\mathbf{k}$, find the surface integral of the normal component of **curl F** (*not* **F**) over (a) the open hemispherical surface $x^2 + y^2 + z^2 = 9$, $z > 0$, and (b) the sphere $x^2 + y^2 + z^2 = 9$. (In both parts, you should be able to write the answer down by inspection.)

26. The abstract concept of a gooney sphere is derived from the shape of a gooney egg. A gooney bird is born with a pointed head and a prominent stubby tail; therefore the shape of the egg is roughly ellipsoidal but with pointed ends. Surface integrals over gooney spheres are difficult to compute; tables of gooney functions are needed, but these were tabulated during the war and are still classified top-secret. All that is known is that a gooney sphere of minimal diameter $d = 1$ has volume approximately 0.7. (a) Find the surface integral of the normal component of **F** $= x\mathbf{i} + y\mathbf{j} + z\mathbf{k}$ over the surface of a gooney sphere with center at the origin and minimal diameter $d = 2$, making any assumptions you deem reasonable. (b) Would your answer be the same if the gooney sphere had center at $(2,7,-3)$?

27. If electric field intensity is **E** $= (x + 1)^2\mathbf{i} + y\mathbf{j} + z\mathbf{k}$, relevant to suitable choices of the units involved, what is the total charge within the cube bounded by the planes $x = 0$, $x = 1$, $y = 0$, $y = 1$, $z = 0$ and $z = 1$? Evaluate the left side of (7), Section 4.6, (a) directly, (b) by the divergence theorem.

28. What is the flux output per unit volume at $(3,1,-2)$ if **F** $= x^3\mathbf{i} + yx\mathbf{j} - x^3\mathbf{k}$?

29. What is the flux output from an ellipsoid of volume v if **F** $= 3x\mathbf{i} + y\mathbf{j} + z\mathbf{k}$?

30. If **F** $= 3x^2\mathbf{i} + y\mathbf{j} + z\mathbf{k}$, would the flux output from an ellipsoid depend on the location of the ellipsoid as well as on its volume?

31. (a) Describe the oriented surface enclosing the region

$$1 \leqq x^2 + y^2 + z^2 \leqq 4$$

assuming the usual convention concerning the orientation of a closed surface. (In Section 4.5 it was mentioned that if a surface encloses a region of space, the unit normal points away from the enclosed region; in this problem, the surface has two disconnected parts.)

(b) How would you compute the surface integral of the normal component of a vector field $\mathbf{F}$ over this surface?

(c) If div $\mathbf{F} = 0$ except perhaps at the origin, what can you say about

$$\iint \mathbf{F} \cdot \mathbf{n} \, dS$$

over the two parts comprising this surface, taking $\mathbf{n}$ to be the unit normal outward from the origin in each case?

(d) Would your answer to (c) be any different if the region were that between the sphere $x^2 + y^2 + z^2 = 1$ and the ellipsoid

$$\frac{x^2}{4} + \frac{y^2}{9} + \frac{z^2}{16} = 1$$

(e) Compute the surface integral of the normal component of

$$\mathbf{F} = \frac{x\mathbf{i} + y\mathbf{j} + z\mathbf{k}}{(x^2 + y^2 + z^2)^{3/2}}$$

over the ellipsoid

$$\frac{x^2}{4} + \frac{y^2}{9} + \frac{z^2}{16} = 1$$

32. Suppose that u,v,w are orthogonal curvilinear coordinates for which $ds^2 = v^2 \, du^2 + u^2 \, dv^2 + dw^2$.

(a) Calculate the divergence of $\mathbf{u}$, where $\mathbf{u}$ is the unit vector tangent to a u-curve.

(b) Determine the Laplacian of the function $\phi = uww$.

33. Let $\mathbf{R} = x\mathbf{i} + y\mathbf{j} + z\mathbf{k}$ and $r = |\mathbf{R}|$. Show that, under certain circumstances, the integral

$$\omega = \iint \frac{\mathbf{R}}{r^3} \cdot \mathbf{n} \, dS = -\iint \left(\nabla \frac{1}{r} \right) \cdot \mathbf{n} \, dS$$

over a surface gives the solid angle subtended by the surface at the origin.

34. (a) Show that, if ϕ is harmonic, $\nabla \cdot (\phi \nabla \phi) = |\nabla \phi|^2$.

(b) Given $\phi = 3x + 2y + 4z$, evaluate

$$\iint \phi \frac{\partial \phi}{\partial n} \, dS$$

over the surface $x^2 + y^2 + z^2 = 4$. Here, $\partial\phi/\partial n$ represents the normal derivative of ϕ, that is, $\mathbf{n} \cdot \nabla\phi$.

35. Given $\phi(x,y,z) = xyz + 5$, find the surface integral of the normal component of **grad** ϕ over $x^2 + y^2 + z^2 = 9$.

36. Given

$$\mathbf{F} = \frac{x\mathbf{i} + y\mathbf{j} + z\mathbf{k}}{x^2 + y^2 + z^2}$$

find the surface integral of the normal component of **F** over the surface of the sphere $x^2 + y^2 + z^2 = 4$. Can you use the divergence theorem?

37. If $\mathbf{R} = x\mathbf{i} + y\mathbf{j} + z\mathbf{k}$ and $r = |\mathbf{R}|$, find

$$\iint r\mathbf{R} \cdot \mathbf{n} \, dS$$

over the surface of a sphere of radius b and center at the origin,
(a) by interpreting the integrand geometrically;
(b) by using the divergence theorem.

38. Let $\mathbf{F} = \phi\nabla\phi$. Find the surface integral of the normal component of **F** over the surface of a sphere of radius 3 and center at the origin,
(a) if $\phi = x + y + z$;
(b) if $\phi = x^2 + y^2 + z^2$.

39. Let us suppose that a field **F** due to a point "source" of "strength" q located at a point P has potential ϕ at a point Q given by $\phi(Q) = q/r$, where r is the distance from P to Q. Except when $r = 0$, ϕ is a harmonic function, that is, $\nabla^2\phi = 0$. Now suppose that the source is not concentrated at a single point but is distributed uniformly with density σ (source strength per unit area) over the surface of a sphere of radius a. If Q is the point (x_0,y_0,z_0), the potential at Q must then be found by integration,

$$\phi(x_0,y_0,z_0) = \iint \frac{\sigma \, dS}{\sqrt{(x - x_0)^2 + (y - y_0)^2 + (z - z_0)^2}}$$

where the integral is over the surface of the sphere. Give an heuristic line of reasoning to show that the potential is
(a) constant within the sphere, equal to $4\pi a\sigma$;

(b) equal to $4\pi a^2 \sigma / b$ at any point outside the sphere a distance b from the center of the sphere. [Hint: Think of **F** as a scalar multiple of the electric field intensity due to a charge distribution and use Gauss's law.]

40. By interpreting the following integrals as potentials, find their values. Take the surface S to be the sphere $x^2 + y^2 + z^2 = 4$.

(a)
$$\iint_S \frac{dS}{\sqrt{(x-1)^2 + y^2 + z^2}}$$

(b)
$$\iint_S \frac{dS}{\sqrt{(x-3)^2 + y^2 + z^2}}$$

41. Evaluate

$$\iint_S \frac{dS}{\sqrt{(x-3)^2 + (y-2)^2 + z^2}}$$

over the surface $x^2 + y^2 + z^2 = 25$ by interpreting the integral as a potential.

42. Evaluate the following integrals over the region of space within the sphere $x^2 + y^2 + z^2 = 4$, by interpreting them as potentials and using Gauss's law.

(a)
$$\iiint \frac{dx\,dy\,dz}{\sqrt{(x-1)^2 + y^2 + z^2}}$$

(b)
$$\iiint \frac{dx\,dy\,dz}{\sqrt{(x-3)^2 + y^2 + z^2}}$$

43. Evaluate

$$\iiint \frac{dx\,dy\,dz}{\sqrt{(x-9)^2 + (y-2)^2 + z^2}}$$

where the integral extends over the interior of the sphere $x^2 + y^2 + z^2 = 4$, by interpreting the integral as a potential.

44. Let S be a sphere of radius b and center at a point P and let ϕ be a continuous function. Consider the integral

$$\iint_S \phi \nabla \left(\frac{1}{r}\right) \cdot \mathbf{n}\,dS$$

where **n** is the unit outward normal, and $r = |\mathbf{R}|$ where **R** extends from the center of the sphere to a variable point on the surface. What is the limit of this integral as b tends to zero?

(You cannot use the divergence theorem since $1/r$ is not defined at $r = 0$. Observe that

$$\nabla\left(\frac{1}{r}\right) = -\frac{\mathbf{R}}{r^3} \quad \text{and} \quad \mathbf{n} = \frac{\mathbf{R}}{r}$$

whence

$$\nabla\left(\frac{1}{r}\right) \cdot \mathbf{n} = -\frac{1}{r^2} = -\frac{1}{b^2}$$

for points on the surface.)

45. Let $\mathbf{F}$ be a vector field, defined and continuously differentiable everywhere except at a point P, and having zero divergence (except at P). Let S' be a closed surface (say, an ellipsoid) enclosing P, and let S denote the surface of a small sphere with center at P completely within S'. Compare

$$\iint_S \mathbf{F} \cdot \mathbf{n}\, dS \quad \text{and} \quad \iint_{S'} \mathbf{F} \cdot \mathbf{n}\, dS$$

where $\mathbf{n}$ denotes the *outward* unit normal in each case.

46. Let ϕ be a function that is continuously differentiable and harmonic in a region bounded by a (suitably smooth) surface S, and let r denote the distance from a fixed point P in the interior of the region. Show that the value of ϕ at P is given by the formula

$$\phi(P) = \frac{1}{4\pi} \iint_S \left[\frac{1}{r}\frac{\partial\phi}{\partial n} - \phi\frac{\partial}{\partial n}\left(\frac{1}{r}\right)\right] dS$$

[Hint: Use the results of Exercises 38 and 39.] (This formula is of considerable importance in the theory of harmonic functions.)

47. Evaluate

$$\iint_S \left[\frac{1}{r}\frac{\partial\phi}{\partial n} - \phi\frac{\partial}{\partial n}\left(\frac{1}{r}\right)\right] dS$$

over the surface of the sphere $(x - 3)^2 + y^2 + z^2 = 25$, where $r^2 = x^2 + y^2 + z^2$ and $\phi = xyz + 5$. By using the formula given in Exercise 46, you should be able to write the answer down at once.

48. Evaluate

$$\iint_S \left[\phi\frac{\partial}{\partial n}\left(\frac{1}{r}\right) - \frac{1}{r}\frac{\partial\phi}{\partial n}\right] dS$$

(a) over the surface of the ellipsoid $\dfrac{x^2}{9} + \dfrac{y^2}{16} + \dfrac{z^2}{25} = 1$ where

$$r^2 = x^2 + (y - 1)^2 + z^2 \quad \text{and} \quad \phi = x^2 + y^2 - 2z^2 + 4$$

(b) over the surface of the cylindrical pillbox bounded by $x^2 + y^2 = 25$ and $z = \pm 10$, where

$$r^2 = (x - 2)^2 + (y - 1)^2 + (z - 3)^2$$

and

$$\phi = x^2 - z^2 + 5$$

49. What is the value of the surface integral (Exercise 46) if P is outside the closed surface S?

50. Give a vector interpretation of each of the following. The notation is that used in Section 4.9.

(a) $\displaystyle \lim_{V \to 0} \frac{\iint_S \mathbf{n} \cdot \mathbf{F}\, dS}{V}$

(b) $\displaystyle \lim_{V \to 0} \frac{\iint_S \mathbf{n} \times \mathbf{F}\, dS}{V}$

(c) $\displaystyle \lim_{V \to 0} \frac{\iint_S \mathbf{n} f\, dS}{V}$ where f is a scalar field.

(d) $\displaystyle \lim_{V \to 0} \frac{\iint_S (\partial f / \partial n)\, dS}{V}$

F I V E

GENERALIZATIONS

5.1 : Introduction

The preceding four chapters were devoted to vector algebra and vector analysis. Vector algebra includes the study of scalar and vector products, and vector analysis centers mostly about the various integral theorems, such as the divergence theorem and Stokes' theorem. The reader who wishes to study these topics more intensively may proceed from here in many directions. If interested in studying more of the same material, he can study many excellent books on vector analysis that carry the integral theorems further to give a more complete analysis of vector fields. If interested mainly in applications, he is already prepared to study texts on hydrodynamics or electromagnetic wave theory, or he can proceed to the study of tensor analysis, with its interesting applications to elasticity and the theory of relativity. If interested in pure mathematics, he can proceed either in an algebraic direction, to study vector spaces and normed linear spaces, or in a geometrical direction to study Riemannian geometry.

But if he does this immediately, he will always thereafter think

of vector analysis as an isolated part of his curriculum, a good preparation for certain specialized courses but not in the main stream of
his mathematical development. There is a simple reason for this,
which is that vector analysis, as usually presented (and as presented
in the preceding four chapters), is in certain respects old-fashioned.
The classical treatment covers up many essential aspects of the subject. When the student studies topics in mathematics presented
from a modern viewpoint, he does not even recognize that he has
learned some of this material before in another context.

It is not the purpose of this chapter to introduce the reader to
a superficial smattering of other topics related to vector analysis.
Rather, it is our purpose to recast what we have already learned in a
more modern format. This involves introducing new ideas that
will seem very foreign at first.

Before proceeding, we note that many of the theorems in this
chapter are stated without proof. This does not mean the proofs
are difficult, but simply that these theorems are more appropriately
proved in a course in modern algebra. In this chapter, geometrical
ideas are emphasized, with a minimum of digression to algebraic
generalizations.

5.2 : Cartesian Spaces

As motivation, let us contemplate the equations

$$\begin{aligned}
x + y - 2z &= -3 \\
x + y + z &= 6 \\
2x - y - z &= -3
\end{aligned}$$

(1)

We assume that the reader knows at least one method for solving
such a system of equations; for those interested, the solution in this
case is $x = 1$, $y = 2$, $z = 3$.

It is possible to think of each of these equations as an equation
of a plane; the solution $(1,2,3)$ is the point of intersection of the planes.
There is, however, another point of view that is sometimes useful.
Let us consider the equations

$$\begin{aligned}
x' &= x + y - 2z \\
y' &= x + y + z \\
z' &= 2x - y - z
\end{aligned}$$

(2)

as representing a transformation of each ordered triple (x,y,z) into a new ordered triple (x',y',z'). If these triples represent points in space, then (2) defines a transformation of each point (x,y,z) to a new location (x',y',z'). Equations (1) pose the problem: what was the old location of the point whose new location is $(-3,6,-3)$?

Alternatively, we can think of (2) as defining a new coordinate system. From this point of view, (1) states that some point (x,y,z) has $x'y'z'$ coordinates $(-3,6,-3)$.

Either point of view gives a valuable geometrical interpretation to the study of systems of equations like (1).

Now suppose we are given, instead, a system of linear equations having more than three unknowns, say

(3)
$$\begin{aligned}
x + y + z - u &= 2 \\
2x - y + z - u &= -1 \\
x + y + z + u &= 10 \\
x - y + z - u &= -2
\end{aligned}$$

(The solution is $x = 1$, $y = 2$, $z = 3$, $u = 4$.)

In the study of such equations, it is useful to think of (x,y,z,u) as representing a point in a four-dimensional space. The left side of (3) represents a transformation of points (x,y,z,u) into points (x',y',z',u'), and in solving (3) we are finding that point which transforms into $(2,-1,10,-2)$.

This partially motivates the following definition: an *n-dimensional Cartesian space* is the set of all sequences $(x^1,x^2,\dots,x^n)$ of n real numbers. The sum of two sequences

$$\begin{aligned}
\mathbf{x} &= (x^1,x^2,\dots,x^n) \\
\mathbf{y} &= (y^1,y^2,\dots,y^n)
\end{aligned}$$

is defined to be

$$\mathbf{x} + \mathbf{y} = (x^1 + y^1,\ x^2 + y^2,\ \dots,\ x^n + y^n)$$

For any real number c, we define

$$c\mathbf{x} = (cx^1,cx^2,\dots,cx^n)$$

We denote the n-dimensional Cartesian space by R^n. In particular, R^1 is the ordinary real number system, R^2 represents the plane, and R^3 represents what we have been calling "space."

Note the change in notation. A single letter $\mathbf{x}$ may represent a sequence $(x^1,x^2,\dots,x^n)$ of n numbers, rather than a single number as in (1). If we think of $\mathbf{x}$ as a point, then x^i denotes the ith *coordinate* of the point. If we think of **x** as a vector, then x^i denotes the ith *component* of the vector. The superscript i is *not* an exponent. We could have used subscripts just as well; the author's preference for superscripts will be explained later.

It is a matter of taste whether we think of a sequence as a point or a vector. The author tends to think of **x** as a vector, represented by a directed line segment extending from the origin $(0,0, \ldots ,0)$ to a point $(x^1,x^2, \ldots ,x^n)$; thus **x** is both a vector and the point whose position is prescribed by the vector.

For positive integers n greater than 3, it may not be possible to "visualize" R^n, but this is of little consequence. Some students can't even visualize R^3, but manage nevertheless to pass courses in solid analytic geometry.

Spaces of dimension greater than three occur also in theoretical physics. In the theory of relativity there occurs a space of four dimensions; roughly speaking, three coordinates refer to position in space and the fourth is related to time. The "phase space" of statistical mechanics is six-dimensional, with three coordinates of position and three of velocity. In the theory of linear oscillations, the displacement from equilibrium of a system with n degrees of freedom is represented by a point in an n-dimensional space. However, our study of n-dimensional spaces is motivated more by mathematical than by physical considerations. The n-dimensional spaces occurring in physics may have quite a different structure than R^n; for instance, the coordinates may be complex numbers rather than real numbers.

If a sequence is denoted by **x**, then the letter x is called the *kernel letter* of the sequence. By convention, if a sequence has kernel letter x, then its ith component is denoted x^i. Thus if we are told that $\mathbf{x} = (1,3,8,7,-2)$, we know automatically that x^4 denotes the number 7.

Sometimes, as above, when two sequences are involved, we use different letters of the alphabet, x and y, as kernel letters. Sometimes we use the same letters of the alphabet, distinguishing them by subscripts, placed *directly underneath* the letter. (Otherwise we might run out of letters of the alphabet.) Thus, if we have $\underset{1}{\mathbf{x}} = (3,2,0,9)$ and $\underset{2}{\mathbf{x}} = (5,9,3,7)$, we understand that $\underset{1}{x^1} = 3$, $\underset{2}{x^1} = 5$, $\underset{2}{x^2} = 9$, etc., and the sum of the sequences is $\underset{1}{\mathbf{x}} + \underset{2}{\mathbf{x}} = (8,11,3,16)$. The subscripts are placed directly under the letter because they are really to be considered as part of the kernel letter.

We now introduce the following definition.   A *linear transformation* of R^n is a rule that associates with each sequence $\mathbf{x}$ a sequence $\mathbf{y} = T(\mathbf{x})$, where the components of $\mathbf{y}$ are related to those of $\mathbf{x}$ by equations of the form

(4)
$$y^1 = T_1{}^1 x^1 + T_2{}^1 x^2 + \ldots + T_n{}^1 x^n$$
$$y^2 = T_1{}^2 x^1 + T_2{}^2 x^2 + \ldots + T_n{}^2 x^n$$
$$\ldots$$
$$y^n = T_1{}^n x^1 + T_2{}^n x^2 + \ldots + T_n{}^n x^n$$

where the $T_j{}^i$ are numbers.

For example, a linear transformation of R^2 is defined by the equations
$$y^1 = 3x^1 - x^2$$
$$y^2 = \ x^1 + x^2$$

Thus if $\mathbf{x} = (3,2)$, then $T(\mathbf{x}) = (7,5)$.

For brevity, it is possible to write (4) in the abbreviated form

(5) $$y^i = T_1{}^i x^1 + T_2{}^i x^2 + \ldots + T_n{}^i x^n$$

It is understood that there are n such equations, one for each value of i from 1 to n.   By use of summation notation, this can be written even more briefly

(6) $$y^i = \sum_{j=1}^{n} T_j{}^i x^j$$

Or, since we always know the summation will extend from 1 to n, we can write simply

(7) $$y^i = \sum T_j{}^i x^j$$

In (7) there is no difficulty determining that it is the index j over which we are summing, since j occurs both in $T_j{}^i$ and in x^j; moreover, i is the only index appearing on both sides of the equation, so we expect i to remain fixed in summing.   If, therefore, we wish to cut our notation to the bare minimum, we can write simply

(8) $$y^i = T_j{}^i x^j$$

provided we adopt the convention (sometimes called the *Einstein summation convention*) that a summation is implied whenever the same index occurs twice, once as a subscript and once as a superscript. This convention is quite dangerous in the hands of novices, since they tend to forget that any summation is involved and consequently may do stupid things. For example, it would not make sense to divide both sides of (8) by x^j to obtain $y^i/x^j = T_j{}^i$ since the x^i, $j = 1$, $2, \ldots, n$, need not be equal to each other. For this reason, we shall not use the Einstein convention in this book.

The letter j in (7) is called a *dummy index*, since it can be replaced by any other letter (except, in this case, i) without changing the meaning of (7). For instance, there is no difference between $\sum T_j{}^i x^j$ and $\sum T_k{}^i x^k$, since they both stand for the sum

$$T_1{}^i x^1 + T_2{}^i x^2 + \ldots + T_n{}^i x^n$$

It is easy to spot a dummy index with the notation we are using, since it always occurs once as a subscript and once as a superscript, and never appears on both sides of the same equation.

For example, by this convention, $\sum u_i v^i$ means

$$u_1 v^1 + u_2 v^2 + \ldots + u_n v^n$$

and $\sum S_{kp} y^p$ stands for $S_{k1} y^1 + S_{k2} y^2 + \ldots + S_{kn} y^n$.

EXAMPLE 1: Letting $n = 2$, write out $\sum \sum U_{ij} x^i y^j$.
Solution:

$$\sum \sum U_{ij} x^i y^j = \sum (U_{i1} x^i y^1 + U_{i2} x^i y^2)$$
$$= U_{11} x^1 y^1 + U_{12} x^1 y^2 + U_{21} x^2 y^1 + U_{22} x^2 y^2$$

EXAMPLE 2: Letting $n = 3$, how many equations are represented by $x^j = \sum \sum Y_{mp}{}^j u^m v^p$, and how many terms are there on the right side of each equation?
Solution: There are three equations, one for each $j = 1,2,3$. Both m and p are dummy variables running from 1 to 3, so that there are nine terms on the right side of each equation.

EXAMPLE 3: Letting $n = 4$, write out $\sum T_j{}^j$.
Solution:

$$\sum T_j{}^j = T_1{}^1 + T_2{}^2 + T_3{}^3 + T_4{}^4$$

EXERCISE

Let $T_j{}^i$ denote the entry in the ith row and jth column of the array of numbers

$$\begin{pmatrix} 3 & 4 & 0 & 2 \\ 2 & 1 & -1 & 5 \\ 1 & 5 & 0 & 4 \\ 0 & -2 & 3 & 3 \end{pmatrix}$$

and let $x^1 = 2$, $x^2 = 0$, $x^3 = 9$, $x^4 = 3$. Compute (a) $\sum T_j{}^i$, (b) $\sum T_k{}^2 x^k$, (c) $\sum T_k{}^3 T_4{}^k$, and (d) $\sum \sum T_k{}^3 T_j{}^k x^j$.

5.3 : Vector Spaces

The purpose of this section is to introduce an axiomatic approach to vector algebra. This is the approach favored by most mathematicians today.

In this approach, no attempt is made to define the term *vector*. Instead, we list the fundamental properties that we require a *collection* of objects to possess in order that the objects themselves may qualify to be called vectors. This makes it possible for some rather weird things to be called "vectors," but, to avoid frightening the reader, we shall ignore this for the moment.

A collection of objects is called a *vector space*, and the objects themselves called *vectors*, provided that the following axioms are satisfied.

An operation of *addition* is defined, whereby to each pair of vectors **u** and **v** there is assigned a sum **u** + **v** which is also a vector. An operation of *multiplication by a scalar* is defined, assigning to each vector **v** and each real number c a vector $c\mathbf{v}$. These operations are required to have the properties:

(1) $$\mathbf{u} + \mathbf{v} = \mathbf{v} + \mathbf{u}$$

(2) $$(\mathbf{u} + \mathbf{v}) + \mathbf{w} = \mathbf{u} + (\mathbf{v} + \mathbf{w})$$

(3) There is a unique vector **0**, called the zero vector, such that $\mathbf{0} + \mathbf{v} = \mathbf{v}$ for every vector **v**.

(4) To each vector **v** there corresponds a unique vector $-\mathbf{v}$ with the property $\mathbf{v} + (-\mathbf{v}) = \mathbf{0}$.

(5) $$c(\mathbf{u} + \mathbf{v}) = c\mathbf{u} + c\mathbf{v}$$

(6) $$(c + d)\mathbf{u} = c\mathbf{u} + d\mathbf{u}$$

(7) $$(cd)\mathbf{u} = c(d\mathbf{u})$$

(8) $$0\mathbf{u} = \mathbf{0}$$

(9) $$1\mathbf{u} = \mathbf{u}$$

(10) $$(-1)\mathbf{u} = -\mathbf{u}$$

valid whenever $\mathbf{u}$, $\mathbf{v}$, and $\mathbf{w}$ are vectors, and c and d are real numbers.

The interested student may consider as an exercise: Derive (8) and (10) from the other axioms.

The *difference* $\mathbf{u} - \mathbf{v}$ of two vectors is defined to be $\mathbf{u} + (-\mathbf{v})$.

It follows from (2) and the principle of finite induction that there is no need for parentheses in writing the sum $\mathbf{v}_1 + \mathbf{v}_2 + \ldots + \mathbf{v}_k$ of k vectors. Making use of (1) it also follows that such a sum is independent of the order of the terms.

Any vector that can be obtained as a sum

$$c^1\mathbf{v}_1 + c^2\mathbf{v}_2 + \ldots + c^k\mathbf{v}_k$$

is called a *linear combination* of the vectors $\mathbf{v}_1, \mathbf{v}_2, \ldots, \mathbf{v}_k$. (For the last time, we emphasize that superscripts are not exponents in this chapter, unless stated otherwise. The $c^1, c^2, \ldots, c^k$ are arbitrary numbers.)

If we have

(11) $$c^1\mathbf{v}_1 + c^2\mathbf{v}_2 + \ldots + c^k\mathbf{v}_k = \mathbf{0}$$

where at least one of the coefficients $c^1, c^2, \ldots, c^k$ is nonzero, then the set of vectors $\mathbf{v}_1, \mathbf{v}_2, \ldots, \mathbf{v}_k$ is said to be *linearly dependent*. If, on the other hand, (11) implies $c^1 = 0$, $c^2 = 0$, $\ldots$, $c^k = 0$, then the set of vectors is *linearly independent*.

A set of vectors $\mathbf{e}_1, \mathbf{e}_2, \ldots, \mathbf{e}_n$ is called a *basis* for a vector space if (i) these vectors are in the vector space and form a linearly independent set, and (ii) every vector in the vector space is a linear combination of these vectors.

If a vector space has a basis consisting of exactly n vectors, where n is a positive integer, then the vector space is said to be *n-dimensional*, or to be *finite-dimensional* with dimension n.

Infinite-dimensional vector spaces will not be discussed in this book. When we say a vector space is finite-dimensional, we imply that it has at least one basis with a finite number of vectors. It is natural to ask: can a vector space have more than one basis, and if so, do all bases have the same number of vectors? The answer to both questions is *yes*. In any n-dimensional vector space, there will be an infinite number of ways we can choose a basis $\underset{1}{\mathbf{e}}, \underset{2}{\mathbf{e}}, \ldots, \underset{n}{\mathbf{e}}$, but no matter how we make the choice, we will always wind up with n vectors. In other words, it is impossible for a vector space to be n-dimensional and also m-dimensional if $n \neq m$. We omit the proof.

As a matter of convention in this book, we shall always consider a basis as an ordered set. That is, we will take the vectors $\underset{1}{\mathbf{e}}, \underset{2}{\mathbf{e}}, \ldots, \underset{n}{\mathbf{e}}$ in a definite order, and consider the same vectors in a different order as constituting a distinct basis. With this convention, it makes sense to speak of the kth base vector of the basis: it is $\underset{k}{\mathbf{e}}$.

By (ii), every vector $\mathbf{v}$ in the vector space can be written as a linear combination of the base vectors,

(12) $$\mathbf{v} = v^1 \underset{1}{\mathbf{e}} + v^2 \underset{2}{\mathbf{e}} + \ldots + v^n \underset{n}{\mathbf{e}}$$

Moreover, there is only one way we can do this, for if we also have

$$\mathbf{v} = c^1 \underset{1}{\mathbf{e}} + c^2 \underset{2}{\mathbf{e}} + \ldots + c^n \underset{n}{\mathbf{e}}$$

then by subtracting, we obtain

$$(v^1 - c^1) \underset{1}{\mathbf{e}} + (v^2 - c^2) \underset{2}{\mathbf{e}} + \ldots + (v^n - c^n) \underset{n}{\mathbf{e}} = \mathbf{0}$$

By the definition of linear independence, it follows that $v^k - c^k = 0$, $k = 1, 2, \ldots, n$, and so the sequences $(v^1, v^2, \ldots, v^n)$ and $(c^1, c^2, \ldots, c^n)$ are identical.

The number v^k is called the kth *component* of $\mathbf{v}$ relative to the basis, and the sequence $(v^1, v^2, \ldots, v^n)$ is said to *represent* $\mathbf{v}$ relative to the basis. The word *coordinate* is often used instead of *component*, and the sequence is then called the *coordinate sequence* or *coordinate n-tuple* of $\mathbf{v}$ relative to the given basis. We say that the basis determines a *coordinate system* in the vector space. (Note, however, that a coordinate system is simply a rule that assigns to each vector some sequence of numbers, and not all coordinate systems are obtained in the above manner.)

It is easy to see that if $\mathbf{v}$ is represented by $(v^1, v^2, \ldots, v^n)$ and $\mathbf{u}$ by $(u^1, u^2, \ldots, u^n)$ relative to the same basis, then $\mathbf{u} + \mathbf{v}$ is represented by $(u^1 + v^1, u^2 + v^2, \ldots, u^n + v^n)$, and for any number c, $c\mathbf{v}$ is represented by $(cv^1, cv^2, \ldots, cv^n)$. It follows that, if we work with coordinate sequences, we can treat an n-dimensional vector space as though it were R^n.

Thus the concept of an n-dimensional vector space, as we have defined it, does not constitute any generalization. Such a space can be identified with R^n. There is, generally, no one natural way that such a space can be identified with R^n. An n-dimensional vector space can be represented by R^n in as many different ways as there are different bases in the space.

EXAMPLE 1: In the plane, let $\underset{1}{\mathbf{e}}$ and $\underset{2}{\mathbf{e}}$ be any two vectors, neither of which is a scalar multiple of the other. The set $\underset{1}{\mathbf{e}}, \underset{2}{\mathbf{e}}$ is linearly independent, and every vector in the plane can be written as a linear combination of these two vectors; that is, $\underset{1}{\mathbf{e}}, \underset{2}{\mathbf{e}}$ constitute a basis. In Figure 96, we have $\mathbf{v} = 3\underset{1}{\mathbf{e}} + 2\underset{2}{\mathbf{e}}$, so the coordinate sequence representing $\mathbf{v}$ relative to this basis is (3,2).

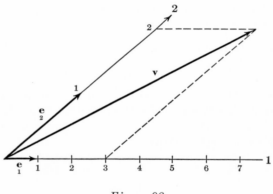

Figure 96

EXAMPLE 2: In space, let $\underset{1}{\mathbf{e}}, \underset{2}{\mathbf{e}}, \underset{3}{\mathbf{e}}$ be three nonzero vectors, not all in the same plane. Then these vectors constitute a basis for the vector space of all vectors in space. Compare Section 1.5, where we required the three vectors to be mutually perpendicular and have unit length. Note that the axioms for a vector space make no mention of metric concepts such as length or angle; when using only these axioms, it makes no sense to speak of "perpendicular vectors" or "unit vectors."

EXAMPLE 3: For every positive integer n, R^n is an n-dimensional vector space. It is routine to verify that the axioms are satisfied. To see that R^n is n-dimensional according to the definition given in this section, one need only verify that the vectors $\underset{1}{\mathbf{e}} = (1,0,\ldots,0)$, $\underset{2}{\mathbf{e}} = (0,1,\ldots,0)$, $\ldots$, $\underset{n}{\mathbf{e}} = (0,0,\ldots,1)$ constitute a basis for R^n. This is called the *natural basis* for R^n.

EXAMPLE 4: Besides the natural basis, every R^n has an infinite number of other bases. For example, the vectors

$$\underset{1}{\mathbf{e}} = (1,-1,0,0) \qquad \underset{3}{\mathbf{e}} = (0,0,2,0)$$

$$\underset{2}{\mathbf{e}} = (1,1,0,0) \qquad \underset{4}{\mathbf{e}} = (0,0,0,1)$$

constitute a basis for R^4.

EXAMPLE 5: Prove in detail that the vectors given in Example 4 constitute a basis for R^4.

Solution: $c^1\underset{1}{\mathbf{e}} + c^2\underset{2}{\mathbf{e}} + c^3\underset{3}{\mathbf{e}} + c^4\underset{4}{\mathbf{e}} = 0$ implies

$$(c^1 + c^2, -c^1 + c^2, 2c^3, c^4) = (0,0,0,0)$$

hence $c^1 + c^2 = 0$, $-c^1 + c^2 = 0$, $2c^3 = 0$, $c^4 = 0$, implying $c^1 = 0$, $c^2 = 0$, $c^3 = 0$, $c^4 = 0$, and hence the four vectors are linearly independent. Any vector (x^1,x^2,x^3,x^4) can be written in the form $v^1\underset{1}{\mathbf{e}} + v^2\underset{2}{\mathbf{e}} + v^3\underset{3}{\mathbf{e}} + v^4\underset{4}{\mathbf{e}}$ by taking

$$v^1 = (x^1 - x^2)/2, \quad v^2 = (x^1 + x^2)/2$$

$$v^3 = x^3/2, \quad v^4 = x^4$$

EXERCISES

1.   (a) If $v^1(1,1) + v^2(1,-1) = (4,6)$, what are the values of v^1 and v^2?

      (b) What coordinate sequence represents $(4,6)$ relative to the basis $\underset{1}{\mathbf{e}} = (1,1)$, $\underset{2}{\mathbf{e}} = (1,-1)$ in R^2?

2. (a) What is the natural basis for R^3?
    (b) What coordinate sequence represents (x^1, x^2, x^3) relative to the natural basis?
    (c) What coordinate sequence represents (x^1, x^2, x^3) relative to the basis $\underset{1}{e} = (0,1,0)$, $\underset{2}{e} = (2,0,1)$, $\underset{3}{e} = (0,0,1)$?

3. What coordinate sequence represents $(3,7,9)$ relative to the basis $\underset{1}{e} = (0,0,1)$, $\underset{2}{e} = (0,1,0)$, $\underset{3}{e} = (3,0,0)$ in R^3?

4. Classify the following sets of vectors in R^4 as linearly dependent or linearly independent:
    (a) $(1,0,1,0)$, $(0,1,0,1)$
    (b) $(1,1,0,0)$, $(0,0,1,1)$, $(2,2,-1,-1)$
    (c) $(1,2,3,4)$, $(2,1,3,4)$, $(0,0,0,0)$, $(3,0,0,0)$
    (d) $(1,0,0,1)$, $(0,1,0,0)$, $(2,0,0,0)$, $(1,0,3,0)$
    (e) $(2,4,8,4)$, $(1,2,4,2)$

5.4 : Matrices

A *matrix* is an array of numbers.   An $n \times m$ (n by m) matrix is a matrix with n rows and m columns.   By convention, if T denotes a matrix, then $T_j{}^i$ denotes the entry in the ith row and jth column of the matrix.   This convention can be easily remembered by either of the mnemonic devices

$$T_{\text{Catholic}}^{\text{Roman}} \quad \text{or} \quad T_{\text{Car}}^{\text{Railway}}$$

the initial letters suggesting row and column.
    An $n \times 1$ matrix has but a single column and is called a *column vector*.   If v is a column vector, the entry in the ith row is denoted v^i, there being little point in retaining the subscript $j = 1$.   Similarly, a matrix having only one row is called a *row vector* and the superscript $i = 1$ is deleted, so the jth entry of a row vector w is denoted w_j.
    For example, if we have

$$w = (1 \ 3 \ 2 \ -4) \qquad T = \begin{pmatrix} 3 & 4 & 0 \\ 2 & -1 & 8 \\ 0 & 6 & 3 \\ 3 & 3 & 4 \end{pmatrix} \qquad v = \begin{pmatrix} 9 \\ 8 \\ 2 \end{pmatrix}$$

w is a 1×4 matrix, T is a 4×3 matrix, and v is a 3×1 matrix.
We have $w_2 = 3$, $T_3{}^2 = 8$, $T_3{}^4 = 4$, $v^1 = 9$, etc.

The notation $(T_j{}^i)$ will sometimes be used instead of T to
denote a matrix.

The sum of two $n \times m$ matrices, $R = S + T$, is defined by
adding corresponding entries,

$$R_j{}^i = S_j{}^i + T_j{}^i$$

and if T is a matrix, we define cT to be the matrix whose entry in the
ith row and jth column is $cT_j{}^i$.

With these operations, the collection of all $n \times m$ matrices, for
fixed n and m, is a vector space. For instance, the collection of all
4×3 matrices is a 12-dimensional vector space. Each "vector" in
the vector space is a matrix.

If S is an $n \times k$ matrix, and T is a $k \times m$ matrix, their product
$R = ST$ is the $n \times m$ matrix defined by

$$R_j{}^i = \sum S_p{}^i T_j{}^p$$

where we are using the summation convention mentioned in Section
5.2. In other words, the entry in the ith row and jth column is the
formal scalar product of the ith row of S with the jth column of T.
For example,

$$\begin{pmatrix} 3 & 2 & 0 \\ 1 & 9 & 4 \\ -3 & 5 & 5 \\ 1 & 0 & -1 \end{pmatrix} \begin{pmatrix} -3 & 1 & 1 \\ 0 & 3 & 2 \\ 0 & -2 & 0 \end{pmatrix} = \begin{pmatrix} -9 & 9 & 7 \\ -3 & 20 & 19 \\ 9 & 2 & 7 \\ -3 & 3 & 1 \end{pmatrix}$$

The product ST is defined only if S has the same number of columns
as T has rows. The motivation for this apparently arbitrary way of
multiplying matrices will be given later.

Row and column vectors are treated just like other matrices.
If w, T, and v are as defined above, we have

$$wT = (-3 \ 1 \ 14)$$

$$Tv = \begin{pmatrix} 59 \\ 26 \\ 54 \\ 59 \end{pmatrix} \qquad vw = \begin{pmatrix} 9 & 27 & 18 & -36 \\ 8 & 24 & 16 & -32 \\ 2 & 6 & 4 & -8 \end{pmatrix}$$

but the products Tw, wv, vT are not defined.

The reader will observe that the system of equations (4), Section 5.2, can be written $y = Tx$, if we take x and y to be column vectors and let $T = (T_j{}^i)$.

EXERCISES

In these exercises, let

$$w = (1\ 2\ 3\ 4) \qquad v = \begin{pmatrix} 4 \\ 3 \\ 2 \\ 1 \end{pmatrix}$$

$$T = \begin{pmatrix} 0 & 1 & -1 & 1 \\ 1 & 2 & -1 & 2 \\ 5 & 0 & 0 & 3 \end{pmatrix} \qquad S = \begin{pmatrix} 2 & 2 & 2 & 2 \\ 1 & -1 & 1 & -1 \\ 0 & 1 & 2 & 3 \\ 3 & 2 & 1 & 0 \end{pmatrix}$$

1. Compute TS.
2. Is ST defined?
3. Compute wv.
4. Compute vw.
5. What is $T_4{}^3$? What is v^2? What is w_1?
6. Compute Tv.
7. Is vT defined? If so, compute it.
8. Compute wS.
9. Compute $(wS)v$ and $w(Sv)$. Are they equal?
10. Let
$$R = \begin{pmatrix} 2 & 1 \\ 0 & 6 \end{pmatrix} \quad \text{and} \quad P = \begin{pmatrix} 4 & 4 \\ 7 & 7 \end{pmatrix}$$
Compute RP and PR. Are they equal?
11. Is $S + T$ defined? If so, compute it.
12. With R and P defined as in Exercise 10, compute $2R - P$.
13. Let
$$I = \begin{pmatrix} 1 & 0 \\ 0 & 1 \end{pmatrix}$$
With R defined as in Exercise 10, compute IR and RI. Are they equal?

14. For any positive integer n, the "Kronecker delta" is defined by

$$\delta_j{}^i = \begin{cases} 1 \text{ if } i = j \\ 0 \text{ if } i \neq j \end{cases}$$

$i = 1, 2, \ldots, n$; $j = 1, 2, \ldots, n$. The matrix $I = (\delta_j{}^i)$ is called the *identity matrix*. Convince yourself that, if R is any $n \times n$ matrix, $IR = RI = R$. (Compare Exercise 13.)

5.5 : Linear Transformations

Let V and U be vector spaces. A *linear transformation* of V into U is a rule T that associates with each vector $\mathbf{v}$ in V exactly one vector $T(\mathbf{v})$ in U, and that has the properties

$$(1) \qquad\qquad T(\mathbf{v}_1 + \mathbf{v}_2) = T(\mathbf{v}_1) + T(\mathbf{v}_2)$$

$$(2) \qquad\qquad T(c\mathbf{v}) = cT(\mathbf{v})$$

whenever $\mathbf{v}, \mathbf{v}_1, \mathbf{v}_2$ are vectors and c is a number.

It follows from these properties that for any vectors $\mathbf{v}_1, \mathbf{v}_2, \ldots, \mathbf{v}_k$ we have

$$T(c^1\mathbf{v}_1 + c^2\mathbf{v}_2 + \ldots + c^k\mathbf{v}_k) = c^1 T(\mathbf{v}_1) + c^2 T(\mathbf{v}_2) + \ldots + c^k T(\mathbf{v}_k)$$

so that we can compute the transform of any linear combination of k vectors once we know the transform of each of the vectors.

Now suppose that V has a basis $\mathbf{e}_1, \mathbf{e}_2, \ldots, \mathbf{e}_m$ and that U has a basis $\mathbf{f}_1, \mathbf{f}_2, \ldots, \mathbf{f}_n$. For each j, $T(\mathbf{e}_j)$ is a vector in U and is represented by a coordinate sequence relative to the chosen basis in U. Let us form a matrix $(T_j{}^i)$ whose jth *column* (for each j) is the coordinate sequence representing $T(\mathbf{e}_j)$. This matrix is said to *represent* T relative to the two bases involved. Using the summation convention of Section 5.2, we have $T(\mathbf{e}_j) = \sum_i T_j{}^i \mathbf{f}_i$.

Now suppose that $\mathbf{v} = \sum_j v^i \mathbf{e}_i$ is an arbitrary vector in V, and that $T(\mathbf{v}) = \mathbf{u}$. Then we have

$$\mathbf{u} = T(\mathbf{v}) = T\left(\sum_j v^i \mathbf{e}_i\right) = \sum_j v^i T(\mathbf{e}_i) = \sum \sum v^i T_j{}^i \mathbf{f}_i$$

Comparing this with $\mathbf{u} = \sum_i u^i \mathbf{f}$ (recall that the coordinate sequence is unique) we have

(3) $$u^i = \sum T_j{}^i v^j$$

If the coordinate sequences representing $\mathbf{u}$ and $\mathbf{v}$ are written as column vectors, (3) can be written in the matrix form $u = Tv$, where now we are letting T denote the matrix $(T_j{}^i)$.

We shall be interested mainly in the special case where V and U are the same space. We then speak of a "linear transformation of V." If V is n-dimensional, any linear transformation of V is represented, relative to a basis for V, by an $n \times n$ matrix. In the special case R^n this was discussed in Section 5.2, but the possibility of using any basis other than the natural basis in R^n was not mentioned.

As an example, which the reader should study carefully, let us consider the linear transformation $\mathbf{y} = T(\mathbf{x})$ of R^2 defined by the equations

$$y^1 = 2x^1 + 4x^2$$
$$y^2 = 6x^1 - 2x^2$$

Let us first find the matrix representing T relative to the natural basis $\mathbf{e}_1 = (1,0)$, $\mathbf{e}_2 = (0,1)$. Directly from the equations we see that $T(\mathbf{e}_1) = (2,6) = 2\mathbf{e}_1 + 6\mathbf{e}_2$, so the first column of the matrix must be $\binom{2}{6}$. Similarly, we have $T(\mathbf{e}_2) = 4\mathbf{e}_1 - 2\mathbf{e}_2$ so the second column is $\binom{4}{-2}$.

Thus the matrix is

$$\begin{pmatrix} 2 & 4 \\ 6 & -2 \end{pmatrix}$$

which is simply the matrix of coefficients of the system of equations.

But now suppose we choose another basis, say $\mathbf{e}_1 = (1,1)$ and $\mathbf{e}_2 = (1,-1)$. We have $T(\mathbf{e}_1) = (6,4) = 5\mathbf{e}_1 + \mathbf{e}_2$ and

$$T(\mathbf{e}_2) = (-2,8) = 3\mathbf{e}_1 - 5\mathbf{e}_2$$

Relative to this basis, the matrix representing T is

$$\begin{pmatrix} 5 & 3 \\ 1 & -5 \end{pmatrix}$$

Again the reader is cautioned to study this example, lest he

make the very common error of forgetting that $T(\underset{j}{\mathbf{e}})$ must be written
in terms of the $\underset{j}{\mathbf{e}}$'s.   In every class there is at least one student who
will give the answer

$$\begin{pmatrix} 6 & -2 \\ 4 & 8 \end{pmatrix}$$

which is incorrect.

EXERCISE

A linear transformation of R^3 is defined by the equations

$$y^1 = 4x^1 - 6x^2$$
$$y^2 = 2x^1 + 8x^2$$
$$y^3 = 3x^3$$

Find the matrix representing this linear transformation relative to

(a) the basis $\underset{1}{\mathbf{e}} = (1,0,0)$, $\underset{2}{\mathbf{e}} = (0,0,1)$, and $\underset{3}{\mathbf{e}} = (0,1,0)$;

(b) the basis $\underset{1}{\mathbf{e}} = (2,0,0)$, $\underset{2}{\mathbf{e}} = (0,3,0)$, and $\underset{3}{\mathbf{e}} = (0,0,4)$;

(c) the basis $\underset{1}{\mathbf{e}} = (-1,1,0)$, $\underset{2}{\mathbf{e}} = (1,1,0)$, and $\underset{3}{\mathbf{e}} = (0,0,2)$.

5.6 : Linear Functionals

From this point on, we drop the use of boldface letters to denote
vectors.   The reason for this will become evident as we proceed.

A *linear functional* on a vector space is a rule that assigns to
each vector v a real number $f(v)$, such that

(1) $$f(\underset{1}{v} + \underset{2}{v}) = f(\underset{1}{v}) + f(\underset{2}{v})$$

(2) $$f(cv) = cf(v)$$

for all vectors v, $\underset{1}{v}$, $\underset{2}{v}$ and every real number c.

In other words, a linear functional is a linear transformation of
the vector space into the space R^1.

There is no basic significance to the use of the word *functional* rather than *function*. Some authors use the term "linear function" in a different sense, and what we call "linear functionals" are called "linear homogeneous functions."

If $e_1, e_2, \ldots, e_n$ is a basis for an n-dimensional vector space, the number $f(e_i)$ is called the ith component of the linear functional f, relative to this basis. Denoting this number by f_i, for each $i = 1,2, \ldots, n$, the row vector $(f_1, f_2, \ldots, f_n)$ is said to *represent* f relative to the given basis. We recall that, if v is a vector in the space, we have $v = \sum_i v^i e_i$, and we can represent v by a *column* vector having v^i as ith entry. Making use of (1) and (2) we have

$$f(v) = f\left(\sum_i v^i e_i\right) = \sum_i v^i f(e_i) = \sum f_i v^i$$

From the matrix viewpoint, this says that $f(v)$ is the only entry in the 1×1 matrix obtained by multiplying the row vector representing f with the column vector representing v relative to the same basis.

If f and g are linear functionals on the same vector space, their sum $f + g$ is defined in the obvious way,

$$(f + g)(v) = f(v) + g(v)$$

for every vector v, and if c is a real number, cf is defined by $(cf)(v) = cf(v)$. Thus defined, $f + g$ and cf are also linear functionals, and it is routine to verify that the collection of all linear functionals satisfies all the axioms for a vector space. The collection of all linear functionals on a given space is called the *dual space* of the given space. Each of the "vectors" in the dual space is a linear functional on the given space.

If f is represented by the row vector $(f_1, f_2, \ldots, f_n)$ and g by $(g_1, g_2, \ldots, g_n)$, then it is easy to see that $f + g$ is represented by $(f_1 + g_1, f_2 + g_2, \ldots, f_n + g_n)$ and cf is represented by $(cf_1, cf_2, \ldots, cf_n)$. From this it follows that, once we have prescribed a basis in an n-dimensional vector space, enabling us to identify the space with the vector space of all column vectors, we can then identify the dual space with the vector space of all row vectors. The dual space of an n-dimensional vector space is also n-dimensional.

The more sophisticated reader is advised to supply detailed proofs of the facts we have stated.

Now suppose we are given an n-dimensional vector space, and

that a basis $e, e, \ldots, e$ has been prescribed.   The ith *coordinate func-*
$\quad\;\; 1\;\; 2 \qquad\quad n$
tion is then defined to be the function that assigns to each vector v
the ith coordinate v^i of the vector, relative to the basis.   The ith
coordinate function is easily seen to be the linear functional represented by the row vector with the number one in the ith place, and
zero in every other place.   Denoting the ith coordinate function by $\overset{i}{e}$,
we have $\overset{i}{e}(v) = v^i$ for every vector v, and in particular

$$\overset{i}{e}(e) = \begin{cases} 1 & \text{if } i = j \\ 0 & \text{if } i \neq j \end{cases}$$
$$\quad\; j$$

The linear functionals $\overset{1}{e}, \overset{2}{e}, \ldots, \overset{n}{e}$ constitute a basis for the dual
space.   This basis is said to be *dual* to the basis $e, e, \ldots, e.$
$\qquad\qquad\qquad\qquad\qquad\qquad\qquad\qquad\qquad\qquad\qquad\;\; 1\;\; 2 \qquad n$
It is, of course, important to distinguish between e, which is a
$\qquad\qquad\qquad\qquad\qquad\qquad\qquad\qquad\qquad\qquad\qquad\qquad\; i$
vector in the space, and $\overset{i}{e}$, which is a linear functional on the space.
The weird notation facilitates use of the summation convention; for
example, we have $f = \sum f_i \overset{i}{e}$, for every linear functional f, since

$$\left(\sum f_i \overset{i}{e}\right)(v) = \sum f_i \overset{i}{e}(v) = \sum f_i v^i = f(v)$$

for every vector v.

To conserve space, we shall continue to write an arbitrary vector
in R^n as $x = (x^1, x^2, \ldots, x^n)$, although it would be more consistent
notationally to write

$$x = \begin{pmatrix} x^1 \\ x^2 \\ \cdot \\ \cdot \\ \cdot \\ x^n \end{pmatrix}$$

The linear functionals on R^n are functions of the form

$$f(x^1, x^2, \ldots, x^n) = f_1 x^1 + f_2 x^2 + \ldots + f_n x^n$$

The reader may now be able to see why we have dropped the
use of boldface letters to denote vectors.   Carried to extremes, we
would have to use boldface letters to denote linear functionals, since
they are vectors in the dual space.   Our original reason for using
boldface letters was to continually remind the reader of the distinc-

tion between vectors and numbers.   However, from the vector space viewpoint, most of the objects we are now working with are "vectors" in some vector space.   Even numbers are vectors when we consider R^1 as a vector space!

Now let us drop all pretense to sophistication, and give a down-to-earth geometrical interpretation of linear functionals, along lines similar to the geometrical introduction to vectors given in Section 1.1.

Let us consider two parallel planes P and Q in space.   If the planes are distinct (i.e., they do not coincide) we say they determine a *plane pair*.   A plane pair is said to be *directed* if the planes are given in a definite order.   The same plane pair determines two directed plane pairs, one denoted PQ and the other QP (or $-PQ$).   Two directed plane pairs PQ and $P'Q'$ are said to be *equal* if it is possible to superimpose P with P' and Q with Q' by moving them through space, always keeping the planes parallel to their original positions and not changing the separations between the planes of each plane pair.

We say that PQ and $P'Q'$ are *parallel* if P and P' are parallel. This implies, of course, that all of the planes P, P', Q, and Q' are mutually parallel.

If d is the distance between P and Q, we define the *magnitude* of the plane pair to be $1/d$.   Thus, the farther apart the planes are, the smaller is the magnitude.

If two directed plane pairs are parallel and have the same magnitude, then either they are equal or one is the "negative" of the other, i.e., they have oppositely directed sense.

If PQ and RS are directed plane pairs that are parallel and have the same directed sense, and the magnitude of PQ is s times that of RS, we can write $PQ = s(RS)$.   In this way we define multiplication of a plane pair by a nonzero scalar.

We shall now explain how to add directed plane pairs.   The reader is advised to omit this paragraph on first reading.   The motivation for the rule of addition will be apparent after reading the rest of the section.   If PQ and RS are directed plane pairs, their sum is a directed plane pair UV determined in the following manner.   If PQ and RS are parallel, let UV be any plane pair whose magnitude is the sum of the magnitudes of PQ and RS, or the difference of these magnitudes, depending on whether PQ and RS have the same or opposite sense; UV is required to be parallel to PQ (and hence to RS

also). If this rule assigns zero magnitude to UV, then UV is not defined. If PQ and RS are not parallel, then they must intersect. Call the line of intersection of P and R the "zero line," the line of intersection of Q and R a "one line," and the line of intersection of P and S a "one line." Let V be the plane containing both one lines, and U a plane parallel to V passing through the zero line. Then UV is the desired sum.

Given any directed plane pair PQ, and a vector v, we define the *measure* of v by PQ, denoted $f(v)$, as follows. If v is parallel to PQ, or if v is the zero vector, we define $f(v)$ to be zero. Otherwise, there will be a unique number m such that mv may be represented by a directed line segment extending from a point in P to a point in Q, and we take $f(v) = 1/m$. This is illustrated in Figure 97, where $m = \frac{1}{2}$ and $f(v) = 2$.

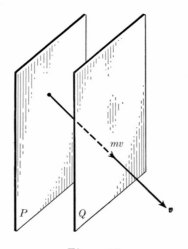

Figure 97

It is easy to verify that $f(v + w) = f(v) + f(w)$, and $f(cv) = cf(v)$, for vectors v and w and any number c. Thus to every directed plane pair PQ there is an associated linear functional f.

If we introduce a coordinate system, in the manner of Section 1.5, and revert to our old i, j, and k notation, the components of the linear functional f are the numbers $f(i)$, $f(j)$, and $f(k)$. The absolute values of these numbers are the reciprocals of the lengths of the line segments cut off on the x, y, and z axes, respectively, by the plane pair. In the example shown in Figure 98, these numbers are $-\frac{1}{6}$, $\frac{1}{3}$, and $\frac{1}{6}$ respectively. If $v = xi + yj + zk$, we have (in this case)

$$f(v) = -\frac{x}{6} + \frac{y}{3} + \frac{z}{6}$$

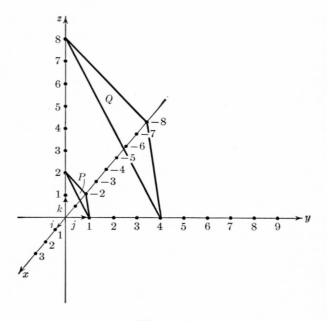

Figure 98

On the other hand, if we are given a linear functional f, then if we let $f(i) = a$, $f(j) = b$, and $f(k) = c$, the ordered plane pair PQ defined by the equations

(3)
$$P: \quad ax + by + cz = 0$$
$$Q: \quad ax + by + cz = 1$$

will be associated with the linear functional in the manner described above. Of course, there will be many other ordered plane pairs equal to PQ associated with the same linear functional.

There is one exception to this. The trivial linear functional that assigns zero to every vector v is called the *zero functional*. If f is the zero functional, we will have $a = 0$, $b = 0$, and $c = 0$, and (3) does not define a plane pair. It is easy to see that the zero functional is not associated with any ordered plane pair.

If P passes through the origin, the ordered plane pair PQ is said to *extend from the origin*. For example, if a, b, and c are not all zero, (3) defines a plane pair extending from the origin. Every ordered plane pair is equal to an ordered plane pair extending from the origin.

If we take every vector as extending from the origin, we can identify each point (x,y,z) with its position vector $xi + yj + zk$, and thereby pass to the R^3 point of view. Similarly, let us take every ordered plane pair as extending from the origin. Then if $v = xi + yj + zk$, we can write $f(x,y,z)$ instead of $f(v)$. With notation as above, we have $f(x,y,z) = ax + by + cz$. We see from (3) that the planes P and Q are the isotimic surfaces on which f takes the values zero and one respectively.

Now we can understand the reason for the addition rule given above. If f is the linear functional associated with PQ, and g is the linear functional associated with RS, then since f is zero on P and g is zero on R, their sum $f + g$ is zero at every point on the line of intersection of P and R, called the zero line above. Since f is zero on P, and g takes the value one on S, $f + g$ is equal to unity on the intersection of P and S. Similarly, $f + g$ equals one on the intersection of Q and R. These two lines, called one lines above, determine the isotimic surface on which $f + g$ equals one, since the isotimic surface of a linear functional (other than the zero functional) must be a plane.

Ordered plane pairs fall short of forming a vector space because there is no ordered plane pair corresponding to a zero vector.

A linear functional is sometimes called a *covariant vector*. Thus, instead of speaking of a linear functional *on* a vector space, we speak of a covariant vector *in* the vector space. Ordinary vectors in the space are then called *contravariant vectors*.

Let us recapitulate these notions in the three-dimensional case. A contravariant vector may be represented by a directed line segment. A covariant vector is a linear functional, and (if not the zero vector) may be represented geometrically by an ordered pair of planes. In matrix notation, relative to a basis in the space, we represent a contravariant vector v by a column vector whose ith entry is denoted

v^i; a covariant vector f is represented by a row vector with ith entry denoted f_i. The value the function f assigns to v is $f(v) = \sum f_i v^i$; matrixwise this is the matrix product of a row vector with a column vector (in that order). Geometrically, $f(v)$ is the *reciprocal* of the scalar m needed to "fit" mv properly between the two planes.

We shall not pause here to give any detailed physical applications of these ideas. It may be worth mentioning, however, that similar concepts enter into the theory of x-ray crystallography. Let us digress briefly to give some idea of what this theory involves. This discussion is considerably oversimplified.

Just as the design in a wallpaper is a regular pattern in the plane, a crystal may be thought of as a regular pattern in space; in either case, a certain unit of structure is repeated over and over again. For simplicity, let us imagine the crystal to consist of a regular array of identical atoms. (The crystallographer will flinch at this!) Any three of these atoms will determine a plane, called a *lattice plane*. Because of the regularity of the crystal, any lattice plane will contain many atoms (infinitely many, if we imagine the crystal to extend throughout space). Moreover, given any lattice plane P, there will be many other lattice planes parallel to P. The collection of all lattice planes parallel to a given lattice plane will be called a *parallel family*. The distance between successive planes in the same parallel family is the same throughout, and is called the *spacing* of the family. There may be a great number of different parallel families of lattice planes, with different spacings (infinitely many, if the crystal is imagined to extend throughout space) but the density of atoms per unit area in some lattice planes will be too small for these lattice planes to be of practical importance in the diffraction of x-rays.

When a beam of x-rays impinges upon an atom, the atom will absorb and then partially re-emit some of the energy. The combined effect of this energy scattering by all the atoms in a lattice plane is to produce a reflected beam (Huyghens' principle). In other words, x-rays are reflected from the lattice planes in much the same way that light is reflected from a mirror. Indeed, the same law holds: the angle of reflection equals the angle of incidence. However, each lattice plane reflects only a very small fraction of the incident beam, and unless the beams reflected from successive planes of a parallel family are exactly in phase, destructive interference will occur and no reflection will be observed. If θ is the glancing angle of incidence of the beam on the parallel family, d is the spacing of the family, and λ is the wavelength of the beam of x-rays, reflection will occur only if $2d \sin \theta$ is an integral multiple of λ (Bragg's law).

In other words, for a given glancing angle, only certain wavelengths will be reflected from a parallel family, making it possible experimentally to determine the spacing of the family.

Now suppose the incident beam is not monochromatic but contains a wide range of frequencies. Then each parallel family will reflect its characteristic frequencies, and since no two parallel families have the same angle of incidence, there will be a large number of reflected beams. These show up as spots on the x-ray film. If these beams were in the optical range, we would see the spots in a variety of colors. Each spot corresponds to some parallel family of lattice planes in the crystal.

The crystallographer does not obtain direct information about the positions of the individual atoms in the crystal. His data tell him about the lattice planes instead. The points on the film do not represent individual atoms but lattice planes of atoms. Roughly speaking, he obtains a photograph of the dual space, rather than of the space itself. His data enable him to construct the *reciprocal lattice* of the crystal, which is a three-dimensional array of points, each point representing a lattice plane of the crystal.

EXERCISE

In any book on x-ray crystallography, look up the term "Miller indices." Explain how the Miller indices of a plane are related to the concept of a covariant vector.

5.7 : Grassmann Products

For simplicity, we restrict ourselves to a three-dimensional vector space with an arbitrary basis e_1, e_2, e_3. We introduce a symbol ε_{ijk}, where the subscripts may be 1, 2, or 3. It is defined to be equal to one if i, j, and k, in that order, constitute an even permutation of 1, 2, and 3, and equal to minus one if they constitute an odd permutation of 1, 2, and 3. We let ε_{ijk} equal zero if two or more of the subscripts are equal. Thus we have

$$\varepsilon_{123} = 1, \qquad \varepsilon_{231} = 1, \qquad \varepsilon_{312} = 1$$

$$\varepsilon_{213} = -1, \qquad \varepsilon_{132} = -1, \qquad \varepsilon_{321} = -1$$

$$\varepsilon_{111} = 0, \qquad \varepsilon_{222} = 0, \qquad \varepsilon_{333} = 0, \quad \varepsilon_{112} = 0, \text{ etc.}$$

We define the *Grassmann product* of three vectors $\underset{1}{v}, \underset{2}{v}, \underset{3}{v}$ to be the sum

$$(1) \qquad \underset{1}{v} \wedge \underset{2}{v} \wedge \underset{3}{v} = \sum \sum \sum \varepsilon_{ijk} \underset{1}{v^i} \underset{2}{v^j} \underset{3}{v^k}$$

The sum is taken over all possible values of i, j, and k, but since the symbol ε_{ijk} equals zero whenever any subscripts are repeated, we can ignore all terms except those for which i, j, and k are a permutation of 1, 2, and 3. Thus the sum has only six terms that can possibly be nonzero.

The reader will immediately recognize (1) as the *determinant* of the matrix

$$\begin{pmatrix} \underset{1}{v^1} & \underset{2}{v^1} & \underset{3}{v^1} \\ \underset{1}{v^2} & \underset{2}{v^2} & \underset{3}{v^2} \\ \underset{1}{v^3} & \underset{2}{v^3} & \underset{3}{v^3} \end{pmatrix}$$

so we can write (1) in the abbreviated form

$$(2) \qquad \underset{1}{v} \wedge \underset{2}{v} \wedge \underset{3}{v} = \det \left(\underset{j}{v^i} \right)$$

provided we keep in mind that the parentheses around $\underset{j}{v^i}$ mean that we are thinking of the entire matrix, not just one entry in the matrix.

The Grassmann product is computed formally just the same way the triple scalar product (Section 1.11) is computed. Here, however, we are not considering the base vectors to be of unit length, or to be mutually perpendicular, so we avoid using the term "triple scalar product." The Grassmann product of three vectors depends on the basis we select, since the components $\underset{j}{v^i}$ depend on the basis. Therefore it would be more proper to speak of the Grassmann product $\underset{1}{v} \wedge \underset{2}{v} \wedge \underset{3}{v}$ *relative* to the basis $\underset{1}{e}, \underset{2}{e}, \underset{3}{e}$.

It is easy to verify that the Grassmann product is *homogeneous* and *linear* in each of its factors (see Section 1.11 to review the meanings of these words) and equals zero if any factors are repeated. Moreover, $\underset{i}{v} \wedge \underset{j}{v} \wedge \underset{k}{v} = \underset{1}{v} \wedge \underset{2}{v} \wedge \underset{3}{v}$ if i,j,k is an even permutation of

1,2,3, and $v_i \wedge v_j \wedge v_k = -v_1 \wedge v_2 \wedge v_3$ if i,j,k is an odd permutation of 1,2,3.

If the set of vectors v_1, v_2, v_3 is another basis for the space, then $v_1 \wedge v_2 \wedge v_3$ is not equal to zero. To see this, imagine each of the vectors $e_1, e_2,$ and e_3 written as a linear combination of $v_1, v_2,$ and v_3 (possible if v_1, v_2, v_3 form a basis) and think of what will happen if we replace the factors in $e_1 \wedge e_2 \wedge e_3$ by these linear combinations. On expanding the product and simplifying, using the above properties of the Grassmann product, we find that $e_1 \wedge e_2 \wedge e_3$ equals some number times $v_1 \wedge v_2 \wedge v_3$. Since $e_1 \wedge e_2 \wedge e_3 = 1$ (why?) it follows that $v_1 \wedge v_2 \wedge v_3$ is nonzero.

We now demonstrate the converse, that if $v_1 \wedge v_2 \wedge v_3 \neq 0$, then these three vectors constitute a basis for the space. A routine calculation (Exercise 1) shows that, for any four vectors $v_1, v_2, v_3,$ and w, we have

$$(3) \qquad (w \wedge v_2 \wedge v_3)v_1 + (v_1 \wedge w \wedge v_3)v_2 + (v_1 \wedge v_2 \wedge w)v_3 = (v_1 \wedge v_2 \wedge v_3)w$$

From this we see that, if $v_1 \wedge v_2 \wedge v_3$ is nonzero, we can write every vector w as a linear combination $w = C_1 v_1 + C_2 v_2 + C_3 v_3$ where

$$C_1 = \frac{w \wedge v_2 \wedge v_3}{v_1 \wedge v_2 \wedge v_3}, \quad C_2 = \frac{v_1 \wedge w \wedge v_3}{v_1 \wedge v_2 \wedge v_3}, \quad \text{and} \quad C_3 = \frac{v_1 \wedge v_2 \wedge w}{v_1 \wedge v_2 \wedge v_3}$$

Moreover, it is easy to show (Exercise 2) that these vectors form a linearly independent set.

It follows then that $v_1 \wedge v_2 \wedge v_3 \neq 0$ if and only if the set v_1, v_2, v_3 is a basis for the space. Moreover, since the property of being a basis has nothing to do with the particular coordinate system, we see that if $v_1 \wedge v_2 \wedge v_3 \neq 0$ when computed relative to one basis, then it is also $\neq 0$ relative to *every* basis.

Expression (3) is closely related to Cramer's rule, a method for solving simultaneous equations by determinants. This method is of theoretical importance but is quite inferior as a practical procedure. To see the connection with (3), let T be a linear transformation such that $Te_1 \wedge Te_2 \wedge Te_3 \neq 0$. Then the set of vectors Te_1, Te_2, Te_3 is a basis, and any vector w can be written as a linear combination

$$w = v^1 T e_1 + v^2 T e_2 + v^3 T e_3$$

where v^1, v^2, and v^3 are unique. Since T is a linear transformation, we have

$$w = Tv$$

where $v = v^1 e_1 + v^2 e_2 + v^3 e_3$. As noted above, we have

$$v^1 = (w \wedge T e_2 \wedge T e_3)/(T e_1 \wedge T e_2 \wedge T e_3)$$

with similar expressions for v^2 and v^3. Keeping in mind that the ith column of the matrix representing T gives the components of $T e_i$, we see that the denominator of this expression is the determinant of the matrix representing T, and in computing v^1 the numerator is the determinant of the matrix obtained by replacing the first column by the column vector representing w. For example, given the system of equations

$$
\begin{aligned}
5 &= 2v^1 + 3v^2 - v^3 \\
6 &= v^1 + v^2 + v^3 \\
-4 &= v^1 - v^2 - v^3
\end{aligned}
$$

(4)

we solve for (say) v^1 as follows:

$$
v^1 = \frac{\det \begin{pmatrix} 5 & 3 & -1 \\ 6 & 1 & 1 \\ -4 & -1 & -1 \end{pmatrix}}{\det \begin{pmatrix} 2 & 3 & -1 \\ 1 & 1 & 1 \\ 1 & -1 & -1 \end{pmatrix}} = \frac{8}{8} = 1
$$

Similar calculations yield $v^2 = 2$ and $v^3 = 3$, so it is the vector $e_1 + 2e_2 + 3e_3$ that is transformed by T to the vector $5e_1 + 6e_2 - 4e_3$.

A linear transformation T is said to be *nonsingular* if, given any vector w, there is a unique vector v such that $Tv = w$. We then write $v = \overset{-1}{T}w$, and this defines a transformation $\overset{-1}{T}$, called the *inverse* of T.

If $v_1 = \overset{-1}{T}w_1$ and $v_2 = \overset{-1}{T}w_2$, then by definition $Tv_1 = w_1$ and $Tv_2 = w_2$, and since T is linear, $T(v_1 + v_2) = w_1 + w_2$, hence

$$\overset{-1}{T}(w_1 + w_2) = v_1 + v_2 = \overset{-1}{T}w_1 + \overset{-1}{T}w_2$$

Similarly, $\overset{-1}{T}(cw) = c\overset{-1}{T}w$ (Exercise 6). Therefore *the inverse of a linear transformation is also a linear transformation.*

From the above discussion, we see that T is nonsingular if $T\underset{1}{e} \wedge T\underset{2}{e} \wedge T\underset{3}{e} \neq 0$. Conversely, if T is nonsingular, then

$$T\underset{1}{e} \wedge T\underset{2}{e} \wedge T\underset{3}{e} \neq 0$$

(Exercise 7). *A linear transformation is nonsingular if and only if it is represented, relative to an arbitrary basis, by a matrix with nonzero determinant.* Since the definition of "nonsingular" does not involve any mention of the basis, it follows that, if T is represented relative to some basis by a matrix with nonzero determinant, then it will also be represented by a matrix with nonzero determinant relative to any other basis. Later on, we will find that the matrices representing a linear transformation T relative to various bases all have the same determinant, so that it makes sense to speak of the "determinant of T" without the qualifying phrase "relative to a particular basis."

EXERCISES

1. Go through the following derivation of (3), giving reasons for each step.

   It suffices to show that the mth component of the left side equals $(v \underset{1}{} \wedge v \underset{2}{} \wedge v \underset{3}{})w^m$. We have

$$(w \wedge \underset{2}{v} \wedge \underset{3}{v})v^m_1 + (\underset{1}{v} \wedge w \wedge \underset{3}{v})v^m_2 + (\underset{1}{v} \wedge \underset{2}{v} \wedge w)v^m_3$$

$$= (w \wedge \underset{2}{v} \wedge \underset{3}{v})v^m_1 - (w \wedge \underset{1}{v} \wedge \underset{3}{v})v^m_2 + (w \wedge \underset{1}{v} \wedge \underset{2}{v})v^m_3$$

$$= \sum\sum\sum \varepsilon_{ijk}w^i v^j v^k v^m_{2\,3\,1} - \sum\sum\sum \varepsilon_{ijk}w^i v^j v^k v^m_{1\,3\,2}$$

$$\qquad\qquad + \sum\sum\sum \varepsilon_{ijk}w^i v^j v^k v^m_{1\,2\,3}$$

$$= \sum\sum\sum \varepsilon_{ijk}w^i[v^j v^k v^m_{2\,3\,1} - v^j v^k v^m_{1\,3\,2} + v^j v^k v^m_{1\,2\,3}]$$

Consider the nonzero terms for which $i \neq m$. Then j or k equals m, and there will be two terms in which j and k play interchanged roles. That is, if $j = m$ and $k = p$ in one term, there will be another term where $k = m$ and $j = p$. These two terms are

$$\varepsilon_{imp} w^i \left[v^m_{\ 2} v^p_{\ 3} v^m_{\ 1} - v^m_{\ 1} v^p_{\ 3} v^m_{\ 2} + v^m_{\ 1} v^p_{\ 2} v^m_{\ 3} \right] = \pm w^i \left[v^m_{\ 1} v^p_{\ 2} v^m_{\ 3} \right]$$

and

$$\varepsilon_{ipm} w^i \left[v^p_{\ 2} v^m_{\ 3} v^m_{\ 1} - v^p_{\ 1} v^m_{\ 3} v^m_{\ 2} + v^p_{\ 1} v^m_{\ 2} v^m_{\ 3} \right] = \mp w^i \left[v^p_{\ 2} v^m_{\ 3} v^m_{\ 1} \right]$$

It follows that the terms for which $i \neq m$ cancel in pairs.
When $i = m$ we have

$$\sum_k \sum \varepsilon_{mjk} w^m \left[v^i_{\ 2} v^k_{\ 3} v^m_{\ 1} - v^i_{\ 1} v^k_{\ 3} v^m_{\ 2} + v^i_{\ 1} v^k_{\ 2} v^m_{\ 3} \right]$$

$$= w^m \sum_j \sum_k \varepsilon_{mjk} \left[v^m_{\ 1} v^i_{\ 2} v^k_{\ 3} - v^i_{\ 1} v^m_{\ 2} v^k_{\ 3} + v^i_{\ 1} v^k_{\ 2} v^m_{\ 3} \right]$$

$$= w^m \sum_j \sum_k \left[\varepsilon_{mjk} v^m_{\ 1} v^i_{\ 2} v^k_{\ 3} + \varepsilon_{jmk} v^i_{\ 1} v^m_{\ 2} v^k_{\ 3} + \varepsilon_{jkm} v^i_{\ 1} v^k_{\ 2} v^m_{\ 3} \right]$$

$$= w^m (v_{\ 1} \wedge v_{\ 2} \wedge v_{\ 3})$$

which is what we desired to prove.

2. Show that if $v_1 \wedge v_2 \wedge v_3 \neq 0$, then $C_1 v_1 + C_2 v_2 + C_3 v_3 = 0$ only if $C_1 = 0$, $C_2 = 0$, and $C_3 = 0$. [Hint: If $C_1 v_1 + C_2 v_2 + C_3 v_3 = 0$, then

$$0 = (C_1 v_1 + C_2 v_2 + C_3 v_3) \wedge v_2 \wedge v_3 = C_1 (v_1 \wedge v_2 \wedge v_3)$$

hence $C_1 = 0$.]

3. Using Cramer's rule, solve (4) for v^2 and v^3.

4. Show that, if every vector v is of the form $C_1 v_1 + C_2 v_2 + C_3 v_3$, then $v_1 \wedge v_2 \wedge v_3 \neq 0$.

5. Show that if the set v_1, v_2, v_3 is linearly independent, then it is a basis. [Hint: Reason purely algebraically without using Grassmann products. Consider the set v_3, e_1, e_2, e_3. Since the first of these vectors is a linear combination of the last three, we can delete one of the last three and still have a set whose linear combinations exhaust the entire space. If, say, e_3 is deleted, consider the set v_2, v_3, e_1, e_2. The first of these vectors is a linear combination of the last three, so either e_1 or e_2 can be deleted, etc.]

6.   Let T be a linear transformation, nonsingular, with $\overset{-1}{T}$ defined as described in the text.   Prove in detail that for every number c, $\overset{-1}{T}(cw) = c\overset{-1}{T}(w)$.

7.   Show that, if T is nonsingular, then $T\underset{1}{e} \wedge T\underset{2}{e} \wedge T\underset{3}{e} \neq 0$.   [Hint: If T is nonsingular, every vector w can be written as a linear combination of $T\underset{1}{e}, T\underset{2}{e}$, and $T\underset{3}{e}$.   Use Exercise 4.]

5.8 : Scalar Products and Vector Products

     In Section 1.9, the scalar product of two vectors in space was defined to be $\mathbf{u} \cdot \mathbf{v} = |\mathbf{u}| \, |\mathbf{v}| \cos \theta$.   This has been shown to be equivalent to $u \cdot v = u^1 v^1 + u^2 v^2 + u^3 v^3$, provided the components of u and v are taken relative to a basis consisting of three mutually orthogonal unit vectors i, j, and k.   However, what we call a "unit vector" depends arbitrarily on the choice of scale.   In other words, there is no *unique* way of defining a scalar product.   There are infinitely many ways of defining one.   However, no matter what the choice of scale may be, the following fundamental properties are satisfied:

(1) $v \cdot v \geq 0$ for every vector v, and $v \cdot v = 0$ if and only if v is the zero vector.

(2) $u \cdot v = v \cdot u$ for all vectors u and v.

(3) $(u + v) \cdot w = u \cdot w + v \cdot w$ for all vectors u, v, and w.

(4) $(cu) \cdot v = c(u \cdot v)$ for all vectors u and v and every scalar c.

     These properties provide the foundation for the following axiomatic definition of "scalar product."   Any rule which assigns to each pair of vectors u and v in a vector space a scalar $u \cdot v$ is called a *scalar product* (or an *inner product*) in the vector space if the above four axioms are satisfied.

     From (2) and (3) it follows that

(5) $$w \cdot (u + v) = w \cdot u + w \cdot v$$

and using (2) and (4) we see that

(6) $$u \cdot (cv) = c(u \cdot v)$$

Once a scalar product has been defined in a vector space, one can then use this scalar product to define such metric concepts as "length" and "angle." This is just the opposite of the geometrical approach used in Section 1.9.

In any vector space in which a scalar product is defined, the *length* or *norm* of a vector v is defined to be the nonnegative square root of $v \cdot v$. That is, we have *by definition*

$$(7) \qquad |v| = \sqrt{v \cdot v}$$

The first three of the following properties are readily verified:

(8) $\quad |v| \geqq 0$

(9) $\quad |v| = 0$ if and only if v is the zero vector

(10) $\quad |cv| = |c|\,|v|$, valid for every vector v and every scalar c. Notice that $|c|$ is the absolute value of a *number*, but $|v|$ is the length of a *vector*.

(11) $\quad |u \cdot v| \leqq |u|\,|v|$ (Schwarz inequality)

(12) $\quad |u + v| \leqq |u| + |v|$

If either u or v is the zero vector, we see that $u \cdot v = 0$ (by taking $c = 0$ in (4) or (6)), and in this case the Schwarz inequality is clearly valid. To prove it for nonzero vectors u and v, we apply (1) to the vector $(v \cdot v)u - (u \cdot v)v$. This gives

$$[(v \cdot v)u - (u \cdot v)v] \cdot [(v \cdot v)u - (u \cdot v)v] \geqq 0$$

which on being expanded and simplified, with the use of the properties of the scalar product, gives

$$[|u|^2\,|v|^2 - (u \cdot v)^2](v \cdot v) \geqq 0$$

and since $(v \cdot v)$ is positive, we have

$$|u|^2\,|v|^2 \geqq (u \cdot v)^2$$

The Schwarz inequality follows by taking positive square roots. This proof is admittedly somewhat tricky; another proof is outlined in the exercises.

Using the Schwarz inequality, we prove (12) as follows:

$$\begin{aligned}
|u + v|^2 &= (u + v) \cdot (u + v) = (u \cdot u) + (v \cdot v) + 2(u \cdot v) \\
&= |u|^2 + |v|^2 + 2(u \cdot v) \leqq |u|^2 + |v|^2 + 2|u|\,|v| \\
&= (|u| + |v|)^2
\end{aligned}$$

Taking nonnegative square roots gives the desired result.

The *distance* between two vectors u and v is defined to be $|u - v|$. The fundamental properties of distance are:

(13) $|u - v| \geqq 0$,   and $|u - v| = 0$ if and only if $u = v$

(14) $|u - v| = |v - u|$

(15) $|u - w| \leqq |u - v| + |v - w|$,   for all vectors u, v, and w

These properties are quite easy to prove; for instance, (15) is proved by applying (12) to the two vectors $u - v$ and $v - w$.

The geometrical significance of the Schwarz inequality is that, if u and v are nonzero vectors, then

$$-1 \leqq \frac{u \cdot v}{|u|\,|v|} \leqq 1$$

and therefore it is possible to find θ such that

$$\cos \theta = \frac{u \cdot v}{|u|\,|v|}$$

In this way we define the *angle* between two vectors u and v. We then have $u \cdot v = |u|\,|v| \cos \theta$, already familiar to us in the three-dimensional case. However, in the general case, we are seldom concerned with angles, except when $\theta = 0$ or $\pi/2$.

Vectors u and v are said to be *orthogonal* if $u \cdot v = 0$. A *basis* in a vector space is said to be *orthogonal* if it is composed of mutually orthogonal vectors, i.e., if every pair of base vectors is orthogonal. If each of these base vectors has unit length, the basis is said to be *orthonormal*. That is, a basis $e_1, e_2, \ldots, e_n$ is orthonormal if $e_i \cdot e_j = 0$ when $i \neq j$ and $e_i \cdot e_j = 1$ when $i = j$.

It can be shown that every finite-dimensional vector space can be equipped with a scalar product; indeed, there are an infinite number of different ways that this can be done, as will be demonstrated below in the special case of R^n. Once the space is equipped with a scalar product, there exists at least one orthonormal basis, and if the space has dimension $n \geqq 2$ there are an infinite number of distinct orthonormal bases. When the base vectors in a three-dimensional space are denoted i, j, and k, it is always understood that this basis is orthonormal.

In R^n it is customary to define the scalar product of two vectors

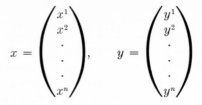

to be $x \cdot y = x^1y^1 + x^2y^2 + \ldots + x^ny^n$. It is quite easy to verify that the fundamental properties (1), (2), (3), and (4) are all satisfied. Relative to this scalar product, the vectors

$$
e_1 = \begin{pmatrix} 1 \\ 0 \\ 0 \\ \cdot \\ \cdot \\ 0 \end{pmatrix}, \quad e_2 = \begin{pmatrix} 0 \\ 1 \\ 0 \\ \cdot \\ \cdot \\ 0 \end{pmatrix}, \quad \ldots, \quad e_n = \begin{pmatrix} 0 \\ 0 \\ 0 \\ \cdot \\ \cdot \\ 1 \end{pmatrix}
$$

constitute an orthonormal basis. This scalar product will be called the *usual scalar product* in R^n, and the vectors $e_1, e_2, \ldots, e_n$ will be called the *natural basis*.

Before we continue, we digress somewhat to make two side remarks. These remarks are concerned with the definition we have given of "vector space," and also with the definition of "scalar product."

This book is primarily concerned with finite-dimensional vector spaces (indeed, with three-dimensional spaces), and the word "number" is always taken to mean "real number." More sophisticated students will, of course, wince at this. It is possible to consider vector spaces in which "multiplication of a vector by a scalar" does not mean "multiplication of a vector by a real number." The scalars may be complex numbers, or they may be elements of other mathematical systems also not discussed in this book. Most of these more general vector spaces are, so far as is known now, of no importance in any physical applications. Some of them are, however. For example, vector spaces in which the components of a vector may be complex numbers are quite convenient in some branches of physics and engineering, especially in connection with the theory of linear oscillations. This may seem quite surprising, since physical measurements do not (to the knowledge of this author) ever yield complex numbers.   Moreover, the differential equations fundamental to linear oscillation theory are real differential equations, and consequently have solutions that do not in any way involve complex numbers. The reason for using functions with complex values, and also vectors with complex components, is that the fundamental differential equations have the property that if a complex-valued function satisfies the equation, so also will its real and imaginary parts.   In order to account for phase angles, it is much more convenient to work with complex functions.   (This is the reason that complex numbers are used in electrical theory, also.)   So we work freely with complex functions, and in the final analysis of the answer we look at the real part of the function as the part having physical significance.

However, in at least one branch of physics, namely quantum mechanics, the situation is much deeper than this.   Some of the fundamental equations themselves involve complex quantities and do not have real solutions.   To make things even more complicated, in advanced quantum mechanics one works with vector spaces in which each vector has an infinite number of components.   In the "Hilbert space" that is studied in advanced quantum mechanics, one can find an infinite number of vectors, each one of which is orthogonal to all the others!   The scalar products in such spaces may have complex values, and the properties of the scalar product are somewhat different from those we have given.

This does not mean, however, that what we discuss here is *incorrect*.   It means that we are not considering vector spaces in full generality.

The second side remark is concerned with the scalar product. In any finite-dimensional vector space, there are many different scalar products, all having the properties required by the definition we have given.   For example, in R^n, we can define many scalar products in the following manner: Begin by selecting, once and for all, n arbitrary positive numbers $c_1, c_2, \ldots, c_n$.   Then define the scalar product of x and y to be

$$x \cdot y = c_1 x^1 y^1 + c_2 x^2 y^2 + \ldots + c_n x^n y^n$$

It is easily seen that this definition satisfies all the requirements demanded for a scalar product.   The usual scalar product corresponds to the special case that $c_i = 1$, $i = 1, 2, \ldots, n$.   Two vectors that are orthogonal relative to the usual scalar product in R^n need not be orthogonal when another scalar product is used.   Scalar products in

R^n other than the usual scalar product are not mathematical freaks; such "unusual" scalar products do occur in certain applications. (In studying linear oscillations of a system with n degrees of freedom, the n constants are related to the masses of the oscillating particles involved.)

The *usefulness* of the idea of a scalar product has already been demonstrated. Some additional uses are indicated by the following theorems, in which it is assumed that the vector space V is n-dimensional and is equipped with a scalar product.

THEOREM 1: *If f is a linear functional on V, there exists a unique vector u such that $f(v) = v \cdot u$ for every vector v in V.*

EXAMPLE: In R^4, let us suppose the scalar product is chosen to be $x \cdot y = x^1 y^1 + 2x^2 y^2 + x^3 y^3 + 9x^4 y^4$, and suppose the linear functional is defined by $f(x) = 3x^1 + 6x^2 - x^3 - 18x^4$. Then it is easy to see that the associated vector u is

$$u = \begin{pmatrix} 3 \\ 3 \\ -1 \\ -2 \end{pmatrix}$$

In general, if we let $g_{ij} = e_i \cdot e_j$, where $e_1, e_2, \ldots, e_n$ is a basis for V, then the scalar product in V is given by $x \cdot y = \sum \sum g_{ij} x^i y^j$. In particular, if the basis is orthonormal, $g_{ij} = 0$ when $i \neq j$ and $g_{ij} = 1$ if $i = j$, so the expression becomes $x \cdot y = \sum_{i=1}^{n} x^i y^i$. The vector u associated with a linear functional f is then easily verified to be $u = \sum_{i=1}^{n} f(e_i) e_i$, where $e_1, e_2, \ldots, e_n$ is an arbitrary orthonormal basis.

This theorem shows that every linear functional in V is obtained by holding u constant in the scalar product $v \cdot u$, and therefore every covariant vector can be identified with a contravariant vector u. To each covariant vector f there is a corresponding contravariant vector u, and to each contravariant vector u there is a corresponding covariant vector f. The components of f are generally related to those of u by the expression $f_i = \sum g_{ij} u^j$, where the numbers g_{ij} are defined as above. In some texts the numbers f_i are called the *covariant components* of the contravariant vector u. The ordinary components u^i are then called the *contravariant components*. If the base vectors are not of unit length, the numbers $u^i/|e|_i$ are sometimes called the *actual components* of u. These terms will not be used in this book.

THEOREM 2: *A set of k vectors $\underset{1}{v}, \underset{2}{v}, \ldots, \underset{k}{v}$ is linearly dependent if and only if the determinant of the following matrix is zero:*

$$
\begin{pmatrix}
\underset{1}{v} \cdot \underset{1}{v} & \underset{1}{v} \cdot \underset{2}{v} & \cdots & \underset{1}{v} \cdot \underset{k}{v} \\
\underset{2}{v} \cdot \underset{1}{v} & \underset{2}{v} \cdot \underset{2}{v} & \cdots & \underset{2}{v} \cdot \underset{k}{v} \\
\cdots & & & \\
\underset{k}{v} \cdot \underset{1}{v} & \underset{k}{v} \cdot \underset{2}{v} & \cdots & \underset{k}{v} \cdot \underset{k}{v}
\end{pmatrix}
$$

By making use of the theory of determinants, this theorem is quite simple to prove. Consider the system of k equations

$$
\sum_{j=1}^{k} C_j \underset{i}{v} \cdot \underset{j}{v}, \quad i = 1, 2, \ldots, k
$$

This will have a nontrivial solution (i.e., a solution $C_1, C_2, \ldots, C_k$ where not all the C's are zero) if and only if the determinant of the matrix is zero. Let $u = \sum C_j \underset{j}{v}$; this is equivalent to writing $\underset{i}{v} \cdot u = 0$, $i = 1, 2, \ldots, k$. These k equations are satisfied if u is the zero vector, and conversely if these k equations are satisfied we will have $u \cdot u = \sum C_i \underset{i}{v} \cdot u = 0$ and hence u will be the zero vector. Therefore there exists a nontrivial linear combination of the v's equal to the zero vector if and only if the determinant of the matrix is zero, which is what the theorem states.

Let us now turn to the vector product. It is possible to obtain certain analogs to the vector product in spaces of dimension greater than three, but these generalizations are not nearly so useful as is the usual vector product in three dimensions. Therefore we now restrict ourselves to three dimensions.

Let, then, V denote a three-dimensional vector space. Let us suppose that a scalar product has been defined in V. Then a *vector product* in V is defined to be a rule that assigns to pairs u, v of vectors in V a vector $u \times v$, such that the following properties are satisfied:

(16) $u \times v = -(v \times u)$

(17) $(u + w) \times v = (u \times v) + (w \times v)$

(18) $(cu) \times v = c(u \times v)$

(19) $u \cdot (u \times v) = 0$

(20) $|u \times v|^2 + (u \cdot v)^2 = |u|^2 \, |v|^2$

Except for the last of these, all these properties should be familiar to the reader, in the special case of "ordinary space" with the vector product defined in the usual geometrical manner. The first four of these properties require that the vector product be anti-symmetric, linear in each factor, and that $u \times v$ be orthogonal to both u and v. These properties would be trivially satisfied if we simply took $u \times v$ to be the zero vector, for every u and v. The last of the properties precludes this possibility. It requires the square of the magnitude of $u \times v$ to equal the determinant of the matrix

$$\begin{pmatrix} u \cdot u & u \cdot v \\ v \cdot u & v \cdot v \end{pmatrix}$$

and therefore, by Theorem 2, $u \times v$ cannot be the zero vector if u and v are linearly independent.

The question now arises, are there many different vector products, or is the vector product uniquely determined by these properties? The answer is that *once a particular scalar product has been chosen, there are only two ways in which the vector product can be defined.* In ordinary space, these two ways depend on whether we use a right-hand rule or a left-hand rule in determining the sense of $u \times v$.

To see this, let us suppose that e_1, e_2, e_3 is an orthonormal basis in V. By (20), $e_1 \times e_2$ must be of unit length, and by (19) it must be perpendicular to e_1. Since $e_1 \times e_2 = -e_2 \times e_1$ by (16), then by (19) $e_1 \times e_2$ must also be perpendicular to e_2. Therefore we have either

$$e_1 \times e_2 = e_3 \quad \text{or} \quad e_1 \times e_2 = -e_3$$

First consider the case $e_1 \times e_2 = e_3$. Then by the same argument as above, $e_2 \times e_3 = e_1$ or $-e_1$. However, we cannot have $e_2 \times e_3 = -e_1$ for this would violate (19) (take $u = e_1 + e_3$ and $v = e_2$). Therefore we must have $e_2 \times e_3 = e_1$. A similar argument shows that $e_3 \times e_1 = e_2$ and not $-e_2$. It follows from (16) that $e_1 \times e_1$, $e_2 \times e_2$, and $e_3 \times e_3$ equal the zero vector.

By making repeated application of (16), (17), and (18), we can now compute the vector product of any two vectors $u = \sum_i u^i e_i$ and $v = \sum_i v^i e_i$. Writing the components of $u \times v$ in terms of those of u and v we obtain the usual formula for the vector cross product. If, at the beginning of this argument, we had taken $e_1 \times e_2 = -e_3$ instead of e_3, then we would obtain the usual formula, except with the signs reversed in every term.

Conversely, if we define $u \times v$ for every pair of vectors u and v by selecting an orthonormal basis and using the usual formula (or its negative), it is easy to show that all the properties listed above will be satisfied.

On the other hand, if we change to a basis that is not orthonormal, the formula for computing the components of a vector cross product will be quite different, and perhaps very complicated.

In Section 5.7 we introduced the permutation symbol ε_{ijk}. In terms of this symbol, the usual formula for computing the ith component of $u \times v$ is $\sum \sum \varepsilon_{ijk} u^j v^k$. Now suppose that we define the *axial product* of u and v relative to a basis to be the triple of numbers (p_1, p_2, p_3) where

$$(21) \qquad\qquad p_i = \sum \sum \varepsilon_{ijk} u^j v^k$$

Although the notation p_i may suggest that we obtain the components of a covariant vector, this is in fact not the case (see Exercise 10). Moreover, if u and v are fixed vectors and r is a vector in the space whose components relative to a given basis equal those of the axial product of u and v, it is easy to find another basis relative to which the components of r will *not* equal those of the axial product.

In order to compare the vector product with the axial product, we introduce the notion of *relative area*. Let us refer to the plane containing two distinct base vectors e_i and e_j as the i,j plane. If x and y are two vectors in this plane, let $A(x,y)$ denote the area of the parallelogram having x and y as coterminal edges. In particular, $A(e_i, e_j)$ denotes the area of the parallelogram determined by e_i and e_j. The ratio $A(x,y)/A(e_i, e_j)$ is called the *relative area*. Although the notion of area depends on the idea of length, and hence is dependent on the particular choice of scalar product, it is easy to see that relative area is independent of the choice of scalar product. Indeed, we have $A(x,y)/A(\underset{i}{e},\underset{j}{e}) = |x^i y^j - x^j y^i|$, as the reader can easily verify.

If x and y are two vectors in an n-dimensional vector space V, not necessarily in the i,j plane, then $|x^i y^j - x^j y^i|$ is the relative area of the parallelogram determined by the projection of these vectors onto the i,j plane. If we remove the absolute value signs, letting $T^{ij} = x^i y^j - x^j y^i$, then T^{ij} will equal this relative area, or its negative, depending respectively on whether the orientation of the parallelogram determined by taking x and y in that order is the same as, or opposite to, that determined by taking $\underset{i}{e}$ and $\underset{j}{e}$ in that order.

If we like, we can form a matrix with entries T^{ij}. Along the principal diagonal $i = j$, the entries are zero; moreover, the matrix is skew-symmetric, i.e., $T^{ij} = -T^{ji}$. Therefore $n(n-1)/2$ entries suffice to determine the entire matrix. For instance, if $n = 3$, we need only specify T^{23}, T^{31}, and T^{12}, since $T^{13} = -T^{31}$, $T^{22} = 0$, etc. These three entries are the three numbers denoted p_1, p_2, and p_3 above. We see that the components of the axial product of two vectors represent relative area, with a sign indicating orientation.

In a vector space with dimension, say, $n = 4$, there will be $n(n-1)/2 = 6$ coordinate planes, so it is necessary to specify at least six different entries in the matrix (T^{ij}). There is no temptation here to think of these numbers as the components of a vector, since vectors in R^4 have only four components relative to a given basis. Indeed, it is only when the dimension $n = 3$ that we have $n(n-1)/2 = n$ and therefore are tempted to represent the axial product by a directed line segment, a procedure which we now see is quite artificial.

The vector product, on the other hand, is by definition truly a vector. Its scalar component in any direction equals the area of the projection of a parallelogram on a plane normal to that direction (or its negative, depending on the orientation). Since the notion of area depends on that of length, the vector product depends on the choice of scalar product, as mentioned above. Unfortunately, a base vector $\underset{i}{e}$ need not be perpendicular to the coordinate plane determined by the other base vectors, so the ith component of a vector product need not represent area projected on a coordinate plane. This is why we have not bothered to give a formula for the components of a vector product.

The reader whose primary interest is in physics or engineering is now advised to forget about the vector product as it has been defined in this section and use the term "vector product" to denote the axial product. The axial product will be discussed again in Section 5.10.

EXERCISES

1. Give an alternative proof of the Schwarz inequality along the following lines:
   (a) Explain why, if $f(t) = at^2 + 2bt + c$ is a function that is never negative, then $b^2 \leq ac$.
   (b) Show that, for any two vectors x and y, and any t, we have $(x + ty) \cdot (x + ty) = |x|^2 + 2(x \cdot y)t + |y|^2 t^2$.
   (c) Combine the results of (a) and (b) to prove the Schwarz inequality.

2. (a) Find the fallacy in the following "proof" that any number s equals any number t. Let s and t be arbitrary real numbers, and let A denote their average. Then we have

   $$s + t = 2A$$

   Multiplying both sides by $s - t$ gives

   $$s^2 - t^2 = 2sA - 2tA$$

   hence

   $$s^2 - 2sA = t^2 - 2tA$$

   Adding A^2 to both sides,

   $$s^2 - 2sA + A^2 = t^2 - 2tA + A^2$$

   Taking positive square roots,

   $$s - A = t - A$$

   and therefore $s = t$. This proves that all numbers are equal!
   (b) How can you be certain that the same fallacy does not invalidate the proof of the Schwarz inequality given in this section?

3. You are given eight numbers $x_1, x_2, \ldots, x_8$. Is it necessarily true that

   $$|x_1 x_5 + x_2 x_6 + x_3 x_7 + 2 x_4 x_8|$$
   $$\leq [x_1^2 + x_2^2 + x_3^2 + 2 x_4^2]^{1/2} [x_5^2 + x_6^2 + x_7^2 + 2 x_8^2]^{1/2}$$

   Why? (The superscripts here are exponents.)

4. Prove that the Schwarz inequality becomes an equality if and only if one of the vectors is a scalar multiple of the other.

5. What is the geometrical interpretation of $|u|^2 |v|^2 - (u \cdot v)^2$?

6. Show that, if (19) is dropped from the requirements for the vector cross product, an infinity of distinct "vector products" can be defined relative to each scalar product. [Hint: Consider the "product" $u \overset{.}{\times} v$ defined by reflecting $u \times v$ in a plane.]

7. In R^3, let $e_1 = (1,2,3)$, $e_2 = (2,-1,0)$, and $e_3 = (3,6,-5)$. Find the components of $(2,0,4)$ relative to this basis. [Hint: Use scalar products.]

8. Find a matrix S such that $ST = I$, where

$$T = \begin{pmatrix} 1 & 2 & 3 \\ 2 & -1 & 6 \\ 3 & 0 & -5 \end{pmatrix} \qquad I = \begin{pmatrix} 1 & 0 & 0 \\ 0 & 1 & 0 \\ 0 & 0 & 1 \end{pmatrix}$$

    [Hint: The columns of T are orthogonal relative to the usual scalar product in R^3.]

9. In proving the Schwarz inequality, was any use made of the requirement that $v \cdot v = 0$ implies that v is the zero vector?

10. With p defined by (21), show that $\sum p_i w^i$ is the Grassmann product of u, v, and w. Hence show that the axial product does not determine a covariant vector.

11. Derive a formula for a vector product relative to an orthogonal basis e_1, e_2, e_3 where $|e_1| = 1$, $|e_2| = 2$, $|e_3| = 3$.

12. Define a scalar product in R^3 relative to which the vectors $(1,0,0)$, $(0,4,0)$, and $(0,0,9)$ constitute an orthonormal basis.

5.9 : Linear Transformations (continued)

Throughout the remainder of this book, we shall restrict our attention entirely to a three-dimensional space equipped with a scalar product. The reader will have no difficulty generalizing much of this material to spaces of higher dimension. The only concepts we discuss that will not generalize readily are those involving the vector product (or axial product), for reasons noted in the preceding section. The reason for considering three-dimensional spaces is that we can give simple geometrical examples to motivate and illustrate the various concepts.

One concept we have already introduced briefly is that of a linear transformation. In this section we shall review and extend remarks already made, and give several examples.

Let V denote a vector space with basis e_1, e_2, e_3. The reader may think of these as our old friends i, j, and k, if he wishes, but we do not assume these vectors to have unit length or to be mutually orthogonal (perpendicular). Any vector x can be written uniquely in the form $x = x^1e_1 + x^2e_2 + x^3e_3$, or more briefly $x = \sum_i x^ie_i$, where x^1, x^2, and x^3 are numbers, called the coordinates or components of x. By now the reader should understand quite well that $\sum_i x^ie_i$ means exactly the same thing as $\sum_j x^je_j$, just as

$$\int_a^b f(x)\,dx \quad \text{and} \quad \int_a^b f(t)\,dt$$

mean exactly the same thing. The reader confused about this point should pause to reflect on it right now; such a student should review Section 5.2.

Since we are guided by geometrical considerations, it is well to point out again that we use the words "vector" and "point" interchangeably. When we say "the vector y" we are thinking of a directed line segment extending from the origin, and when we say "the point y" we are thinking of the point to which this directed line segment extends. Sometimes we will use matrix notation, in which we write y as a column vector

$$y = \begin{pmatrix} y^1 \\ y^2 \\ y^3 \end{pmatrix}$$

instead of $y = \sum_i y^ie_i$. Of course, relative to another basis, y may be represented by quite a different column vector.

At least three different mental images may be conjured up by the concept of a linear transformation T. The geometrically-minded student may wish to think that such a transformation has the effect of transforming every vector x into another vector Tx, or of moving a point x to a new location Tx. The algebraically-minded person may wish to think of it as a rule whereby to each column vector x there is associated another column vector Tx. The author once heard one of his students say to another, "When he puts that T in front of the x it is like multiplying x by a scalar, except that the direction of x may change, as well as its magnitude." Whatever the mental image, it is the *opinion* of the author that those who identify linear transformations with systems of equations such as

(1)
$$u^1 = T_1{}^1 x^1 + T_2{}^1 x^2 + T_3{}^1 x^3$$
$$u^2 = T_1{}^2 x^1 + T_2{}^2 x^2 + T_3{}^2 x^3$$
$$u^3 + T_1{}^3 x^1 + T_2{}^3 x^2 + T_3{}^3 x^3$$

or with matrices such as

(2)
$$(T_j{}^i) = \begin{pmatrix} T_1{}^1 & T_2{}^1 & T_3{}^1 \\ T_1{}^2 & T_2{}^2 & T_3{}^2 \\ T_1{}^3 & T_2{}^3 & T_3{}^3 \end{pmatrix}$$

are in danger of overlooking two fundamental points. One is that such representations are possible only because linear transformations have the crucial properties $T(x + y) = Tx + Ty$ and $T(cx) = cTx$, where x and y are vectors and c is a scalar. The other is that these representations depend entirely on the choice of basis; the coefficients $T_j{}^i$ usually will change if a new basis is chosen.

We recall that the matrix $(T_j{}^i)$ representing T is the matrix whose columns represent the transforms of the base vectors, relative to the given basis. That is, if a basis is $\underset{1}{e}, \underset{2}{e}, \underset{3}{e}$, then relative to this basis the vectors $\underset{1}{e}, \underset{2}{e}$, and $\underset{3}{e}$ themselves are represented by the column vectors

$$\begin{pmatrix} 1 \\ 0 \\ 0 \end{pmatrix}, \quad \begin{pmatrix} 0 \\ 1 \\ 0 \end{pmatrix}, \quad \begin{pmatrix} 0 \\ 0 \\ 1 \end{pmatrix}$$

respectively, and the vectors $T\underset{1}{e}, T\underset{2}{e}, T\underset{3}{e}$ are represented by the column vectors

$$\begin{pmatrix} T_1{}^1 \\ T_1{}^2 \\ T_1{}^3 \end{pmatrix}, \quad \begin{pmatrix} T_2{}^1 \\ T_2{}^2 \\ T_2{}^3 \end{pmatrix}, \quad \begin{pmatrix} T_3{}^1 \\ T_3{}^2 \\ T_3{}^3 \end{pmatrix}$$

Although it is true that the matrix representing T is also the array of coefficients of the system of equations (1), it is sometimes easier to write down the matrix directly than to derive the equations. The equations may then be written down quite easily.

As a simple example, let us consider *rotations* in space. It is conventional to call any transformation in which all distances are preserved a *rotation*, an *isometry*, or an *orthogonal transformation*. That is, if T is a rotation, we have $|Tx - Ty| = |x - y|$, for every pair of vectors x and y. In particular, the magnitude of Tx equals that of x, for every vector x. It can be shown that every rotation is a linear transformation. One distinguishes between *proper* and *improper* rotations. A proper rotation is described in geometric language quite easily: we simply select some line in space as an axis, and rotate about this axis through some angle θ. (Improper rotations, as for example the transformation $Tx = -x$ where each vector is transformed into its own negative, will not be considered here. They are not rotations in the everyday sense.)

Let us select a unit vector e_3 parallel to the axis of rotation, and take two mutually perpendicular unit vectors e_1 and e_2 both perpendicular to e_3.

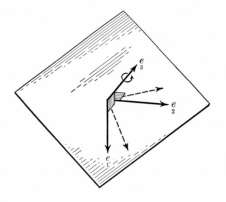

Figure 99

Let us suppose that the sense of rotation is as shown in Figure 99. We see readily from the diagram that $Te_1 = (\cos \theta)e_1 + (\sin \theta)e_2$, $Te_2 = (-\sin \theta)e_1 + (\cos \theta)e_2$, and $Te_3 = e_3$. Therefore the matrix representing T is

$$\begin{pmatrix} \cos\theta & -\sin\theta & 0 \\ \sin\theta & \cos\theta & 0 \\ 0 & 0 & 1 \end{pmatrix}$$

relative to this basis. (A word of caution: Rotations in spaces of higher dimension are more complicated to analyze.)

Returning to the general discussion, if T and S are linear transformations of V, and c is a scalar, then cT is defined to be the linear transformation transforming every vector x to the vector $c(Tx)$, and $T + S$ is defined to be the linear transformation transforming every x into $Tx + Sx$. The product ST is defined by

$$(ST)(x) = S(Tx)$$

In other words, we first apply T and then apply S.

It is easy to see that the matrix representing cT is c times that representing T, and the matrix representing $S + T$ is the sum of those representing S and T. (These operations with matrices were defined in Section 5.4.) We now prove in detail that the matrix representing $R = ST$ is the product of those representing S and T, in that order. By definition, $Rx = S(Tx)$, and since both S and T are linear, we have

$$R(cx) = S(T(cx)) = S(c(Tx)) = c(S(Tx)) = c(Rx)$$

and similarly

$$R(x + y) = S(T(x + y)) = S(Tx + Ty) = S(Tx) + S(Ty)$$
$$= Rx + Ry$$

therefore ST is indeed a linear transformation. The jth column of $R = ST$ is the column vector representing $R\underset{j}{e}$, and this is

$$R\underset{j}{e} = S(T\underset{j}{e}) = S\left(\sum_p T_j{}^p e\right) = \sum_p T_j{}^p S(\underset{p}{e}) = \sum_p T_j{}^p \sum_i S_p{}^i e$$
$$= \sum \sum S_p{}^i T_j{}^p \underset{i}{e}$$

The entry $R_j{}^i$ in the ith row and jth column of the matrix representing R is the ith component of $R\underset{j}{e}$, which we see from this calculation equals $\sum S_p{}^i T_j{}^p$. This is precisely the rule for matrix multiplication, given in Section 5.4.

The product of two transformations S and T depends on the order. It is not necessarily true that ST equals TS. You can demonstrate this yourself, using this or another book, as you sit at your desk.   Let T denote rotation by 90° about a horizontal axis extending from your left to your right, the sense of the rotation being such that the top of any object rotates towards you.   Let S denote rotation by 90° about a vertical axis, the sense of the rotation being such that the right edge of any object rotates towards you.   Now hold an open book in front of you, so that two pages face you, and compare ST with TS.   Remember, ST means: first perform operation T and then perform S.   The book will end up with the two open pages face down.   But after TS (first S, then T) the two open pages will be facing your left instead.

It is easy to see that, if P, S, and T are linear transformations, then $(PS)T = P(ST)$.   Indeed, both sides of this equation simply represent the transformation: first T, then S, and finally P.   It follows that matrix multiplication has the same property.

We shall temporarily denote by $\mathcal{I}$ the *identity transformation* defined by $\mathcal{I}x = x$ (for all x), and by $\mathcal{O}$ the *zero transformation* defined by the requirement that $\mathcal{O}x$ be the zero vector for every vector x. These two transformations are obviously linear.

For reference, we list here the basic properties of the collection of all linear transformations.   First of all, we note that this set is equipped with a law of addition and multiplication by scalars and satisfies all the axioms for a vector space (Section 5.3).   We have also a multiplication defined, and this multiplication is *linear:*

(3) $S(T = P) = ST + ST$, $(S + T)P = SP + TP$

(4) $S(cT) = c(ST)$, $(cS)T = c(ST)$

(5) $(a + b)T = aT + bT$ and $(ab)T = a(bT)$
$$\text{for all scalars } a \text{ and } b.$$

There is an identity element $\mathcal{I}$, with the property

(6) $\mathcal{I}T = T\mathcal{I} = T$ for every T

The zero element has the properties

(7) $\mathcal{O}T = T\mathcal{O} = \mathcal{O}$, and $0T = \mathcal{O}$ for all T

Multiplication is associative:

(8) $S(TP) = (ST)P$

Any collection of objects equipped with these three operations, satisfying the above conditions, is called an *associative algebra*.   The collection of all linear transformations of V is a nine-dimensional associative algebra (Exercise 6).

The reader is already familiar with the real number system (one-dimensional), and the complex number system (two-dimensional), and may be familiar with the quaternions (four-dimensional). These three associative algebras have an additional property, that given any element T, other than the zero element, there exists an element, denoted T^{-1} and called the *inverse* of T, such that $T^{-1}T = TT^{-1} = \mathcal{I}$. An associative algebra with this additional property is called a *division algebra*. It can be proved that every finite-dimensional division algebra is either one of the three just mentioned, or one of them "disguised" by a change in coordinates. *The algebra of linear transformations of V is not a division algebra.*

For this reason, we must distinguish between those linear transformations T that possess inverses and those that do not. We say that T is *nonsingular* if it has an inverse, and is *singular* if it does not. We sometimes denote the inverse of a linear transformation by $\overset{-1}{T}$ rather than T^{-1}.

If T is nonsingular and $Tx = Ty$, then we must have $x = y$, since $x = \mathcal{I}x = T^{-1}Tx = T^{-1}Ty = \mathcal{I}y = y$. Therefore if we are given any vector u, there can be at most one solution of the equation $u = Tx$. Moreover, there must exist such a solution, namely $x = T^{-1}u$, since $T(T^{-1}u) = u$. Geometrically this means that T never transforms distinct points into the same point, and every point is the transform of some point.

T is nonsingular if and only if the columns of any matrix representing T are linearly independent. For, since T is linear, every vector Tx is a linear combination of the three vectors $T\underset{1}{e}$, $T\underset{2}{e}$, $T\underset{3}{e}$. If therefore T is nonsingular, every vector must be a linear combination of these three vectors; so these three vectors cannot be coplanar, and hence are linearly independent. Conversely, if these three vectors are linearly independent, then they are not coplanar, and so every vector u can be written uniquely as a linear combination of these three vectors. But if $u = \sum x^i T\underset{i}{e}$ for unique numbers x^1, x^2, x^3, then by the linearity of T, $x = \sum x^i\underset{i}{e}$ must be a unique solution of $u = Tx$, and so T is nonsingular. As an exercise, the reader is advised to give a rigorous proof not based on a geometrical argument, using the ideas of Section 5.7 (see Exercise 5 of that section).

It follows that T is singular if and only if the columns of $(T_j{}^i)$ are linearly dependent. This is equivalent to saying that there exist numbers x^1, x^2, x^3, not all zero, such that $\sum_i x^i Te$ is the zero vector. This is equivalent to saying there exists a nonzero vector $x = \sum_i x^i e$ such that Tx is the zero vector. *T is singular if and only if there exists a nonzero vector x such that Tx is the zero vector.*

In Section 5.7 we noted that T is nonsingular if and only if it is represented by a matrix with nonzero determinant. Let us now investigate the geometrical content of this statement. This discussion is not rigorous; rigorous derivations will be given later.

Let us suppose for the moment that the basis e, e, e is orthonormal, so these three vectors determine a cube with unit volume. Relative to this basis, the determinant of $(T_j{}^i)$ is our old friend, the triple scalar product of Te, Te, Te, as the reader can investigate for himself. (Recall that the discussion of the triple scalar product given in Chapter One assumes an orthonormal basis. The three vectors were written as row vectors rather than column vectors, but it is easy to see that this makes no difference to the determinant.) This triple scalar product, if it is positive, represents the volume of the parallelepiped determined by Te, Te, Te. Thus T transforms a cube with unit volume into a parallelepiped with volume equal to the determinant of $(T_j{}^i)$. Since T is linear, it is easy to see that T transforms any small cube with edges parallel to e, e, and e, having volume C, to a parallelepiped with volume $C \det (T_j{}^i)$, and from this it is geometrically clear (but a rigorous proof should be given) that all regions having volume C will be transformed into regions with volume $C \det (T_j{}^i)$. Now suppose that S is another linear transformation, and let us follow up T by applying S. Then the region with volume $C \det (T_j{}^i)$ will (by the same argument) be transformed into a region with volume $C \det (T_j{}^i) \det (S_j{}^i)$. The same argument can be applied to the single transformation $R = ST$; a region with volume C will be transformed to a region with volume $C \det (R_j{}^i)$. From this it follows that $\det (R_j{}^i) = \det (T_j{}^i) \det (S_j{}^i)$. Since every matrix represents a linear transformation, and the linear transformations T and S were purely arbitrary, this shows that *the determinant of the product of two matrices equals the product of their determinants.*

We have seen that, if T is represented by a matrix $(T_j{}^i)$ relative to an orthonormal basis, then $\det (T_j{}^i)$ gives the "volume magnification factor" (or its negative; we continue to ignore this complication).

In particular, this shows that det $(T_j{}^i)$ is independent of basis, provided the basis is orthonormal. Actually, the determinant of the matrix representing a linear transformation is the same no matter what basis is used, even if the basis is not orthonormal. We now proceed to show this by a geometrical argument which (we again emphasize) is not rigorous.

We all recall from our school days that numerical volume in cubic inches is $(12)^3$ times as great as volume in cubic feet. More generally, a region having volume C relative to one system of measurement will have volume KC relative to another, and this factor K does not depend on the location or shape of the region.

The volume of a region in a vector space depends on the choice of scalar product, since lengths are defined by means of a scalar product. Let e_1, e_2, e_3 be an arbitrary basis. Define the scalar product of two vectors x and y to be $\sum_{i=1}^3 x^i y^i$, where the components are relative to this basis. With this scalar product, $e_1, e_2,$ and e_3 comprise an orthonormal set, so the determinant of a matrix $(T_j{}^i)$ representing a linear transformation T relative to this basis gives the volume magnification factor, where volumes are relative to this scalar product. A region having volume C will be transformed to one having volume C det $(T_j{}^i)$. Relative to any other scalar product, the region will have volume KC, and will be transformed to one having volume KC det $(T_j{}^i)$. The volume magnification factor is det $(T_j{}^i)$ in any case. This factor is independent of the choice of scalar product or the particular basis used. Therefore it makes sense to say that det $(T_j{}^i)$ is the determinant of the linear transformation T, without adding the qualifying phrase "with respect to the basis." A rigorous proof will be given in the next section.

We now can see quite clearly why it is not possible for a linear transformation with zero determinant to have an inverse. For such a linear transformation, the volume magnification factor is zero. A region having nonzero volume (relative to any scalar product you care to choose) is mapped into a region having zero volume. This means, colloquially speaking, that the region has been squashed flat or compressed into a line or a point. At least one nonzero vector is mapped into the zero vector; so all scalar multiples of this vector will also be mapped into the zero vector. The vector equation $Tv = w$ will either have no solution, for a given w, or it will have infinitely many distinct solutions.

We shall now give the simple examples that we promised earlier. In order to emphasize that linear transformations are very special kinds of transformations, we begin with an example of a class of transformations that are not linear.

EXAMPLE 1:   Let w be a fixed vector, and define $Tv = v + w$ (for every vector v). Such a transformation is called a *translation*. The reader can easily verify that such a transformation is not linear, except in the trivial case where we take w to be the zero vector. Such a transformation cannot be represented by a matrix in the conventional manner. (We shall deliberately avoid answering the question of whether there is some other way of representing a translation by a matrix!)

EXAMPLE 2:   The zero transformation $\mathcal{O}$ is a linear transformation. It is represented (no matter what the basis may be) by a matrix with all nine entries equal to zero. Its determinant is zero. Every region in space is mapped into the point at the origin. It is a very important transformation, just as the number zero is a very important number.

EXAMPLE 3:   The identity transformation $\mathcal{I}$ defined by $\mathcal{I}v = v$ for every vector v is a linear transformation. It is represented, no matter what the basis may be, by the identity matrix

$$\begin{pmatrix} 1 & 0 & 0 \\ 0 & 1 & 0 \\ 0 & 0 & 1 \end{pmatrix}$$

This matrix is often denoted by the symbol $(\delta_j{}^i)$. The symbol $(\delta_j{}^i)$, which stands for unity when $i = j$ and zero when $i \neq j$, is frequently called the *Kronecker delta*. The author would appreciate it if some knowledgeable historian would tell him why.

Since the identity transformation plays a role similar to that played by the number *one*, it is naturally a very important transformation.

EXAMPLE 4:   Let there be given a plane P passing through the origin. If v is the position vector of a point in space, consider the line passing through this point that is perpendicular to P. This line will intersect the plane P in a unique point having position vector w. Let us then define Tv to be w. Such a linear transformation is called *projection on a plane.* If n is a unit vector perpendicular to the plane, it is easy to see that the definition can be given in the following vector form: $Tv = v - (n \cdot v)n$. If w is the position vector of a point in the plane P, then $Tw = w$. It is therefore easy to see that for every vector v, $T(Tv) = Tv$. In other words, the linear transformation T^2 is identical with the linear transformation T. Any linear transformation T with the property $T^2 = T$ is called an *idempotent.* The reader will note that the zero transformation, the identity transformation, and projections as defined in this and the following example, are idempotents.

EXAMPLE 5: Let L be a fixed line through the origin. If v is the position vector of a point, let Tv be the position vector of the point on L where a plane passing through the given point and perpendicular to L intersects L. Such a linear transformation is called *projection on a line.*

Transformations of the type of Examples 4 and 5 quite obviously have zero determinant and cannot possess inverses.

EXAMPLE 6: Let T denote a linear transformation represented, relative to an orthonormal basis e_1, e_2, e_3 by the matrix

$$\begin{pmatrix} \cos\theta & -\sin\theta & 0 \\ \sin\theta & \cos\theta & 0 \\ 0 & 0 & 1 \end{pmatrix}$$

Geometrically, such a linear transformation is a *proper rotation.* If L is the line through the origin parallel to e_3, then points on this line remain fixed, and all other points are rotated about this line through an angle θ. It is clear geometrically that the volume magnification factor of such a transformation is unity, and this can also be seen by computing the determinant of the matrix, since $\cos^2\theta + \sin^2\theta = 1$.

EXAMPLE 7: Let P be a fixed plane passing through the origin, and let Tv denote the "reflected image" of v, thinking of P as a mirror. More precisely, let n denote a unit vector perpendicular to the plane, and define Tv to be $v - 2(n \cdot v)n$. Such a transformation is called *reflection in a plane.*

If we choose an orthonormal basis e_1, e_2, e_3 with e_1 and e_2 parallel to P and e_3 perpendicular to P, the matrix representing T will be

$$\begin{pmatrix} 1 & 0 & 0 \\ 0 & 1 & 0 \\ 0 & 0 & -1 \end{pmatrix}$$

Therefore the determinant of this linear transformation is -1. This brings us back to a point deliberately neglected above. We neglected to consider the possibility that the determinant of a transformation might be negative, and in that case could not possibly represent a volume magnification factor, since as usually defined volume is never negative. If the reader will review what he has read, and recall that it is really the absolute value of the triple scalar product that gives the volume of a parallelepiped, he will see that it is $|\det T|$ and not $\det T$ that gives the volume magnification factor. From a geometrical viewpoint, $\det T$ is positive or negative depending on whether T transforms a right-handed system of vectors into a right-handed or left-handed system, respectively. Obviously, a reflection in a plane maps a right-handed system of vectors into a left-handed one, but does not change volumes, which accounts for $\det T = -1$ in this case.

The more sophisticated reader will realize that there is no way to define "right-handed system" of vectors when the axiomatic definition of vector space is used. The notion of a vector space is a rather abstract one, and has little to do with the fingers of the hand. We have deliberately underplayed this topic, since it would lead us into further discussions of orientation and relative orientation, subjects which, the author has learned (from experience), undergraduates do not understand. It is a paradox of psychology that the concept of orientation is too easy for most undergraduates to comprehend.

EXAMPLE 8: Another type of linear transformation is obtained by taking a fixed vector A, and defining $Tv = A \times v$, for every vector v. If the components of A are A^1, A^2, and A^3 respectively, relative to an orthonormal basis e, e, e, then the matrix representing T
$$ \underset{1\;2\;3}{}$$
relative to this basis is easily seen to be either

$$\begin{pmatrix} 0 & -A^3 & A^2 \\ A^3 & 0 & -A^1 \\ -A^2 & A^1 & 0 \end{pmatrix}$$

or its negative. This matrix has the property $T_j{}^i = -T_i{}^j$ for every i and j. The reader can easily verify that, if T is a linear transformation represented, relative to an orthonormal basis, by a matrix $(T_j{}^i)$

with the property $T_j{}^i = -T_i{}^j$, then there must exist a vector A such that $Tv = A \times v$ for every v. Such linear transformations are said to be *skew-symmetric*, and will be discussed further in the next section.

EXERCISES

1. Let

$$(T_j{}^i) = \begin{pmatrix} 2 & 1 & 0 \\ 1 & 1 & -1 \\ 0 & 4 & 3 \end{pmatrix} \quad \text{and} \quad (S_j{}^i) = \begin{pmatrix} 1 & 3 & 1 \\ 1 & 1 & 1 \\ 2 & 2 & 2 \end{pmatrix}$$

(a) Compute det $(T_j{}^i)$ and det $(S_j{}^i)$.
(b) Find the matrix product $R_j{}^i = \sum T_k{}^i S_j{}^k$.
(c) Compute det $(R_j{}^i)$, verifying that this is the product of the determinants computed in (a).

2. Find a nonzero column vector v such that Mv is the zero vector, where M is the matrix

$$\begin{pmatrix} 2 & 1 & 1 \\ 1 & 2 & 0 \\ 3 & 0 & 2 \end{pmatrix}$$

3. Does the matrix given in Exercise 2 possess an inverse?

4. (a) Relative to an orthonormal basis $\underset{1}{e}, \underset{2}{e}, \underset{3}{e}$, a linear transformation T is represented by the matrix

$$\begin{pmatrix} 0 & 2 & 1 \\ -2 & 0 & 3 \\ -1 & -3 & 0 \end{pmatrix}$$

For what vector A is $Tv = A \times v$ (for all v)? Assume the usual formula for vector products applies when components are relative to this basis. Give A in terms of $\underset{1}{e}, \underset{2}{e}$, and $\underset{3}{e}$.

(b) What is the formula for the vector product of two vectors u and v if components are relative to the basis $\underset{1}{f}, \underset{2}{f}, \underset{3}{f}$ where

$$\underset{1}{f} = \underset{2}{e}, \underset{2}{f} = \underset{3}{e}, \underset{3}{f} = \underset{3}{e}?$$

(c) Write A in terms of $\underset{1}{f}, \underset{2}{f}$, and $\underset{3}{f}$.

(d) What matrix represents T relative to this new basis $\underset{1}{f}, \underset{2}{f}, \underset{3}{f}$?

(e) Verify a second time that $Tv = A \times v$.

5.   Go carefully through the following computational proof that, if $(S_j{}^i)$ and $(T_j{}^i)$ are 3×3 matrices, the determinant of their product equals the product of their determinants. Explain each step to your own satisfaction.

      If $R_k{}^i = \sum S_j{}^i T_k{}^j$, then

$$\det (R_k{}^i) = \sum \sum \sum \varepsilon_{ijk} R_1{}^i R_2{}^j R_3{}^k$$

$$= \sum \sum \sum \varepsilon_{ijk} \sum S_m{}^i T_1{}^m \sum S_p{}^j T_2{}^p \sum S_r{}^k T_3{}^r$$

$$= \sum \sum \sum \sum \sum \sum \varepsilon_{ijk} S_m{}^i S_p{}^j S_r{}^k T_1{}^m T_2{}^p T_3{}^r$$

$$= \sum \sum \sum \sum \sum \sum \varepsilon_{ijk} \varepsilon_{mpr} S_1{}^i S_2{}^j S_3{}^k T_1{}^m T_2{}^p T_3{}^r$$

$$= \sum \sum \sum \varepsilon_{ijk} S_1{}^i S_2{}^j S_3{}^k \sum \sum \sum \varepsilon_{mpr} T_1{}^m T_2{}^p T_3{}^r$$

$$= \det (S_j{}^i) \det (T_j{}^i)$$

6.   Prove in detail that the algebra of all linear transformations of a three-dimensional vector space is nine-dimensional.

5.10 : Change of Basis

      In this section, V denotes a three-dimensional vector space. Let e, e, e be a basis for V, and let another basis be denoted e, e, e.
    _{1 2 3}   _{1' 2' 3'}
We shall call the first basis mentioned the "old" basis, and the second one the "new" basis, simply for convenience in exposition. If we were to have occasion to introduce a third basis, we might denote it e, e, e and call it the "latest" basis.
_{1'' 2'' 3''}

      A word about this unusual notation. Since (for instance) e and
₁
e may be altogether different vectors, it would be more appropriate to
_{1'}
use different letters, writing them e and f perhaps, or to put the prime
₁   ₁
in a different location, writing e and e'. The notation we use here
₁   ₁
has certain advantages, as will soon be demonstrated. Just keep in mind that the stroke (prime) is to distinguish the new-base vectors from the old ones. It is simply a reminder.

      Let us form a three by three matrix, denoted $(A_{j'}{}^i)$, whose columns give the components of the new base vectors relative to the old basis. That is, by definition, we have

$$(1) \qquad\qquad e_{j'} = \sum_i A_{j'}{}^i e_i$$

Keep in mind that $A_{j'}{}^i$ denotes the entry in the ith row and jth column of the matrix. The prime is a suggestive reminder that the jth column gives the components of $e_{j'}$.

We let $(A_j{}^{i'})$ denote the matrix whose jth column gives the components of e_j relative to the new basis. That is,

$$(2) \qquad\qquad e_j = \sum_{i'} A_j^{i'} e_{i'}$$

Although the same letter A is used in the notation for both matrices, it is not to be supposed that any entry in $(A_{j'}{}^i)$ necessarily equals any entry in $(A_j{}^{i'})$. They are generally different matrices. By substituting (2) into (1) or conversely (1) into (2) the reader can readily verify that these matrices are inverses. That is, their product, in either order, equals the identity matrix.

There is no particular significance to the choice of letters used as indices. The symbol $(A_j{}^{i'})$ denotes the same thing as $(A_j{}^{k'})$ or even $(A_p{}^{m'})$. We could not have written simply A, however, since that might be confused with $(A_{j'}{}^i)$. Again we emphasize that $(A_j{}^{i'})$ denotes the entire matrix. The symbol $A_j{}^{i'}$, without parentheses, denotes a single number, the entry in the ith row and jth column of the matrix $(A_j{}^{i'})$.

As an example, suppose that we have

$$(3) \qquad e_{1'} = e_1 + e_2 \qquad e_{2'} = e_1 - e_2$$

$$e_{3'} = \tfrac{1}{2} e_3$$

Then we would have

$$(4) \qquad\qquad (A_{j'}{}^i) = \begin{pmatrix} 1 & 1 & 0 \\ 1 & -1 & 0 \\ 0 & 0 & \tfrac{1}{2} \end{pmatrix}$$

Solving (3) for e_1, e_2, and e_3, we obtain

$$(5) \qquad e_1 = \tfrac{1}{2}(e_{1'} + e_{2'}) \qquad e_2 = \tfrac{1}{2}(e_{1'} - e_{2'})$$

$$e_3 = 2 e_{3'}$$

And therefore the inverse matrix is

$$(6) \qquad (A_j{}^{i'}) = \begin{pmatrix} \frac{1}{2} & \frac{1}{2} & 0 \\ \frac{1}{2} & -\frac{1}{2} & 0 \\ 0 & 0 & 2 \end{pmatrix}$$

There is nothing to memorize here except the form of equations (1) and (2). The notation essentially forces us to do the "right thing" if we remember that our summations are conventionally over indices that appear once *above* and once *below*. Notice that (4) is not obtained by simply duplicating the array of coefficients of (3); because of the definition (1) the rows and columns have become transposed.

    With the aid of these two matrices we can now produce formulas that give old components of a vector in terms of new components, show how the matrix representing a linear transformation changes when we change basis, and so on. The reader will observe that the rather unusual notation we have adopted makes all these formulas quite easy to remember.

    Any vector x is represented by a column vector (x^i) relative to the old basis, and a column vector $(x^{i'})$ relative to the new basis. We have

$$x = \sum x^i e_{\underset{j}{}} = \sum x^j \sum A_j{}^{i'} e_{\underset{i'}{}} = \sum \sum (A_j{}^{i'} x^j) e_{\underset{i'}{}}$$

from which we can read off the new components of x. They are

$$(7) \qquad x^{i'} = \sum A_j{}^{i'} x^j$$

From the matrix standpoint, this is simply the product of a matrix with a column vector.

    A similar calculation yields

$$(8) \qquad x^i = \sum A_{j'}{}^{i} x^{j'}$$

giving the old components in terms of the new.

    Writing out (7) in the special case given above, we have

$$(9) \qquad \begin{aligned} x^{1'} &= \tfrac{1}{2}x^1 + \tfrac{1}{2}x^2 \\ x^{2'} &= \tfrac{1}{2}x^1 - \tfrac{1}{2}x^2 \\ x^{3'} &= 2x^3 \end{aligned}$$

Here the coefficients are in the same position as in the matrix (6).

    Note that, although the matrix (4) gives the new-base vectors in terms of the old, it is not this matrix but its inverse (6) that gives the new components of a vector in terms of its old components.

With tongue in cheek, we suggest this is the reason that components of a vector x relative to a basis are called contravariant components rather than covariant components; they behave under change of basis in a rather contrary way.

Now let us turn to covariant vectors, i.e., linear functionals on V. We recall that the ith component of a linear functional f is the value it assigns to the ith base vector. Therefore we have

$$f_{j'} = f(\underset{j'}{e}) = f(\sum_i A_{j'}{}^i e) = \sum_i A_{j'}{}^i f(\underset{i}{e}) = \sum_i A_{j'}{}^i f_i$$

The transformation law for covariant vectors is therefore

$$(10) \qquad\qquad f_{j'} = \sum f_i A_{j'}{}^i$$

where we have reversed the order to make it more suggestive of matrix notation. From the matrix viewpoint, this is the product of a row vector (f_i) with the matrix $(A_{j'}{}^i)$, in that order.

Comparing this with (7), we see how very different is the transformation law for covariant vectors. The matrices are not the same but are inverses, and the summation is over rows instead of columns.

Next we take up linear transformations. Let T denote a linear transformation of V, represented by a matrix $(T_j{}^i)$ relative to the old basis, and by a matrix $(T_{j'}{}^{i'})$ relative to the new basis. By definition, the jth column of the matrix gives the components of the transformed jth base vector, relative to the same basis. We have

$$T\underset{j'}{e} = (\sum_p A_{j'}{}^p e) = \sum_p A_{j'}{}^p T\underset{p}{e} = \sum_p A_{j'}{}^p (\sum_k T_p{}^k e)$$

$$= \sum\sum_k A_{j'}{}^p T_p{}^k e = \sum\sum A_{j'}{}^p T_p{}^k (\sum_{i'} A_k{}^{i'} e)$$

$$= \sum\sum\sum_{i'} A_{j'}{}^p T_p{}^k A_k{}^{i'} e$$

The coefficient of $\underset{i'}{e}$ is $\sum\sum A_{j'}{}^p T_p{}^k A_k{}^{i'}$. Changing the order of the factors to suggest matrix multiplication, this shows that

$$(11) \qquad\qquad T_{j'}{}^{i'} = \sum\sum A_k{}^{i'} T_p{}^k A_{j'}{}^p$$

the matrix product of $(A_j{}^{i'})$, $(T_j{}^i)$, and $(A_{j'}{}^i)$, in that order.

Since the determinant of the identity matrix is unity, and the determinant of the product of two matrices equals the product of their determinants (Exercise 5, preceding section), we must have $\det (A_j{}^{i'}) = [\det (A_{j'}{}^i)]^{-1}$ and therefore

$$\det (T_{j'}{}^{i'}) = \det [(A_j{}^{i'})(T_j{}^i)(A_{j'}{}^i)]$$

$$= [\det (A_j{}^{i'})][\det (T_j{}^i)][\det (A_{j'}{}^i)]$$

$$= \det (T_j{}^i)$$

This proves the statement made in the preceding section, that the determinant of a linear transformation is independent of the choice of basis. This proof is strictly computational and not very elegant!

Let us now look briefly at the Grassmann product of three vectors $\underset{1}{v}, \underset{2}{v},$ and $\underset{3}{v}$. We recall that this is the determinant of a matrix having as its columns $\underset{1}{v}, \underset{2}{v},$ and $\underset{3}{v}$, in that order. This depends on the choice of basis, since the column vectors representing these three vectors depend on the basis. Now let us denote this matrix by M, i.e., we have $M_j{}^i = \underset{j}{v}{}^i$ for every pair of indices i and j. Let N be a perfectly arbitrary three by three matrix. By just looking at the way matrices multiply, we see that the matrix product NM has three columns, which are the column vectors $N\underset{1}{v}, N\underset{2}{v},$ and $N\underset{3}{v}$, in that order.

In particular, if we take N to be the matrix $(A_j{}^{i'})$, the column vectors $\underset{1}{v}, \underset{2}{v}, \underset{3}{v}$ to be relative to the old basis, then by (7) the column vectors $N\underset{1}{v}, N\underset{2}{v}, N\underset{3}{v}$ are the column vectors representing the same three vectors relative to the new basis. Hence $\det [(A_j{}^i)(M)]$ is the Grassmann product relative to the new basis. Therefore the Grassmann product relative to the new basis is $\det (A_j{}^{i'}) \det (M)$. Since $\det (M)$ is the Grassmann product relative to the old basis, we see that when we change from the old basis to the new basis, all Grassmann products are multiplied by the factor $\det (A_j{}^{i'})$.

The same argument can be used, taking the matrix N to be the matrix representing a linear transformation T, to show that the Grassmann product $T\underset{1}{v} \wedge T\underset{2}{v} \wedge T\underset{3}{v}$ is just $\det (T_j{}^i)$ times the Grassmann product $\underset{1}{v} \wedge \underset{2}{v} \wedge \underset{3}{v}$. Relative to the new basis, both these Grassmann products are different by the same factor $\det (A_j{}^{i'})$, hence their ratio will be the same, and this is another way of showing that the determinant of a linear transformation does not depend on the basis. If we denote this determinant simply by $\det T$, we can write down the formula

$$(12) \qquad T\underset{1}{v} \wedge T\underset{2}{v} \wedge T\underset{3}{v} = [\det (T)]\underset{1}{v} \wedge \underset{2}{v} \wedge \underset{3}{v}$$

valid no matter what basis we use. *The determinant of a linear trans-formation T is the factor by which Grassmann products are magnified by the linear transformation.*

A number, such as det T, that is related to a linear transformation but is independent of basis, is called an *invariant* of T. Another example of an *invariant* of T is the *trace* of T. If T is represented by a matrix $(T_j{}^i)$, then tr T is defined to be the sum of the elements on the principal diagonal of the matrix, i.e.,

(13)
$$\operatorname{tr} T = \sum_{i=1}^{3} T_i{}^i$$

(this is also called the trace of the matrix). To see that this is inde-pendent of basis, we first observe that the trace of the product of two matrices M and N is independent of order, since both are equal to $\sum \sum M_j{}^i N_i{}^j$. Hence the trace of $(A_j{}^{i'})(T_j{}^i)(A_{j'}{}^i)$ is the trace of $(A_{j'}{}^i)(A_j{}^{i'})(T_j{}^i)$. But the first two of these matrices are inverses, so the product matrix is simply $(T_j{}^i)$. Hence tr $(T_{j'}{}^{i'}) = $ tr $(T_j{}^i)$.

The usefulness of the trace will be demonstrated later. Al-though it is an invariant, just as is the determinant, these two in-variants have quite different properties, as will be shown in the exercises.

The process whereby we pass from a matrix to its trace is a special instance of what is called "contraction" in tensor algebra. We do not discuss tensors in this book, but in the next section we shall discuss the *tensor viewpoint* towards vector algebra. This is a rather interesting and sometimes useful concept.

The reader can breathe a sigh of relief that we are through with complicated summations (some people call this "index pushing").

EXERCISES

1. Verify by direct multiplication that (4) and (6) are inverses.

2. If the old components of x are $x^1 = 1$, $x^2 = 3$, $x^3 = -2$, find its new components, where the change of basis is that given by (3).

3. Do the same for a linear functional whose old components are $f_1 = 0$, $f_2 = 1$, $f_3 = -1$.

4. A linear transformation T is represented by the matrix

$$\begin{pmatrix} 1 & 2 & 3 \\ 4 & 5 & 1 \\ -1 & 0 & 2 \end{pmatrix}$$

relative to the old basis, related to a new basis by equations (3). Find the matrix representing T relative to the new basis.

5. A parallelepiped with coterminal edges v_1, v_2, v_3 is said to be *oriented* when these three vectors are given in a definite order. The *oriented volume* of the parallelepiped is defined to be the Grassmann product of these three vectors, in the prescribed order. This depends on the choice of basis.

   (a) For what bases can you say that the absolute value of the oriented volume equals the actual volume of the parallelepiped? (We assume that a scalar product is given, determining the notion of length and hence volume.)

   (b) Give a definition of "relative volume" of a parallelepiped that will depend not on the scalar product but only on the choice of basis. (Compare with the notion of "relative area," introduced earlier.)

   (c) What does the absolute value of the oriented volume represent if the basis is not orthonormal?

   (d) Define det (T) in terms of oriented volume.

   (e) From the simple geometrical viewpoint, what is the significance of an oriented volume that is negative?

6. Determine which of the following statements are always true, and which are not necessarily true, for linear transformations T and S.

   (a) det $(TS) = $ det (T) det (S)

   (b) det $(T + S) = $ det $(T) + $ det (S)

   (c) det $(cT) = c$ det (T) for every scalar c

   (d) tr $(TS) = $ tr (T) tr (S)

   (e) tr $(T + S) = $ tr $(T) + $ tr (S)

   (f) tr $(cT) = c$ tr (T)

   (g) tr $(TS) = $ tr (ST)

   (h) det $(TS) = $ det (ST)

7. Write the matrix elements $A_j^{i'}$ in terms of partial derivatives of the new coordinates $x^{1'}, x^{2'}, x^{3'}$ with respect to the old coordinate functions $x^1, x^2,$ and x^3.

5.11 : The Tensor Viewpoint

This section can be omitted without loss in continuity. Its purpose is to present yet another viewpoint towards the "vector" concept, and to clarify a few points raised earlier in this book.

We continue to use the notation and terminology of the preceding section. In particular, we continue using the term "old basis" and "new basis." However, we introduce a suggestive notational device straightaway. Let us denote the old basis by the single letter B, and let B' denote the new basis. Instead of saying "the column vector representing a (contravariant) vector x relative to the basis B is (x^i)" we simply write $x(B) = (x^i)$. Similarly, the notation $f(B') = (f_{i'})$ means that the row vector representing the covariant vector (linear functional) f relative to the new basis B' is $(f_{i'})$.

Keep in mind that x denotes the vector, but $x(B)$ denotes the column of numbers that represents x relative to the basis B. Thus if the basis is $\underset{1}{e}, \underset{2}{e}, \underset{3}{e}$ and if $x = 3\underset{1}{e} + \underset{2}{e} + 5\underset{3}{e}$, we would have

$$x(B) = \begin{pmatrix} 3 \\ 1 \\ 5 \end{pmatrix}$$

but if B' denotes the basis $\underset{1}{e} + \underset{2}{e}, 2\underset{1}{e}, 5\underset{3}{e}$, then for the same x we have

$$x(B') = \begin{pmatrix} 1 \\ 1 \\ 1 \end{pmatrix}$$

As soon as we do this, we see that we can think of vectors as functions! A vector x is a function that assigns to each basis B a column of numbers.

The reader who finds this hard to swallow should read Section 3.5 once again. We have already seen that a scalar product is a scalar-valued function of two vector variables, a vector product is a vector-valued function of two vector variables, and so on. Now we are thinking of a vector itself as a column-vector-valued function of a variable, the variable in this case being the basis.

(Many physicists say the same thing in a different way, i.e.: a vector in a three-dimensional space is a quantity having three components, which depend on the coordinate system.)

Similarly, a covariant vector is a row-vector-valued function of B.

Let us now be more precise. There is, after all, a lot more difference between contravariant vectors and covariant vectors than whether we write their components in columns or rows. Indeed, it is only when we wish to write equations in matrix form that it makes any difference whether we use columns or rows.

A *contravariant vector* in a three-dimensional vector space is a function x that assigns to each basis B a triple of numbers $x(B)$ with the property that for any two bases B and B' the triples $x(B) = (x^i)$ and $x(B') = (x^{i'})$ are related by the equations

$$(1) \qquad\qquad x^{i'} = \sum A_j{}^{i'} x^j$$

where $(A_j{}^{i'})$ is the matrix whose jth column gives the components of the jth element of B relative to B'.

A similar definition can be given for covariant vector, except that the transformation law is

$$(2) \qquad\qquad f_{i'} = \sum A_{i'}{}^j f_j$$

The reader who thinks that there is a bit of circularity in the logic here is to some extent correct. We are using the notion of a vector in order to define a vector. To avoid being illogical, we must distinguish between at least three objects: vector (element of a vector space), contravariant vector (as defined above), and covariant vector (as defined above). Of course, every vector uniquely determines a contravariant vector, as we have already demonstrated, and it is not hard to see that any contravariant vector (as defined above) uniquely determines an element of the vector space. Hence one can identify vectors with contravariant vectors. If we use the above definition of covariant vector, we should want to prove separately that a covariant vector determines a linear functional, first showing that $\sum f_i x^i = \sum f_{i'} x^{i'}$ (hence to each contravariant vector x and each covariant vector f there is an associated scalar independent of basis) and then demonstrating the linearity.

Let us look briefly at the transformation law for scalar products. Let us denote $\underset{i}{e} \cdot \underset{j}{e}$ by g_{ij} (this is a standard notation). Similarly, let $\underset{i'}{e} \cdot \underset{j'}{e}$ be denoted $g_{i'j'}$. If u and v are arbitrary vectors, we have

$$u \cdot v = \left(\sum u^i \underset{i}{e} \right) \cdot \left(\sum v^j \underset{j}{e} \right) = \sum \sum u^i v^j \underset{i}{e} \cdot \underset{j}{e} = \sum \sum g_{ij} u^i v^j$$

Hence the general formula for the scalar product involves nine terms.

Changing basis, we have

$$g_{i'j'} = e_{i'} \cdot e_{j'} = \left(\sum_k A_{i'}{}^k e\right) \cdot \left(\sum_p A_{j'}{}^p e\right) = \sum_k \sum_p A_{i'}{}^k A_{j'}{}^p (e \cdot e)$$

$$= \sum \sum A_{i'}{}^k A_{j'}{}^p g_{kp}$$

Taking g_{ij} to be the entry in the ith row and jth column, we can form a matrix (g_{ij}), but the transformation law is not the same as that for matrices representing a linear transformation.

It is customary in physics to say that a *tensor* in a three-dimensional space is a "quantity" with nine components. These components vary with changes in coordinate system (in our terminology, since we consider only linear coordinate systems, this simply means a change of basis). Tensors are classified according to their transformation laws. For example, a linear transformation determines a tensor $(T_j{}^i)$ that is called a *mixed tensor*. A scalar product determines a tensor (g_{ij}) that is a special kind of *covariant tensor*. The alternated product of two vectors (to be defined shortly) is a special kind of *contravariant tensor*. We shall not give the precise definitions of these terms, and we warn the reader that the terminology is by no means standard. If the reader wants to know "a little, but not too much" about tensors, he should consult a textbook on theoretical physics. The more advanced student who wishes to gain a much deeper understanding of tensor analysis and its applications should eventually study *Tensor Analysis for Physicists*, by J. A. Schouten (Oxford, 1951). This is quite a difficult book to read and, in the opinion of this author, is not intended so much for physicists as for applied mathematicians. This author knows of no books on tensor analysis written in a modern style for pure mathematicians.

The *alternated product* of two vectors u and v is defined to be the tensor with components $T^{ij} = u^i v^j - v^i u^j$. If the reader has studied carefully the discussion of the axial product, Section 5.8, he will have no trouble understanding its geometrical significance. It transforms under change of basis according to the law

$$(3) \qquad\qquad T^{i'j'} = \sum \sum A_k{}^{i'} A_p{}^{j'} T^{kp}$$

It is closely related to the axial product of u and v. Indeed, the axial product has three components, T^{23}, T^{31}, and T^{12} respectively, and if we know the axial product we can readily determine all the other components of the alternated product from the relation

$T^{ij} = -T^{ji}$. If, for any basis B, we have a rule that associates a triple of numbers $v(B) = (p_1, p_2, p_3)$, and if these three numbers vary with change of basis in the same manner as the entries T^{23}, T^{31}, and T^{12} of an alternated product, then we say that v is an *axial vector*. In other words, an axial vector is an abbreviated way of representing a contravariant tensor with the property $T^{ij} = -T^{ji}$. The axial product of two vectors is an axial vector.

In working with axial vectors, one usually considers only orthonormal bases. As we have already seen, if we have a vector product defined in the vector space, we can identify the axial product of two vectors with either the vector product or its negative. (Returning to the naive geometrical viewpoint of earlier chapters, we can say that the axial product equals the vector product if the basis is a right-handed system, and it equals the negative of the vector product if the basis is a left-handed system. Keep in mind that the basis must be orthonormal—otherwise there is no simple relationship between the vector product and the axial product.)

Figure 100

Axial vectors arise quite naturally in physics if one considers vectors that represent rotations. For instance, the angular velocity vector (Section 1.14) is an axial vector if one considers only orthonormal bases. A somewhat fanciful way of seeing this is to consider a cylinder rotating about an axis that is parallel to the face of a mirror. (The reflected image of a right-handed system is a left-handed system, which is why the analogy has some validity.) The reflected image of the cylinder is rotating in the opposite direction, so we can think of the reflected image of the velocity vector as pointing in the opposite direction. If we wish to violate the usual standards of mathematical rigor, we can define an axial vector as a vector that can be represented by a directed line segment having the mysterious property that its reflected image has a directed sense precisely opposite to that given by the ordinary laws of optics.

To indicate this ambiguity in directed sense, it is customary when giving an elementary geometrical representation of an axial vector to draw a figure like that of Figure 100.

In elementary discussions in which both axial vectors and ordinary vectors occur, it is common to call ordinary (i.e., contravariant) vectors *polar vectors*.

EXERCISES

In R^3, let $\underset{1}{e}, \underset{2}{e}, \underset{3}{e}$ be the natural basis B, and let B' be the basis

$$\underset{1'}{e} = \underset{1}{e} + \underset{2}{e}, \quad \underset{2'}{e} = -\underset{1}{e} + \underset{2}{e}, \quad \underset{3'}{e} = 2\underset{3}{e}$$

Let the scalar product be the usual scalar product in R^3, relative to which the natural basis is orthonormal.

1.   Determine the matrices $(A_{j'}{}^i)$ and $(A_j{}^{i'})$.

2.   Determine the column vector representing $\underset{1}{e} + 5\underset{2}{e} + 4\underset{3}{e}$ relative to B'.

3.   If f is a linear functional with components $f_1 = 1, f_2 = 5, f_3 = 4$ relative to B, find its components relative to B'.

4.   If a linear transformation T is represented by the matrix

$$(T_j{}^i) = \begin{pmatrix} 2 & 3 & 1 \\ 1 & 1 & 1 \\ 3 & 0 & 4 \end{pmatrix}$$

relative to B, what matrix represents T relative to B'?

5.   Is B' an orthonormal basis?

6.   Find the matrix $(g_{i'j'})$ representing the scalar product relative to B'.

7.   Use the matrix obtained in the preceding exercise to compute the scalar product of u and v, given that $u^{1'} = -1, u^{2'} = 1, u^{3'} = 1, v^{1'} = 2, v^{2'} = 3, v^{3'} = -1$. Check your answer by finding the components of u and v relative to the natural basis and computing the scalar product in the usual way.

8. Let S be a contravariant tensor represented by the matrix

$$(S^{ij}) = \begin{pmatrix} 2 & 3 & 1 \\ 1 & 1 & 1 \\ 3 & 0 & 4 \end{pmatrix}$$

relative to B.   What matrix represents S relative to B'?

9. Find the "covariant components" of the vector given in Exercise 2 relative to both B and B'.

10. Match
   (a) $A_j{}^{i'}$ (i) $\partial x^i / \partial x^{j'}$
   (b) f_i (ii) $f(\underset{i}{e})$
   (c) $A_{j'}{}^i$ (iii) $\underset{j}{e^{i'}}$
   (d) x^i
                                   (iv) $\underset{i}{e}(x)$

11. (a) Prove the relation $\sum f_i x^i = \sum f_{i'} x^{i'}$ mentioned in the text.
    (b) Is it true that $f_i x^i = f_{i'} x^{i'}$ for each fixed i?

5.12 : Special Classes of Transformations

We consider a three-dimensional vector space, equipped with both a scalar product and a vector product.   Almost everything we discuss in this section is relative to the choice of scalar or vector product.   For instance, the "symmetric transformations" introduced below are symmetric with respect to the particular choice of scalar product.   Relative to another scalar product, the transformation might not be symmetric.   To avoid undue repetition, we shall not continually use the phrase "relative to the scalar product."

Before giving the definitions, let us derive a simple and useful expression for the entries in the matrix representing a linear transformation T.   If T is a linear transformation of the space, and if $\underset{1}{e}, \underset{2}{e}, \underset{3}{e}$ is an orthonormal basis, then relative to this basis we have

(1) $$T_j{}^i = \underset{i}{e} \cdot T\underset{j}{e}$$

Indeed, we have $T\underset{j}{e} = \sum T_j{}^k \underset{k}{e}$, and therefore $\underset{i}{e} \cdot T\underset{j}{e} = \underset{i}{e} \cdot (\sum T_j{}^k \underset{k}{e}) = \sum T_j{}^k (\underset{i}{e} \cdot \underset{k}{e})$.   Since the basis is orthonormal, $\underset{i}{e} \cdot \underset{k}{e} = 0$ except when

$k = i$, so that all terms in this sum vanish except one. That one term is $T_j{}^i(\underset{i}{e} \cdot \underset{i}{e})$, and since $(\underset{i}{e} \cdot \underset{i}{e}) = 1$, this equals $T_j{}^i$.

Again we emphasize that this expression is valid only if the basis is orthonormal.

A linear transformation is said to be *symmetric* if for every pair of vectors x and y we have

(2) $$x \cdot Ty = Tx \cdot y$$

It follows from this definition and from (1) that, if T is symmetric, then relative to an orthonormal basis T will be represented by a *symmetric matrix* $(T_j{}^i)$, i.e., we will have

(3) $$T_j{}^i = T_i{}^j$$

for every pair of indices i and j. Conversely, if a matrix representing T relative to an orthonormal basis is symmetric, a simple calculation shows that T is a symmetric transformation.

The following examples are somewhat artificial, since we are restricting ourselves to a three-dimensional vector space, but the interested reader can easily generalize them.

EXAMPLE 1: Consider a system of three particles joined together by springs, as shown in Figure 101. These particles are numbered $i = 1,2,3$.

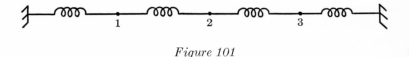

Figure 101

Let the displacement from equilibrium of any particle be denoted x^i (taken positive to the right), and let the resultant force on the ith particle be denoted F^i taken positive if the force is directed to the right. (Since the system is rectilinear, we can represent displacements and forces by signed numbers, the sign indicating the direction.) Let $T_j{}^i$ represent the force exerted on the ith particle due to a unit displacement (to the right) of the jth particle (the other two particles being held fixed). Then it is easy to see that, for an arbitrary displacement of the particles, $F^i = \sum T_j{}^i x^i$. The matrix $T_j{}^i$ is symmetric. For example, if the spring constant of the spring joining particles 1 and 2 is k, then $T^{12} = T^{21} = k$. We have $T^{13} = T^{31} = 0$, etc. This example is far too transparent to indicate the importance of symmetric transformations in the theory of linear oscillations.

EXAMPLE 2: The reader familiar with the concept of angular momentum knows that the angular momentum vector for a rotating rigid body need not be in the same direction as the angular velocity vector. This is the reason one obtains side-thrust on the bearings when an object is rotated that is not symmetrical about its axis of rotation. If p denotes angular momentum and ω denotes angular velocity, and if the components of these vectors are taken relative to an orthonormal basis rotating with the body, it can be shown that $p^i = \sum M_j{}^i \omega^j$, where $M_j{}^i = M_i{}^j$. The "quantity" $(M_j{}^i)$ is sometimes called the *moment of inertia tensor*. In elementary mechanics, the body is taken to be symmetrical about the axis of rotation, whence $M_j{}^i = 0$ whenever $i \neq j$, and the three components $M_1{}^1$, $M_2{}^2$, and $M_3{}^3$ are the moments of inertia about the three coordinate axes.

EXAMPLE 3: It can be shown that any symmetric transformation has the geometrical significance of transforming any sphere into an ellipsoid. If the base vectors are chosen to point along the principal axes of such an ellipsoid, then the matrix representing T will be diagonal. The entries along the principal diagonal of the matrix give the factor by which T magnifies distances in these three directions. The product of these three numbers then obviously gives the volume magnification factor of T, and this of course equals the determinant of T.

It would take us too far afield to elaborate on Examples 1 and 2. We shall now discuss Example 3 in greater detail.

A *nonzero* vector v is said to be an *eigenvector* for a linear transformation T if $Tv = cv$ for some scalar c. (Mathematicians generally prefer the terms *characteristic vector* or *proper vector*.) The scalar c is called the *eigenvalue* corresponding to v. Geometrically, this means simply that all points on a line through the origin parallel to v are shifted to a position that is also along the same line. Worded yet another way, an eigenvector is one whose magnitude may be altered by T but whose direction is not changed. (This is naive and in fact incorrect, since it is possible for the eigenvalue to be zero, whence the transform has no direction.)

Not all linear transformations have eigenvectors. For example, if T is a rotation in the plane through an angle of 30°, there will be no nonzero vector v for which Tv is parallel to v. Some linear transformations have eigenvectors in only one direction. For example, if T is a rotation of space through an angle of 30°, about an axis, the only eigenvectors will be the nonzero vectors along this axis. Symmetric transformations, however, all have a remarkable property: for them *there can be found an orthonormal basis consisting entirely of eigenvectors.*

If, then, T is a symmetric transformation, and if $\underset{1}{e}, \underset{2}{e}, \underset{3}{e}$ is an orthonormal basis with the property $\underset{1}{Te} = c_1\underset{1}{e}, \ \underset{2}{Te} = c_2\underset{2}{r}, \ \underset{3}{Te} = c_3\underset{3}{e}$, the matrix representing T relative to this basis will be diagonal:

$$\begin{pmatrix} c_1 & 0 & 0 \\ 0 & c_2 & 0 \\ 0 & 0 & c_3 \end{pmatrix}$$

The numbers along the principal diagonal will be the eigenvalues of T.

This is the substance of the statement made in Example 3. The proof will be left as a project for the reader; it is outlined in the exercises, so the student should have very little difficulty. The proof for spaces of dimension greater than three is more difficult; the interested reader is referred to *Finite Dimensional Vector Spaces*, by Paul R. Halmos (Van Nostrand, 1958) which is one of the finest mathematical textbooks in the English language.

Now let us turn to *skew-symmetric transformations*. These are linear transformations with the property

(4) $x \cdot Ty = -Tx \cdot y$

We leave to the reader the elementary proof that a linear transformation is skew-symmetric if and only if it is represented, relative to at least one orthonormal basis (and hence to all), by a *skew-symmetric matrix:*

(5) $T_j{}^i = -T_i{}^j$

Given any skew-symmetric transformation T, there exists a unique vector A such that

(6) $Tx = A \times x$

for all x. This has already been pointed out in Section 5.9. On writing out both sides of this equation in components, relative to an orthonormal basis with the property $\underset{1}{e} \times \underset{2}{e} = \underset{3}{e}$, it is trivial to see that such a vector A exists. Since (6) is independent of coordinate system, this relation will hold quite independent of the basis. Note, however, that if one interprets the right side of (6) as an axial product, then (6) will not be valid, since the right side would be an axial vector, whereas the left side is not.

We now point out that *every* linear transformation T can be written as the sum of a symmetric transformation and a skew-symmetric transformation. That is,

$$(7) \qquad\qquad T = \overset{+}{T} + \overset{-}{T}$$

where $\overset{+}{T}$ is symmetric and $\overset{-}{T}$ is skew-symmetric. We call $\overset{+}{T}$ the *symmetric part* of T, and $\overset{-}{T}$ the *skew-symmetric part* of T.

To prove this, we note that it is sufficient to show that there exists a symmetric transformation $\overset{+}{T}$ and a skew-symmetric transformation $\overset{-}{T}$ such that $(T_j{}^i) = (\overset{+}{T}_j{}^i) + (\overset{-}{T}_j{}^i)$ relative to some basis, for linear transformations are identical if and only if they are represented by identical matrices relative to one basis (and hence all bases). Therefore, let us take an orthonormal basis, and let $(T_j{}^i)$ be the matrix representing T relative to this basis. Define $\overset{+}{T}_j{}^i$ to be $\frac{1}{2}(T_j{}^i + T_i{}^j)$ and $\overset{-}{T}_j{}^i$ to be $\frac{1}{2}(T_j{}^i - T_i{}^j)$. Since the basis is orthonormal and $(\overset{+}{T}_j{}^i)$ and $(\overset{-}{T}_j{}^i)$ are symmetric and skew-symmetric respectively, they represent symmetric and skew-symmetric transformations that we will denote $\overset{+}{T}$ and $\overset{-}{T}$. Clearly $(T_j{}^i) = (\overset{+}{T}_j{}^i) + (\overset{-}{T}_j{}^i)$, and so by the remarks above the proof is complete.

EXERCISES

1. Prove in detail that, if $(T_j{}^i)$ is a symmetric matrix representing a linear transformation T relative to an orthonormal basis, then T is a symmetric transformation.

2. Show that, if v is an eigenvector of a symmetric transformation, and w is orthogonal to v, then Tw is also orthogonal to v. [Hint: $Tw \cdot v = w \cdot Tv = w \cdot cv = c(w \cdot v)$.]

3.   Let T denote a symmetric transformation in a three-dimensional space, and let $\mathcal{I}$ denote the identity transformation. Show that if $\det (T - c_1 \mathcal{I}) = 0$ then there exists an eigenvector of T with corresponding eigenvalue c_1.

4.   Show that every symmetric transformation T in a three-dimensional space has at least one eigenvector.   [Hint: $\det (T - c\mathcal{I})$ is a cubic polynomial in c.]

5.   Show that, if T is a symmetric transformation in a three-dimensional space, there exists an orthonormal basis e_1, e_2, e_3 relative to which T is represented by a matrix of the form

$$\begin{pmatrix} c_1 & 0 & 0 \\ 0 & a & d \\ 0 & d & b \end{pmatrix}$$

[Hint: Let e_1 be an eigenvector of T, and take e_2 and e_3 both to be perpendicular to e_1.   Use Exercise 2.]

6.   Show that there exists at least one real number c_2 such that

$$\det \begin{pmatrix} (a - c_2) & d \\ d & (b - c_2) \end{pmatrix} = 0$$

no matter what the real numbers a, b, and d may be.   [Hint: Look at the discriminant of the expression $(a - c)(b - c) - d^2$, which is quadratic in c.]

7.   Show that, if T is a symmetric transformation in a three-dimensional space, there exists an orthonormal basis relative to which T is represented by a diagonal matrix

$$\begin{pmatrix} c_1 & 0 & 0 \\ 0 & c_2 & 0 \\ 0 & 0 & c_3 \end{pmatrix}$$

8.   Show that, if T is an arbitrary linear transformation in a three-dimensional space, the trace of T equals the trace of its symmetric part.

9.   Let M be a symmetric 3×3 matrix, and let v_1, v_2, v_3 be mutually orthogonal vectors, each an eigenvector for M, that is, $Mv_i = c_i v_i$ $(i = 1,2,3)$. Let P be a matrix whose columns are

v, v, and v respectively, that is, $P_j{}^i = v^i$. Describe explicitly
$\underset{1}{} \quad \underset{2}{} \qquad \underset{3}{} \qquad\qquad\qquad\qquad \underset{j}{}$
the matrix $P^{-1}MP$.

10. (a) For an arbitrary basis e, e, e, show that the matrix (g_{ij}),
$\qquad\qquad\qquad\qquad\qquad \underset{1}{} \ \underset{2}{} \ \underset{3}{}$
where $g_{ij} = e \cdot e$, is nonsingular and hence possesses an
$\qquad\qquad\qquad\quad \underset{i}{} \ \underset{j}{}$
inverse.

(b) Let this inverse matrix be denoted (g^{ij}). For any linear
transformation T, represented by a matrix $(T_j{}^i)$ relative to
the same basis, let $\overset{*}{T}$ be the linear transformation repre-
sented by the matrix $(\overset{*}{T}_j{}^i)$, where $\overset{*}{T}_j{}^i = \sum \sum g^{ik}g_{jp}T_k{}^p$.
Show by direct calculation that, for any pair of vectors x
and y, $x \cdot Ty = \overset{*}{T}x \cdot y$.

(c) The transformation $\overset{*}{T}$ is called the *adjoint* of T. Write
down expressions for $\overset{+}{T}$ and $\overset{-}{T}$ in terms of T and $\overset{*}{T}$.

(d) Ignoring the above computations, show that, for any linear
transformation T, there exists a linear transformation $\overset{*}{T}$
such that $x \cdot Ty = \overset{*}{T}x \cdot y$ for every pair of vectors x and
y. [Hint: For each fixed x let $f(y) = x \cdot Ty$. This is a
linear functional, and so there exists a unique vector u such
that $f(y) = u \cdot y$ for all y. Define $\overset{*}{T}x$ to be this vector u.
Prove that $\overset{*}{T}$ is linear.]

5.13 : Scalar Fields and the Gradient

As before, V denotes a three-dimensional vector space equipped
with a scalar product, and for any vector x, $|x|$ is defined to be
$(x \cdot x)^{\frac{1}{2}}$. A sequence of vectors x, x, x, . . . , is said to *converge* to x if
$\qquad\qquad\qquad\qquad\qquad\qquad\qquad \underset{1}{} \ \underset{2}{} \ \underset{3}{}$

$$\lim_{n \to \infty} |x - x_n| = 0$$

A scalar-valued function f is said to be *continuous* at x if, for every
sequence x, x, x, . . . , converging to x, we have
$\qquad\quad \underset{1}{} \ \underset{2}{} \ \underset{3}{}$

$$f(x) = \lim_{n \to \infty} f(x)$$

A function f is said to be *continuous* in a region if it is continuous at every x in that region. It can be shown (but we omit the proof) that the notion of convergence of a sequence, and continuity of a function, is independent of the choice of scalar product, despite the fact that the definitions just given seem to depend on the scalar product. (Thus, for example, it makes sense to speak of a *continuous* temperature distribution, without specifying whether we are measuring distance in feet or centimeters when we define continuity.)

We shall now sketch briefly a coordinate-free treatment of the gradient concept. Before doing so, and in motivation for the definition about to be given, let us review briefly some ideas of elementary calculus.

Let f be a real-valued function of a real variable, the kind of function considered in elementary calculus. We recall that the derivative $f'(x)$ is defined by the expression

$$(1) \qquad\qquad f'(x) = \lim_{\Delta x \to 0} \frac{f(x + \Delta x) - f(x)}{\Delta x}$$

provided this limit exists. This derivative is also denoted df/dx, but the symbol df/dx does not, to begin with, represent a quotient. It can be made to represent one if, for an arbitrary increment Δx, we decree that $dx = \Delta x$, and then *define df* to be $f'(x)\,\Delta x$. Geometrically, $f'(x)$ denotes the slope of a line tangent to the graph of f. The differential df is sometimes said to be the "closest linear approximation" to Δf, at the point x. Geometrically, this is illustrated by a diagram like that of Figure 102; Δf is the change in f that arises from a change

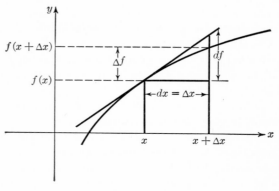

Figure 102

of amount Δx in the independent variable, whereas df is the change that would take place if we moved along the tangent line rather than along the graph.

A point that students frequently miss here is that it is *not* true that dx or df are necessarily "small" quantities. With df and dx defined in this manner, we have $f'(x) = df/dx$ even if dx is a number exceeding ten million. The reader must clearly understand this, or he will misunderstand the following discussion.

It will be observed that, for each fixed x, the differential $df = f'(x)\, dx$ is a linear function of dx. In particular, if $dx = 0$, then $df = 0$. If we multiply dx by an arbitrary factor k, then df will also change by the same factor k.

Now let us *recast* the definition of df in the following manner. For arbitrary dx and nonzero h, let us form the quotient

$$(2) \qquad \frac{f(x + h\, dx) - f(x)}{h}$$

and let us define the *differential of f with respect to dx* to be the limit of this expression (if it exists) as h tends to zero. If $dx = 0$, then obviously this gives zero. If we multiply dx by an arbitrary factor k, then the differential of f will be multiplied by this same factor; this is obvious for $k = 0$, and for $k \neq 0$ we have

$$\frac{f(x + hk\, dx) - f(x)}{h} = k \cdot \frac{f(x + hk\, dx) - f(x)}{hk} = k \cdot \frac{f(x + h'\, dx) - f(x)}{h'}$$

where $h' = hk$ tends to zero as h tends to zero.

We recognize immediately that the limit of (2), as h tends to zero, is our old friend $f'(x)\, dx$. [To see this, replace $h\, dx$ by Δx in the numerator, and h by $\Delta x/dx$ in the denominator, then compare with (1).] The point is that it is possible to define df directly, without ever having defined $f'(x)$. It is in this form that we shall generalize the notion of the differential of a function to functions of more than one variable.

Again we warn the reader that he will not understand this generalization if he does not understand the elementary discussion above. In particular, if he is under the mistaken impression that dx is a "small quantity," he will be definitely handicapped. The number dx is a perfectly arbitrary real number. The differential of f with respect to dx, at any point x, is the limit of the quotient (2) as h tends to zero. This is a linear function of dx, and therefore can be written as some constant times dx. This constant turns out to be our old friend $f'(x)$. With this approach, the differential is defined first, and the notion of derivative appears later.

In the following discussion, we shall let R denote a fixed vector, and dR another fixed vector. Think of R as the position vector of a point in space, and of dR as a directed line segment extending away from this point. Let f be an arbitrary scalar-valued function of a vector variable (i.e., a scalar field). For any nonzero h, we form the quotient

$$(3) \qquad \frac{f(R + h\,dR) - f(R)}{h}$$

The *differential* of f with respect to dR is defined to be the limit of (3), if it exists, as h tends to zero. Let us denote this $df(R, dR)$. If $df(R, dR)$ exists for every R and dR, the function f is said to be *differentiable*. If, for each fixed dR, $df(R, dR)$ is a continuous function of R, then f is said to be *continuously differentiable*.

By an argument similar to that given above for a function of a single variable, it is easy to show that if $df(R, dR)$ exists, then for every scalar k, $df(R, k\,dR)$ exists and

$$(4) \qquad df(R, k\,dR) = k\,df(R, dR)$$

Now suppose that f is differentiable along a line passing through R parallel to dR. That is, suppose that $df(R + t\,dR, dR)$ exists for all t. Then by applying the mean value theorem of elementary calculus to the function $g(t) = f(R + t\,dR)$ one easily obtains a *generalized mean value theorem:*

$$(5) \qquad f(R + dR) - f(R) = df(R + \theta\,dR, dR) \qquad (0 < \theta < 1)$$

In other words, the change in f as we move along the line from R to $R + dR$ equals the differential of f with respect to dR at some point between R and $R + dR$. If f is continuously differentiable, then for small dR, the right side of (1) is "nearly equal" to $df(R, dR)$, and therefore df is "approximately" the change in f, whatever these colloquial expressions may mean.

Keep in mind that the notation dR is used merely to suggest the terminology and notation used earlier in this book. We need not think of dR as a "small vector" in any sense, and indeed, we would prefer to use another letter, say S, instead. The advantage of using dR is that, later on, if the reader wishes to take

$$dR = dx\,\mathbf{i} + dy\,\mathbf{j} + dz\,\mathbf{k}$$

reverting to our old notation, he will obtain the usual formulas he would expect to obtain, for of course we are thinking of df as our old friend

$$\frac{\partial f}{\partial x}\,dx + \frac{\partial f}{\partial y}\,dy + \frac{\partial f}{\partial z}\,dz$$

but—hush!—we should not be admitting this so soon.

We now claim that, if f is continuously differentiable, then for arbitrary vectors dR and dP we have

(6) $$df(R, dR + dP) = df(R, dR) + df(R, dP)$$

We leave the proof to the reader (Exercise 1, where abundant hints are given).

It follows from (4) and (6) that, for fixed R (and assuming that f is continuously differentiable), $df(R, dR)$ is a *linear functional*. This linear functional is called the *derivative* of f at R.

In this manner we have defined the derivative of a scalar field. This definition is completely independent of choice of basis; we have not even mentioned a basis in this section.   If we now introduce a basis e, e, e, we can write out the derivative of a scalar field in terms
       $\underset{1}{}\ \underset{2}{}\ \underset{3}{}$
of components relative to this basis. Suppose for example that $dR = e$.   Then $h\,dR$ has three components, h, 0, and 0, respectively,
        $\underset{1}{}$
and (3) becomes

$$\frac{f(x^1 + h,\, x^2,\, x^3) - f(x^1, x^2, x^3)}{h}$$

and the limit as h tends to zero is, by definition, the partial derivative $\partial f/\partial x^1$ at the point (x^1, x^2, x^3).   Similarly, $df(R, e)$ and $df(R, e)$ are $\partial f/\partial x^2$
                                          $\underset{2}{}$ $\underset{3}{}$
and $\partial f/\partial x^3$ respectively.   It follows that at each point R the linear functional (covariant vector) determined by the differential has components $(\partial f/\partial x^1,\ \partial f/\partial x^2,\ \partial f/\partial x^3)$.   If the vector dR is written in terms of its components,

$$dR = dx^1 \underset{1}{e} + dx^2 \underset{2}{e} + dx^3 \underset{3}{e}$$

then we have

$$df(R, dR) = df(R\, dx^1 \underset{1}{e} + dx^2 \underset{2}{e} + dx^3 \underset{3}{e})$$

$$= dx^1 df(R, \underset{1}{e}) + dx^2 df(R,\ \underset{2}{e}) + dx^3 df(R, \underset{3}{e})$$

$$= \frac{\partial f}{\partial x^1}\,dx^1 + \frac{\partial f}{\partial x^2}\,dx^2 + \frac{\partial f}{\partial x^3}\,dx^3$$

This is what we usually mean by the "total differential" of f.

Now for the first time in this section we shall make use of the scalar product. We recall that every linear functional can be obtained by taking the scalar product with a fixed vector (Section 5.8). It follows that $df(R, dR)$ is the scalar product of dR with a vector, depending only on f and R, and it is this vector that we call the gradient of f at R. That is, grad f at the point R is defined by requiring that

$$(7) \qquad\qquad df(R, dR) = \operatorname{grad} f \cdot dR$$

be valid for every dR.

Putting this another way, we see that the derivative of f at a point R is a covariant vector. The gradient of f at R is the contravariant vector that can be uniquely associated with f by making use of the scalar product. The notion of "derivative" is independent of scalar product, but the notion of "gradient" depends on the scalar product. In this sense, the gradient of a function is a somewhat artificial thing. It is generally easier to work directly with the derivative.

If we use the tensor viewpoint, this is especially easy to discuss. We simply define the derivative of f, relative to a given basis, to be the "vector" with components

$$(8) \qquad\qquad \partial_i f = \partial f/\partial x^i$$

at each point x. From this definition it follows easily that the derivative at a fixed point is a covariant vector, for if we recall that $x^i = \sum A_{j'}{}^i x^{j'}$, we see that $\partial x^i/\partial x^{j'} = A_{j'}{}^i$, and by the chain rule for partial derivatives, valid for a continuously differentiable function, we have

$$\partial_{i'} f = \partial f/\partial x^{i'} = \sum \frac{\partial f}{\partial x^i} \frac{\partial x^i}{\partial x^{i'}} = \sum A_{i'}{}^j f_j$$

which is precisely the transformation law for covariant vectors. Of course, if our earlier discussion is accepted, there is no need for this separate calculation to show that the derivative is a covariant vector. It follows from the fact that the differential of f is linear in dR. Indeed, the proof that $df(R, dR)$ is linear in dR for each fixed R is essentially equivalent to proving the validity of the chain rule for partial derivatives, and is a much more elegant way of looking at the whole matter.

Incidentally, we have now for the first time given an example of a *covariant vector field*. At each point there is a covariant vector $\partial_i f$, which may vary from point to point. A covariant vector field is simply a function that assigns to each point in space a covariant vector.

EXERCISE

Prove that $df(R, dR)$ is linear in its second variable, and especially explain in detail why the requirement of continuous differentiability is imposed. As a "starter" we write down the following equations; you supply the verbiage. Note that (4) is used in one step.

$$\frac{f(R + h\,dR + h\,dP) - f(R + h\,dR)}{h} + \frac{f(R + h\,dR) - f(R)}{h}$$

$$= \frac{df(R + h\,dR + \theta h\,dP, h\,dP)}{h} + \frac{df(R + \theta'h\,dR, h\,dR)}{h}$$

$$= df(R + h\,dR + \theta h\,dP, dP) + df(R + \theta'h\,dR, dR)$$

and now we let h tend to zero.

5.14 : Vector Fields

In Section 3.3 we stated that there are two fundamental measures of the rate of change of a vector field, the divergence and the curl. In this section we give a brief description of an even more fundamental measure of the rate of change of a vector field, and show that the divergence and curl are simply two aspects of this basic derivative.

As before, we use the notation R and dR to denote arbitrary vectors, but we "think" of these vectors differently. We think of R as the position vector of a point, and dR as a directed line segment extending away from this point.

Let F be a vector field. The differential of F with respect to dR at the point R is defined to be the limit, if it exists, of the difference quotient

(1)
$$\frac{F(R + h\,dR) - F(R)}{h}$$

as h tends to zero. We denote this by $dF(R, dR)$. We say that F is *differentiable* at a point R if this derivative exists at R for every dR. It is said to be *continuously differentiable* if it exists for every R and dR and is continuous in R. As in the preceding section, we simplify our discussion by ignoring fields that are not defined at every point in space.

When we say that (1) has limit $dF(R, dR)$ we mean that the norm

$$\left| dF(R, dR) - \frac{F(R + h\,dR) - F(R)}{h} \right|$$

tends to zero as h tends to zero. Despite the fact that many different ways are available for defining the norm, it can be shown that this is independent of the norm. The proof is omitted.

For every h, (1) is a vector, and therefore the differential $dF(R, dR)$ is a vector, for each fixed R and dR.

If F is continuously differentiable, then it can be shown that

(2) $dF(R, k\,dR) = k\,dF(R, dR)$

for every scalar k, and

(3) $dF(R, dR + dP) = dF(R, dR) + dF(R, dP)$

In other words, the differential is linear in its second variable. The proof might appear to follow at once from the exercise of the preceding section, by considering the components of F as scalar fields, but there is a little subtlety involved and therefore we omit the proof.

It follows from (2) and (3) that for fixed R the differential dF determines a linear transformation. Each vector dR is transformed into the vector $dF(R, dR)$. This linear transformation is sometimes called the *derivative* of F at R (by analogy with the motivating discussion in the preceding section) or the *Jacobian* of F at R. (Caution: What some books call the Jacobian is the determinant of this linear transformation rather than the transformation itself.) The term *Frechet derivative* is also used.

Let us now see what matrix represents this linear transformation, relative to a basis in the vector space.

It is rather obvious from the definition that, if we take dR to be (say) $\underset{1}{e}$, where the basis is $\underset{1}{e}, \underset{2}{e}, \underset{3}{e}$, then the limit of (1) is the partial derivative of the vector field with respect to the coordinate function x^1. Therefore the first column of the matrix representing the Jacobian is a column vector representing $\partial F / \partial x^1$. More generally, the ith column is $\partial F/\partial x^i$, and therefore the matrix representing the Jacobian is

$$(4) \qquad (\partial_j F^i) = \begin{pmatrix} \dfrac{\partial F^1}{\partial x^1} & \dfrac{\partial F^1}{\partial x^2} & \dfrac{\partial F^1}{\partial x^3} \\[2ex] \dfrac{\partial F^2}{\partial x^1} & \dfrac{\partial F^2}{\partial x^2} & \dfrac{\partial F^2}{\partial x^3} \\[2ex] \dfrac{\partial F^3}{\partial x^1} & \dfrac{\partial F^3}{\partial x^2} & \dfrac{\partial F^3}{\partial x^3} \end{pmatrix}$$

For convenience, we sometimes write $\partial_j F^i$ instead of $\partial F^i/\partial x^i$.

We recall that any linear transformation determines a mixed tensor. If we like, we may think of $dF(R, dR)$ as a *tensor field*. That is, at each point R, there is an associated tensor $\partial_j F^i(R)$. The tensor analyst might prefer to define the derivative at each point formally to be $\partial_j F^i$ at that point, and then verify that the transformation law for mixed tensors is valid. This would run as follows:

$$\partial_{j'} F^{i'} = \partial_{j'}(A_k^{i'} F^k) = \sum A_k^{i'} \partial_{j'} F^k$$

since the $A_k^{i'}$ are constants. By the chain rule for partial derivatives, this equals

$$\sum \sum A_k^{i'} \partial_p F^k \partial_{j'} x^p = \sum \sum A_k^{i'} \partial_p F^k A_{j'}^p$$

which is the transformation law for mixed tensors.

Intuitively, we think of $dF(R, dR)$ as the closest linear approximation to the change that takes place in the field F as we move from R to the point $R + dR$. For points "close" to a fixed point $\underset{0}{R}$ we may think of $F(R)$ as approximately equal to $F(\underset{0}{R}) + dF(\underset{0}{R}, R - \underset{0}{R})$, just as for ordinary functions of a single real variable we may approximate $f(x)$ by $f(x_0) + f'(x_0)(x - x_0)$. This idea is made somewhat more precise by the generalized mean value theorem, which asserts that under certain conditions

$$(5) \qquad F(R + dR) - F(R) = dF(R + \theta \, dR, dR) \qquad (0 < \theta < 1)$$

In particular, (5) is valid if F is continuously differentiable, and if dR is sufficiently small we can then take $dF(R, dR)$ to be approximately equal to the right side of (5). We omit the proof.

We have already noted that it is possible to split a linear transformation into its symmetric and skew-symmetric parts. Therefore we can write

(6) $$dF(R, dR) = d\overset{+}{F}(R, dR) + d\overset{-}{F}(R, dR)$$

With these preliminaries, we are ready to define the divergence and the curl.

The *divergence* of F is simply the *trace* of the Jacobian of F. We have

(7) $$\operatorname{div} F = \operatorname{tr} dF(R, dR) = \operatorname{tr} d\overset{+}{F}(R, dR) = \frac{\partial F^1}{\partial x^1} + \frac{\partial F^2}{\partial x^2} + \frac{\partial F^3}{\partial x^3}$$

This expression for the divergence is already familiar to us from earlier chapters. The remarkable thing is that the usual formula for the divergence is valid no matter what basis we use. This follows from the fact, already proved, that the trace of a linear transformation is independent of basis. In particular, this shows how very artificial is the notion of writing $\operatorname{div} F = \nabla \cdot F$, as though the concept of divergence depended somehow on the choice of a scalar product. *The divergence of a vector field does not depend on the scalar product and is computed by the same formula whether the basis is orthonormal or not.*

We have already seen that a skew-symmetric transformation can be written in terms of vector products. Thus we can find a vector A such that $d\overline{F}(R, dR) = A \times dR$. We define the curl of F to be twice this vector A. That is, curl F is defined by the formula

(8) $$d\overline{F}(R, dR) = \tfrac{1}{2} \operatorname{curl} F \times dR$$

We recall that the splitting of a linear transformation into symmetric and skew-symmetric parts depends on the scalar product, and that to every scalar product there are two possible ways to define a vector product. The notion of curl therefore does depend on the choice of scalar product and vector product.

If $\underset{1}{e}, \underset{2}{e}, \underset{3}{e}$ is a basis that is orthonormal relative to the scalar product, and if the vector product is such that $\underset{1}{e} \times \underset{2}{e} = \underset{3}{e}$, then we have seen that the usual formula for the vector product is valid. The matrix representing the skew-symmetric part of the Jacobian is

$$\frac{1}{2}\begin{pmatrix} 0 & \left(\dfrac{\partial F^1}{\partial x^2} - \dfrac{\partial F^2}{\partial x^1}\right) & \left(\dfrac{\partial F^1}{\partial x^3} - \dfrac{\partial F^3}{\partial x^1}\right) \\[3mm] \left(\dfrac{\partial F^2}{\partial x^1} - \dfrac{\partial F^1}{\partial x^2}\right) & 0 & \left(\dfrac{\partial F^2}{\partial x^3} - \dfrac{\partial F^3}{\partial x^2}\right) \\[3mm] \left(\dfrac{\partial F^3}{\partial x^1} - \dfrac{\partial F^1}{\partial x^3}\right) & \left(\dfrac{\partial F^3}{\partial x^2} - \dfrac{\partial F^2}{\partial x^3}\right) & 0 \end{pmatrix}$$

relative to any orthonormal basis, and by pulling out the appropriate entries we obtain the usual formula for the curl. It would be more natural, of course, to omit the factor $\frac{1}{2}$ from the definition (8), but then it would appear in the formula for the curl.

Let us now return to the intuitive discussion of divergence and curl, presented in Chapter Three. We have not yet justified the statements made there, although it is easy to do so by making use of the divergence theorem and Stokes' theorem. The discussion we are about to give, based on the Jacobian, is much more satisfying, and can be made into a rigorous argument, but we shall not go into all the details necessary for this.

Let us consider a small body of fluid in the vicinity of a point P, having volume V_0 at time $t = 0$. Let V denote the volume at an arbitrary time t. The ratio V/V_0 is called the *volume factor* at time t. The time rate of change of the volume factor is

$$(9) \qquad \frac{d}{dt}\left(\frac{V}{V_0}\right) = \frac{1}{V_0}\frac{dV}{dt}$$

The discussion in Section 3.3 can be summarized by saying that, if F is the velocity field of the fluid, then div F at a point P is the time rate of change of the volume factor at that point. This is obtained by evaluating (9) at time $t = 0$ and taking the limit as V_0 tends to zero. We shall now attempt to justify this assertion by using this as the *definition* of div F and showing that this leads to div $F = \text{tr}\,(\partial_j F^i)$, the usual expression for the divergence.

If F denotes the velocity field of the fluid, and R denotes the position vector of a particle of fluid, then

$$(10) \qquad dR/dt = F(R)$$

where we write $F(R)$ instead of $F(x^1, x^2, x^3)$. Let us suppose that, at time $t = 0$, the position vector of the particle in question is R_0. For points R near R_0 the right side of (10) is approximately

$$(11) \qquad F(R) = F(R_0) + dF(R_0, R - R_0)$$

where we write $R - R_0$ instead of dR. Let the symmetric part of the Jacobian be denoted S, and let us write $dF(R_0, R - R_0)$ in the form $A \times (R - R_0)$. Then (10) may be written

$$(12) \qquad dR/dt = F(R_0) + S(R - R_0) + A \times (R - R_0)$$

During a short time interval dt, the displacement of the particles in the vicinity of R_0 will be approximately

(13) $dR = F(R_0)\, dt + S(R - R_0)\, dt + A \times (R - R_0)\, dt$

By this, we mean that if the position of a particle at time $t = 0$ is R, then a short time dt later the same particle will have position $R + dR$. The displacement vector dR is the vector sum of three vectors, and one can imagine that the same displacement could be obtained by performing these three displacements in succession.

(The lack of rigor of any argument that uses such terms as "approximately" and "short time" is obvious.   A more fundamental error in this argument is pointed out in Exercise 1.)

Let us look at these three terms separately.   The first term is the only one that does not involve the variable R.   Since $F(R_0)\, dt$ is the same for every particle, this term represents a displacement of the body of fluid involving no change in volume and no rotation.

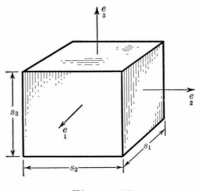

Figure 103

To analyze the other two terms, let us fix ideas by assuming that, at time $t = 0$, the body of fluid occupies a small rectangular parallelepiped whose edges have length s_1, s_2, and s_3.   We choose the faces to be perpendicular to the vectors of an orthonormal basis $e_1,\ e_2,\ e_3$, as shown in Figure 103.   Moreover, we assume that these vectors are eigenvectors for the symmetric transformation S.

If the eigenvalues corresponding to the eigenvectors $\underset{1}{e}$, $\underset{2}{e}$, and $\underset{3}{e}$ are c_1, c_2, and c_3 respectively, then relative to this basis, S is represented by a diagonal matrix with these numbers along the main diagonal, and the displacement $S(R - \underset{0}{R})\, dt$ has components

$$
\begin{aligned}
dx^1 &= c_1(x^1 - \underset{0}{x^1})\, dt \\
dx^2 &= c_2(x^2 - \underset{0}{x^2})\, dt \\
dx^3 &= c_3(x^3 - \underset{0}{x^3})\, dt
\end{aligned}
$$

(14)

These equations are easy to solve, and their solutions can be written in the form

(15) $$ x^i(t) - \underset{0}{x^i} = [x^i(0) - \underset{0}{x^i}]e^{c_i t} \qquad (i = 1,2,3) $$

According to (15), lengths parallel to the vector $\underset{i}{e}$ are multiplied by the factor $e^{c_i t}$, and so the volume of the body of fluid at time t is

$$
\begin{aligned}
V(t) &= (s_1 e^{c_1 t})(s_2 e^{c_2 t})(s_3 e^{c_3 t}) \\
&= s_1 s_2 s_3 e^{(c_1 + c_2 + c_3)t} \\
&= V_0 e^{(\mathrm{tr}\ S)t}
\end{aligned}
$$

approximately, for small V_0. The volume factor is $e^{(\mathrm{tr}\ S)t}$ and its time rate of change is $(\mathrm{tr}\ S)e^{(\mathrm{tr}\ S)t}$, which at time $t = 0$ equals $\mathrm{tr}\ S$. We recall that the trace of the symmetric part of a linear transformation equals the trace of the transformation itself, and so the trace of S equals the trace of the Jacobian, and this gives the usual expression for the divergence.

Now let us consider the third term in (13). This displacement is the vector product $A \times (R - \underset{0}{R})\, dt$ and equals the zero vector whenever $R - \underset{0}{R}$ is parallel to A. Moreover, the velocity $A \times (R - \underset{0}{R})$ is at right angles to both A and $R - \underset{0}{R}$, and therefore the particles must be moving in circular paths around the axis determined by A. The velocity of a particle will have magnitude $|A|\,|R - \underset{0}{R}|\sin\theta$, where $|R - \underset{0}{R}|\sin\theta$ is the distance from the particle to the axis, and therefore the particles are moving with angular velocity $|A|$. This shows that A is the angular velocity vector for the body of fluid in the vicinity of R. Since curl F equals $2A$ by definition, curl F is twice the angular velocity vector at R. This is the justification for the remarks made in Section 3.4.

The material presented above is given in rigorous form in the book *Advanced Calculus*, by H. K. Nickerson, D. C. Spencer, and N. E. Steenrod (Van Nostrand, 1959). Every honors student in mathematics should study this book; it is difficult, but well worth the effort.

We have seen from the above discussion that it is possible to define the derivative of a vector field in a natural manner, quite independently of the basis or the scalar product. This derivative is a linear transformation, and the trace of the transformation is the divergence. Thus divergence is independent of basis and scalar product. On the other hand, the curl of the vector field does depend on the choice of scalar product, and on the related choice of vector product.

Let us now consider briefly the determinant of this linear transformation, called the *Jacobian determinant*. Relative to some basis in the vector space, the field F has components F^1, F^2, and F^3. Let us denote the components of a point R by x^1, x^2, and x^3, as above, and let us look at the equations

$$u^1 = F^1(x^1, x^2, x^3)$$
(16)
$$u^2 = F^2(x^1, x^2, x^3)$$
$$u^3 = F^3(x^1, x^2, x^3)$$

We may think of these equations as determining, for each point (x^1, x^2, x^3), another point (u^1, u^2, u^3). In other words, the vector field F determines a transformation from $x^1 x^2 x^3$ space to $u^1 u^2 u^3$ space; of course, both these spaces are replicas of R^3. A small region in the vicinity of (x^1, x^2, x^3) is transformed to a region in the vicinity of (u^1, u^2, u^3). Assuming the field continuously differentiable, the Jacobian at a point is the linear transformation centered at the point that most closely approximates the transformation (16). Its determinant, therefore, gives the volume magnification factor at that point. More precisely, if V is the volume of a region in the vicinity of a point (x^1, x^2, x^3), and if we let V' denote the volume of the corresponding region in the vicinity of (u^1, u^2, u^3), then

$$(17) \qquad\qquad \lim_{V \to 0} \frac{V'}{V} = |J|$$

where J denotes the Jacobian determinant.

In particular, if $J \neq 0$ at a point, the linear transformation is one to one, and since it approximates (16), it follows that we can expect (16) to determine a one-to-one transformation, at least in some small region containing the point.   Within this region it is therefore possible to consider x^1, x^2, and x^3 as functions of u^1, u^2, u^3:

(18)
$$x^1 = G^1(u^1, u^2, u^3)$$
$$x^2 = G^2(u^1, u^2, u^3)$$
$$x^3 = G^3(u^1, u^2, u^3)$$

Moreover, it is reasonable to suppose that the Jacobian determinant of (18), evaluated at a point (u^1, u^2, u^3), is the reciprocal of the Jacobian determinant of (16) evaluated at the corresponding point (x^1, x^2, x^3).

Let us denote the Jacobian determinant of (18) by

$$\frac{\partial(x^1, x^2, x^3)}{\partial(u^1, u^2, u^3)}$$

and the Jacobian determinant of (16) by

$$\frac{\partial(u^1, u^2, u^3)}{\partial(x^1, x^2, x^3)}$$

(This is the usual notation, by the way.)   Let f be a continuous function and B a region in $x^1 x^2 x^3$ space such that the triple integral

(19)
$$\iiint_B f(x^1, x^2, x^3) \, dx^1 \, dx^2 \, dx^3$$

exists.   We recall that such an integral is the limit of sums of the form

(20)
$$\sum_{k=1}^{n} f(\underset{k}{x^1}, \underset{k}{x^2}, \underset{k}{x^3}) V_k$$

where V_k is the volume of a small region B_k containing $(\underset{k}{x^1}, \underset{k}{x^2}, \underset{k}{x^3})$.   If V_k' denotes the volume of the region corresponding to B_k in $u^1 u^2 u^3$ space, then

$$V_k = \left| \frac{\partial(x^1, x^2, x^3)}{\partial(u^1, u^2, u^3)} \right| V_k'$$

approximately, and the sum (20) is therefore approximately equal to

(21)
$$\sum_{k=1}^{n} g(\underset{k}{u^1}, \underset{k}{u^2}, \underset{k}{u^3}) \left| \frac{\partial(x^1, x^2, x^3)}{\partial(u^1, u^2, u^3)} \right| V_k'$$

where $g(\underset{k}{u^1}, \underset{k}{u^2}, \underset{k}{u^3})$ is defined to be equal to the value of f at the point corresponding to (u_k^1, u_k^2, u_k^3) and the Jacobian is evaluated at this same point. This heuristic line of reasoning leads us to the familiar *change of variables theorem:*

$$\iiint_B f(x^1, x^2, x^3)\ dx^1\ dx^2\ dx^3 = \iiint_{B'} g(u^1, u^2, u^3) \left| \frac{\partial(x^1, x^2, x^3)}{\partial(u^1, u^2, u^3)} \right| du^1\ du^2\ du^3$$

As a simple example, suppose we wish to integrate the function $f(x,y,z) = x^2 + y^2 + z^2$ over the unit sphere with center at the origin. If we change to spherical coordinates, we have

$$x = r \sin \phi \cos \theta$$
$$y = r \sin \phi \sin \theta$$
$$z = r \cos \phi$$

and the Jacobian determinant is

$$\frac{(x,y,z)}{(r,\phi,\theta)} = \det \begin{pmatrix} \sin \phi \cos \theta & r \cos \phi \cos \theta & -r \sin \phi \sin \theta \\ \sin \phi \sin \theta & r \cos \phi \sin \theta & r \sin \phi \cos \theta \\ \cos \phi & -r \sin \phi & 0 \end{pmatrix}$$

$$= r^2 \cos^2 \phi \sin \phi \cos^2 \theta + r^2 \sin^3 \phi \sin^2 \theta$$
$$\qquad\qquad + r^2 \cos^2 \phi \sin \phi \sin^2 \theta + r^2 \sin^3 \phi \cos^2 \theta$$

$$= r^2 \cos^2 \phi \sin \phi + r^2 \sin^3 \phi$$

$$= r^2 \sin \phi$$

Since $x^2 + y^2 + z^2 = r^2$, $g(r,\phi,\theta) = r^2$, and the integral becomes

$$\int_0^{2\pi} \int_0^{\pi} \int_0^1 r^4 \sin \phi\ dr\ d\phi\ d\theta = \frac{4\pi}{5}$$

For a rigorous treatment of the change of variables theorem, the author recommends *Advanced Calculus,* by R. C. Buck (McGraw-Hill, 1956). This book is written in a more sophisticated style than most textbooks on advanced calculus, but is quite readable nonetheless.

EXERCISES

1.   If $dR_1/dt = F(R_0)\ dt$, $dR_2/dt = S(R_2 - R_0)$, and

$$dR_3/dt = A \times (R_3 - R_0).$$

and we let $R = R_1 + R_2 + R_3$, does R satisfy (12)? Hence, criticize the rigor of the treatment given in this section.

2. If $u = x - y$ and $v = x + y$, find $\partial(u,v)/\partial(x,y)$ and hence $\partial(x,y)/\partial(u,v)$.

3. Let B be the region in the xy plane bounded by the lines $x = 0$, $y = 0$, $x + y = 1$. Evaluate the integral

$$\iint_B \exp\left(\frac{x - y}{x + y}\right) dx\, dy$$

5.15 : Historical Notes

It is not really possible to appreciate the history of vector algebra without knowing something of the history of algebra in general, and this is too broad a topic for us to discuss here. We shall confine our remarks to certain specific topics, and let the interested reader pursue the subject further elsewhere.

The word "vector" comes from a Latin word meaning "to carry," and was used earlier in astronomy with a somewhat different meaning. The notion of vector addition was arrived at independently by Möbius and others in the early part of the nineteenth century. Vector analysis as such is somewhat more recent. For example, the notion of *curl* was apparently introduced by J. C. Maxwell in his *Treatise on Electricity and Magnetism* (1873). The notation used most commonly now is essentially due to J. Willard Gibbs, whose book on vector analysis was printed privately in the early 1880's, and Oliver Heaviside, whose book on *Electromagnetic Theory* (1893) makes hilarious reading because of his jibes at mathematicians.

One of the most interesting events in the history of vector analysis is the controversy that once existed between exponents of vector analysis and a few other mathematicians who felt that *quaternions* were most suitable for solving problems in physics. Before proceeding, let us briefly discuss the algebra of quaternions. The algebra of quaternions is a four-dimensional vector space made into a division algebra in the following manner. Since one element in this algebra must play the part of a multiplicative identity, let us select an arbi-

trary basis and denote the four vectors in this basis by $1, i, j,$ and k.
(The first of these vectors is to be the identity.)   Thus any vector x
can be written in the form

$$x = x_0 + x_1 i + x_2 j + x_3 k$$

Let us call the vectors *quaternions*.   They are added and multiplied
by real numbers in the usual manner.   The product of two quaternions is defined by formally multiplying them out, according to the
usual rules of algebra (except that we must be careful to preserve
the order) and then simplifying the resulting expression by using the
following rules:

(1) $$i^2 = -1, \quad j^2 = -1, \quad k^2 = -1$$

(2) $$ij = k, \qquad jk = i, \qquad ki = j$$

(3) $$ji = -k, \quad kj = -i, \quad ik = -j$$

An example will illustrate the procedure.   If, for instance,
$x = 3 - i + 2j + k$ and $y = 3j - 2k$, we have

$$xy = (3 - i + 2j + k)(3j - 2k)$$
$$= 9j - 6k - 3ij + 2ik + 6j^2 - 4jk + 3jk - 2k^2$$
$$= 9j - 6k - 3k - 2j - 6 - 4i + 3i + 2$$
$$= -4 - i + 7j - 9k$$

It can be shown that the quaternions constitute a division algebra.   That is, to each quaternion $x \neq 0$, there is a quaternion x^{-1}
such that $xx^{-1} = x^{-1}x = 1$.   We shall not digress to show how an
inverse is computed.   It is important to note, however, that we cannot write y/x, since this would be ambiguous.   We must write either
$x^{-1}y$ or yx^{-1}, and since multiplication of quaternions is not commutative, these two expressions may not be equal.

The *real part* of a quaternion $x_0 + x_1 i + x_2 j + x_3 k$ is the number x_0.   If the real part of a quaternion is zero, the quaternion is
called a *pure quaternion*.   In applying quaternions to problems in
physics or geometry, pure quaternions are identified with ordinary
vectors in three-dimensional space, as the notation suggests.

If x and y are pure quaternions, the real part of xy turns out
to be the negative of the scalar product $x \cdot y$ (computed by the usual
formula), and the pure quaternionic part represents the vector product $x \times y$.   Thus it is possible to do with quaternions many of the

things one ordinarily does in vector analysis by using scalar and vector products.

We see that quaternions form a sort of generalization of complex numbers, and to appreciate their historical significance, one must really consider the background of the idea of a complex number.

As long ago as 1545 a mathematician (Cardan) "solved" a problem in algebra that has no real solutions. The problem is to find two numbers whose sum is 10 and whose product is 40. Cardan gave a formal solution, involving the square root of a negative number, and verified by substitution that these "fictitious numbers" have the required properties. As early as 1629, Girard suggested that such "impossible solutions" should be considered for three reasons: one can give a general rule for finding roots of certain equations, these solutions supply the lack of other solutions, and they may in any event have their own usefulness. In 1673, Wallis pointed out that numbers such as $\sqrt{-1}$ should be just as legitimate in mathematics as negative numbers. One cannot have $\sqrt{-1}$ eggs in a basket, but then neither can one have -7 eggs in a basket. Wallis came very close to giving the usual geometrical interpretation of complex numbers. It remained for a Norwegian surveyor Wessel to do this in 1797. (Argand did it independently in 1806, which is why the term Argand diagram is used. Wessel published his work in an obscure journal and hence did not receive credit during his lifetime.)

It was not until 1831 that Gauss put complex numbers on a respectable basis. Since some readers of this book may have learned complex numbers from a viewpoint (still common among many school-teachers) that predates 1831, let us briefly review complex numbers. A complex number is an ordered pair (x,y) of real numbers. With the usual addition and multiplication by (real) scalars, the set of all complex numbers forms a two-dimensional vector space. It is made into an algebra by defining the product of two complex numbers according to

$$(4) \qquad (x_1,y_1)(x_2,y_2) = (x_1x_2 - y_1y_2,\ x_1y_2 + x_2y_1)$$

It can then be verified that the set of all complex numbers forms a division algebra. If we identify $(1,0)$ with the real number 1, and let i denote $(0,1)$, then

$$(x,y) = (x,0) + (0,y) = x(1,0) + y(0,1) = x + yi$$

which is the usual notation for a complex number. Moreover, we have $i^2 = (0,1)(0,1) = (-1,0) = -1$, so it is now possible to square a number and obtain a negative number. Any school-teacher who defines i to be the square root of -1 is, of course, talking nonsense, since until we introduce complex numbers -1 has no square root.

Now we recall that multiplication by $\cos \theta + i \sin \theta$ has the effect of rotating a complex number through an angle θ. Hence rotations in a plane can be obtained by identifying the plane with the Argand diagram and the rotation with the operation of multiplying by $\cos \theta + i \sin \theta$. This suggested to W. R. Hamilton that rotations in space might be similarly obtained, if there were some way to make *triples* of numbers into a division algebra. (This is modern terminology; the term "division algebra" was not used by Hamilton.) Apparently this problem troubled him for a period of fifteen years. This is not too surprising when one considers that, up to the time of Hamilton, it was generally assumed that the commutative law $xy = yx$ was a necessary condition for the consistency of the rules of algebra. Hamilton is credited with the realization that this is not the case; actually, Gauss had the same idea earlier but did not publish his work.

Hamilton was trying to do the impossible. It was proved later, by Frobenius in 1878, that the only finite-dimensional division algebras are of dimensions one, two, and four. The real numbers are one-dimensional, the complex number system is two-dimensional. It was on a famous day, October 16, 1843, when he was out walking with his wife, that Hamilton, in a great flash of insight, conceived of the quaternions. It is said that he carved the fundamental formulas

$$i^2 = j^2 = k^2 = ijk = -1$$

of this new algebra in the stone of Brougham Bridge, on which he happened to be at the moment. He immediately recognized the importance of his discovery (some might say invention) and devoted the remainder of his life to quaternions.

Although the quaternions comprise a four-dimensional division algebra, rather than a three-dimensional one, it turned out that quaternions fulfilled the needs envisaged by Hamilton. It is possible to represent rotations by the use of quaternions, although not so simply as one might have wished, and in general there is a certain awkwardness in the use of quaternions. After working for ten years, Hamilton published his *Lectures on Quaternions* (1853); his *Elements of Quaternions* appeared in 1866, the year after his death. Incidentally, the earliest use of the word *vector* (in the mathematical sense), according to the Oxford dictionary, is in this work.

Hamilton had one devoted disciple, P. G. Tait, who mastered all the tricks of quaternions, and devoted himself to the cause of convincing one and all that quaternions were the ultimate tool for geometers and physicists. There were others who disagreed.

At about the same time that Hamilton made his remarkable discovery, H. G. Grassmann published a work called the Theory of Extension (*Ausdehnungslehre*). In this remarkable book, both matrix theory and tensor algebra are developed implicitly, but because he filled the book with philosophical abstractions, and because of its difficulty, the book was essentially ignored by mathematicians. A second edition was published in 1862, but the work was not much appreciated until the twentieth century.

The vector analysis of Gibbs and Heaviside, and the various generalities in this chapter, are more closely related to the *Ausdehnungslehre* than to anything Hamilton did. Grassmann introduced various types of "products" of vectors, and set things up for Gibbs to invent dyadics (not discussed in this book) and discussed linear transformations in general. The notion of a linear associative algebra was developed by Benjamin Peirce in the 1860's. The only other name we shall mention is that of Cayley, who was eminent for (among other things) conceiving of n-dimensional space (as did Grassmann) and who published a *Memoir on the Theory of Matrices* in 1858.

A delightful controversy took place between Gibbs and Tait concerning the merits of the use of quaternions in solving problems in geometry and physics. There is a certain beauty and mathematical elegance in the quaternions, but they are not very well adapted to practical use. Tait viewed vector analysis as a "hermaphroditic monster" and did not hesitate to express this view in print. The replies of Gibbs can be found in his collected works, available in any library, and they are both entertaining and instructive to read. By the beginning of the twentieth century, vector analysis was well established, and it was amply demonstrated that Hamilton and Tait were overly optimistic in their thought that quaternions would be as revolutionary to mathematics as was the invention of calculus. The revolutionary idea contributed by Hamilton was simply that it is possible to have a self-consistent algebra in which multiplication is not commutative.

ANSWERS AND NOTES

Important: Not all the notes given here will be understood by a beginner. Some of them are intended for graduate students or teachers who may be teaching vector analysis for the first time.

In the first four chapters, vectors are represented by bold-face letters, such as $\mathbf{A}$, $\mathbf{B}$, $\mathbf{C}$, . . . Since you cannot conveniently imitate this, the author suggests that you either underline the letter, $\underline{A}$, or put an arrow above it, $\vec{A}$. Be sure to distinguish between the number 0 and the vector $\mathbf{0}$.

Section 1.1   PAGE 1

Note: If the reader has studied modern algebra or logic, he will recognize that a vector is an *equivalence class* of directed line segments. This is a geometrical definition; other definitions will be found in Sections 5.2, 5.3, and 5.11. Note that parallel vectors having the same length in feet will also have the same length in meters or centimeters. That is, vector equality is not a metric property; it does not depend on choice of unit of length.

Section 1.2   *PAGE 5*

1.   Arrow extending from the same initial point and forming the diagonal of the parallelogram determined by the two vectors, as shown in Figure 2.

2.   Notice that $\mathbf{C} - \mathbf{A} = \mathbf{C} + (-\mathbf{A}) = (-\mathbf{A}) + \mathbf{C}$.

3.   Yes, the statement is correct.

4.   This is easy if you observe that a regular hexagon is composed of six equilateral triangles. (a) $\mathbf{B} - \mathbf{A}$, $-\mathbf{A}$, $-\mathbf{B}$, $\mathbf{A} - \mathbf{B}$ (b) the zero vector.

5.   In problems of this type, think of the vectors as displacements. The displacement $\mathbf{C}$ can be obtained by first moving backwards along $\mathbf{F}$, then moving along $\mathbf{E}$, then upwards in a direction opposite to $\mathbf{D}$. Hence $\mathbf{C} = -\mathbf{F} + \mathbf{E} - \mathbf{D}$.

6. $\mathbf{F} = \mathbf{E} - \mathbf{D} - \mathbf{C}$

7. $\mathbf{H} = \mathbf{D} - \mathbf{E} + \mathbf{F} + \mathbf{K}$. Check this by putting your pencil at the initial point of $\mathbf{D}$ and moving it along $\mathbf{D}$, $-\mathbf{E}$, $\mathbf{F}$, and $\mathbf{K}$. You will find that the resulting displacement is equivalent to $\mathbf{H}$.

8. $\mathbf{G} = -\mathbf{K} + \mathbf{C} + \mathbf{D} - \mathbf{E}$

Historical Note: This kind of addition was called *geometrical addition* when it was first introduced by Möbius and others over a century ago.

Personal Note: If your father is or has been an engineer, ask him when he learned vector analysis. Be prepared for a surprise.

Mathematical Note: The length of $\mathbf{A} + \mathbf{B}$ does not equal the length of $\mathbf{A}$ plus the length of $\mathbf{B}$. A student of mine once announced happily that he had won a bet in a tavern by showing an instance in which three units added to four units produce five units (see Exercise 4, Section 1.4).

Section 1.3   *PAGE 7*

1.   No, length is never a negative number.

2. $|4\mathbf{A}| = 12$, $|-2\mathbf{A}| = 6$, $|s\mathbf{A}| \leqq 6$

3. $|s\mathbf{A}| = 1$, $|-s\mathbf{A}| = 1$

4.   Equals the magnitude of $\mathbf{A}$.

5.   Not necessarily true, since the vectors may not point in the same direction.

6. Yes.

7. Two. Think of the plane as the top of your desk. One of the vectors points upward and the other downward. Many students say, "There are infinitely many." This is incorrect, since we do not distinguish between vectors that are equal.

8. Two, pointing in opposite directions.

9. $\mathbf{C} = \frac{1}{2}(\mathbf{A} + \mathbf{B})$

10. Infinitely many. Think of the line as perpendicular to the xy plane. The unit vector might make any angle θ with the x axis.

11. $$|\mathbf{A}| = |\mathbf{A} - \mathbf{B} + \mathbf{B}| \leq |\mathbf{A} - \mathbf{B}| + |\mathbf{B}|$$

Hence $|\mathbf{A}| - |\mathbf{B}| \leq |\mathbf{A} - \mathbf{B}|$. If you prefer a less tricky method, draw a diagram and use a well-known theorem in geometry.

12. No, $\mathbf{A}$ might be the zero vector.

Note: If s is a nonzero number and $\mathbf{A}$ is a vector, the vector $s^{-1}\mathbf{A}$ is sometimes said to be "$\mathbf{A}$ divided by s." Thus, if we divide a nonzero vector by its own length we obtain a vector of unit magnitude. This is the point of the first part of Exercise 3.

Section 1.4 *PAGE 8*

Note: I think the only reason some students have trouble with some of these exercises is that they think more is expected of them than simply writing down the answer. When I work one of these problems by drawing a diagram and looking at it, students sometimes say, "Oh, is that all you want?" It is not necessary for you to use any equations or formulas in giving the answer to a trivial exercise.

1. 1

2. 0

3. $\sqrt{2}$

4. 5

5. $A_x = 3\sqrt{3}, \quad A_y = 3$

6. $A_x = |\mathbf{A}| \cos\theta, \quad A_y = |\mathbf{A}| \sin\theta$

7. $\mathbf{A} = \mathbf{i} - 3\mathbf{j}$

8.   (a) $\dfrac{1}{2}\mathbf{i} + \dfrac{\sqrt{3}}{2}\mathbf{j}$ (d) $\dfrac{1}{2}\mathbf{i} + \dfrac{\sqrt{3}}{2}\mathbf{j}, \ \dfrac{1}{2}\mathbf{i} - \dfrac{\sqrt{3}}{2}\mathbf{j}$

  (b) $\dfrac{\sqrt{3}}{2}\mathbf{i} - \dfrac{1}{2}\mathbf{j}$ (e) $\pm\left(\dfrac{\sqrt{2}}{2}\mathbf{i} + \dfrac{\sqrt{2}}{2}\mathbf{j}\right)$

  (c) $\dfrac{3}{5}\mathbf{i} + \dfrac{4}{5}\mathbf{j}$

9. $10, 3, \sqrt{1 + s^2}, 1$

10. $2\mathbf{i} + 6\mathbf{j}$

11. $-\mathbf{i}, -\mathbf{j}, \dfrac{\sqrt{2}}{2}\mathbf{i} + \dfrac{\sqrt{2}}{2}\mathbf{j}$

Section 1.5   PAGE 10

1. $5, 3, 5$

2. $5\mathbf{i} + 6\mathbf{j} - \mathbf{k}, \ 4\mathbf{j} + 4\mathbf{k}$

3. $4\sqrt{2}$

4. $\pm\frac{1}{3}$

5. $\frac{3}{5}\mathbf{i} + \frac{4}{5}\mathbf{j}$

6.   (a) $4\sqrt{2}$ (b) yz plane

7. $\cos \alpha = \frac{3}{5}$.   In general, $\cos \alpha = A_x/|\mathbf{A}|$.

8. $\pm\mathbf{j}$

9. $\sqrt{3}$

10. $\mathbf{i} - 5\mathbf{j} - \mathbf{k}$

11. $x\mathbf{i} + y\mathbf{j} + z\mathbf{k}$

12. $s = 2, t = 3, r = -1$

Section 1.6   PAGE 11

No'e: The rotational effect a force produces on a rigid body depends both on the force and on the line of application of the force.   Therefore some books, such as Gibbs' *Vector Analysis* (Yale University Press, 1918), do not consider forces as vector quantities.   Also, some books call a directed line segment a *bound vector* and what we call a vector a *free vector*.

Section 1.7   <small>PAGE 16</small>

1. $\cos^{-1}(-2/15)$

2. $90°$

3. $\cos^{-1}(\sqrt{3}/3)$

4. $\cos^{-1}(\sqrt{1435}/41)$, $\cos^{-1}(\sqrt{246}/41)$, $90°$

5. $90° - \cos^{-1}(1/3)$

6. $A_x/|\mathbf{A}|$, $A_y/|\mathbf{A}|$, $A_z/|\mathbf{A}|$

7. $2/3, 1/3, 2/3$

8. $(\mathbf{i} + \mathbf{j} + \mathbf{k}) \cdot (x\mathbf{i} + y\mathbf{j} + z\mathbf{k}) = 0$ if and only if $x + y + z = 0$. Hence $\theta = 90°$ if and only if $x + y + z = 0$.

9. One method is to show that the desired vector is
$$\mathbf{A} + \tfrac{2}{3}[-\mathbf{A} + \mathbf{B} + \tfrac{1}{2}(\mathbf{C} - \mathbf{B})]$$

Section 1.8   <small>PAGE 20</small>

1. $x = 3t, y = -2t, z = 7t$

2. $\pm\left(\dfrac{3}{5}\mathbf{i} + \dfrac{4}{5}\mathbf{j}\right)$

3. $\pm\left(\dfrac{6}{7}\mathbf{i} + \dfrac{3}{7}\mathbf{j} + \dfrac{2}{7}\mathbf{k}\right)$

4. $\pm\left(\dfrac{3\sqrt{19}}{19}\mathbf{i} - \dfrac{3\sqrt{19}}{19}\mathbf{j} + \dfrac{\sqrt{19}}{19}\mathbf{k}\right)$

5. $x = 1,\quad y = 2$

6. $y = 2,\quad z = 3$

7. $x = (y/4) = -z$

8. $\cos^{-1}(3\sqrt{42}/70)$, about $74°$

9. $x = 3, y = 4$

10. $x - 1 = (y - 4)/(-2) = (z + 1)/8$.   This may be written in other forms.

Section 1.9   PAGE 23

Note: In Section 1.5 we explained what is meant by the components of a vector in the x, y, and z directions.   More generally, we can define the *scalar component* of a vector **A** in any direction to be **A**·**n** where **n** is a *unit* vector in the desired direction.   The *vector component* of **A** in the direction of a unit vector **n** is $(\mathbf{A}\cdot\mathbf{n})\mathbf{n}$.   Unless otherwise stated, "component" means "scalar component" in this book.

1.   19

2. $8 + 27 - 12 = 23$

3.   20

4. $\cos^{-1}(2/15)$

5. $\cos^{-1}(3/5)$

6.   10/3

7. $\sqrt{2}$

8. $\sqrt{5}\,\mathbf{i} + \sqrt{5}\,\mathbf{j}$

9. $|\sin(\theta/2)|$

10.   Expand $(\mathbf{A} + \mathbf{B})\cdot(\mathbf{A} + \mathbf{B}) + (\mathbf{A} - \mathbf{B})\cdot(\mathbf{A} - \mathbf{B})$.

12. $15\sqrt{26}/13$

Section 1.10   PAGE 26

Note: Quite often we speak of *the* equation of a plane where it would be better to speak of *an* equation, since distinct equations may represent the same plane.   For example, $x + y + 2z = 3$ and $2x + 2y + 4z = 6$ both represent the same plane.

1.   (a) $\pm\left(\dfrac{2}{3}\mathbf{i} + \dfrac{1}{3}\mathbf{j} + \dfrac{2}{3}\mathbf{k}\right)$ (d) $\pm\mathbf{i}$

      (b) $\pm\left(\dfrac{\sqrt{2}}{2}\mathbf{i} - \dfrac{\sqrt{2}}{2}\mathbf{k}\right)$ (e) $\pm\left(\dfrac{\sqrt{2}}{2}\mathbf{j} - \dfrac{\sqrt{2}}{2}\mathbf{k}\right)$

      (c) $\pm\left(-\dfrac{\sqrt{37}}{37}\mathbf{j} + \dfrac{6\sqrt{37}}{37}\mathbf{k}\right)$ (f) $\pm\left(\dfrac{\sqrt{2}}{2}\mathbf{i} - \dfrac{\sqrt{2}}{2}\mathbf{j}\right)$

2. $x - 4y + z = 0$

3. $\sqrt{3}/3$

4.   (a) $\sqrt{14}$ (b) $3\sqrt{2}$ (c) 2

5. $3x + y - z = 3$

6.   No.

7.   Sphere of diameter $|\mathbf{A}|$ passing through the origin.

8. $3x - y = C, \quad z = 0$

9. $5\sqrt{2}/2$

10. $3x + 2y = 11, \quad z = 0$

Review Problems   *PAGE 27*

1.   (a) $2\mathbf{i} - \mathbf{j} + 5\mathbf{k}$

     (d) $\pm\left(\dfrac{2}{3}\mathbf{i} - \dfrac{2}{3}\mathbf{j} + \dfrac{1}{3}\mathbf{k}\right)$

     (b) any scalar multiple of $(2\mathbf{i} + 3\mathbf{j} - 4\mathbf{k})$

     (e) $\pm\left(\dfrac{\sqrt{37}}{37}\mathbf{i} - \dfrac{6\sqrt{37}}{37}\mathbf{k}\right)$

     (c) any scalar multiple of $(3\mathbf{i} + \mathbf{j} + 7\mathbf{k})$

     (f) $\pm\left(\dfrac{3}{5}\mathbf{i} + \dfrac{4}{5}\mathbf{j}\right)$

2.   1

3. $|\mathbf{A}| = \sqrt{62}, \quad |\mathbf{B}| = 3\sqrt{6}$

4. $\sqrt{93}/558$

5. $\sqrt{42}/7$

6. $(\mathbf{i} + \mathbf{j} + 3\mathbf{k}) \cdot (2\mathbf{i} - 8\mathbf{j} + 2\mathbf{k}) = 0$

7. $16/3$

8. $\sin^{-1}(5\sqrt{3}/9)$, about $74°$

Section 1.11   *PAGE 32*

1.   (a) 30   (b) -13 (c) 5   (d) 1

2.   5

3.   0

4. $2/3$

5.   1

6. $3x - 17y - 4z = 0$

7. $3x - 7y + z = -20$

Section 1.12   PAGE 36

They do form a right-handed system.

Note to instructor: A k-dimensional vector space (or k-dimensional subspace) is oriented by selecting a linearly independent ordered set consisting of k vectors.   Any other such linearly independent ordered set is said to have "positive" orientation if it can be obtained from the given set in the proper order by a linear transformation with positive determinant.   If an n-dimensional space has been oriented, and if also an $(n - 1)$-dimensional subspace of the same space is oriented by an ordered set $\mathbf{A}_1, \mathbf{A}_2, \ldots, \mathbf{A}_{n-1}$, then the same orientation of the subspace can be prescribed just as well by selecting a single vector $\mathbf{C}$ not in the subspace, using the following convention: the ordered set $\mathbf{A}_1, \mathbf{A}_2, \ldots, \mathbf{A}_{n-1}, \mathbf{C}$ must have positive orientation.

Section 1.13   PAGE 41

1.   (a) $2\mathbf{i} + 14\mathbf{j} + 4\mathbf{k}$ (c) $-11\mathbf{i} - 6\mathbf{j} + \mathbf{k}$
     (b) $-8\mathbf{i} + 23\mathbf{j} - \mathbf{k}$ (d) $\mathbf{k}$
                                              (e) $\mathbf{j} - \mathbf{i}$

2. $\sqrt{26}$

3. $\sqrt{61}/2$

4. $\mathbf{0}$. $\mathbf{A}$ and $\mathbf{B}$ are parallel.

5. $\pm\left(\dfrac{\sqrt{11}}{11}\mathbf{i} - \dfrac{3\sqrt{11}}{11}\mathbf{j} + \dfrac{\sqrt{11}}{11}\mathbf{k}\right)$

6. $\dfrac{x - 2}{8} = \dfrac{y - 3}{-13} = \dfrac{z - 7}{-3}$

7. $x = -y/4 = z/3$

8. $-64\mathbf{j} + 16\mathbf{k}, \quad 16\mathbf{i} - 16\mathbf{j} + 16\mathbf{k}$

9. $17x - y + 9z = 43$

10. $\pm(\sqrt{5}/25)(5\mathbf{i} + 6\mathbf{j} - 8\mathbf{k})$

11. $\sin(\psi - \theta) = \sin\psi\cos\theta - \cos\psi\sin\theta$

13. $2\sqrt{38}/19$

Section 1.14 *PAGE 45*

1. 10 units

2. $x^2 + y^2 + z^2 - xy - yz - zx = 2$; a cylinder of radius $\frac{2}{3}\sqrt{3}$ ft

3. $[\mathbf{R},\mathbf{F},\mathbf{u}] = \dfrac{\sqrt{3}F}{3}(z_0 - y_0)$

Section 1.15 *PAGE 47*

Note to instructor: We see from the Jacobi identity (Exercise 3) that we have here a very special kind of Lie algebra. This is the Lie algebra of the rotation group. The connection between vector products and rotations is not emphasized, but it arises implicitly several places, especially in the last chapter.

Section 1.16 *PAGE 53*

1. $\sin A = (\sin a)/(\sin c)$

2. 3000 nautical miles

3. 1500 nautical miles

4. (a) 34°, 2040 nautical miles   (c) 112°
   (b) 49°, 2940 nautical miles   (d) 4040 nautical miles

5. 41.4° N, 82.7° W

6. (a) 50° W   (b) 33° W   (c) 49°

8. 1.84

Review Problems *PAGE 54*

1. $7\sqrt{3}$

2. $r = 3, \quad s = -27/2$

3. $[\mathbf{K},\mathbf{L},\mathbf{B}]\mathbf{M} - [\mathbf{K},\mathbf{L},\mathbf{M}]\mathbf{B}$

4. -2

5. Only (a), (b), (c), (g), and (h) have meaning if the dot and cross refer to scalar and vector products respectively.

7. (a) $\mathbf{i} + (4\mathbf{k}/3)$ (b) 0   (c) **0**   (d) 2

8. $2x - 2y \div z + 3 = 0$

9. $90° - \cos^{-1}(5\sqrt{3}/9)$

10. (a) circle with diameter $|\mathbf{A}|$
     (b) sphere with diameter $|\mathbf{A}|$

12. (a) $C_z = 2$ (c) Draw a diagram.

Section 2.1   PAGE 60

1.   (a) $\cos t\,\mathbf{i} - \sin t\,\mathbf{j}$ (d) yes, $\sqrt{2}$
     (b) true since $\mathbf{k}\cdot\mathbf{F}'(t) = 0$ (e) yes, 1
     (c) $t = n\pi$ (f) $-\sin t\,\mathbf{i} - \cos t\,\mathbf{j}$
         $(n = 0, \pm 1, \pm 2, \ldots)$

2.   (a) $3\mathbf{i} + 3t^2\mathbf{j}$
     (b) $\cos t\,\mathbf{i} - e^{-t}\mathbf{j}$
     (c) $-2t\mathbf{i} + (e^t + 5t^4)\mathbf{j} + (e^t - 3t^2)\mathbf{k}$
     (d) $(\cos t + 3t^2)(\mathbf{i} + \mathbf{j} + 2\mathbf{k})$
     (e) $\mathbf{0}$

3.   (a) $6t - 10t \sin t - 5t^2 \cos t$
     (b) $(8t\sqrt{8t^2 + 1})/(8t^2 + 1)$
     (c) $1 - 12t^3$

Section 2.2   PAGE 69

1.   No, the tangent may be parallel to the y axis.

2.   If we dropped (iii) then (7) would not make sense, since the denominator might be zero.

3. $x^2 - y^2 = 1$, $z = 0$

4.   At $(0,0,0)$, corresponding to $t = 0$.

5. $T = \dfrac{2\pi\mathbf{i} + \mathbf{k}}{\sqrt{4\pi^2 + 1}}$ where $t = 1$.

6.   Along a straight line, $\mathbf{T}$ is constant.

7.   (a) $\displaystyle\int_0^1 \sqrt{14}\,dt = \sqrt{14}$ (b) Distance between points is $\sqrt{14}$, and the path is straight.

8. 2π

9. $\sqrt{2}(e-1)$

10. (a) $2\sqrt{5}\pi^2$
    (b) $\sqrt{5}(\sin t\,\mathbf{i} + \cos t\,\mathbf{j} + 2\mathbf{k})/5$
    (c) $\sqrt{5}(-\mathbf{j} + 2\mathbf{k})/5$

11. $\mathbf{i}$

Section 2.3 PAGE 79

1. (a) $\sqrt{2}\,e^t$
    (b) $a_t = \sqrt{2}\,e^t,\ a_n = \sqrt{2}\,e^t$
    (c) $(\sqrt{2}/2)[(\cos t - \sin t)\mathbf{i} + (\sin t + \cos t)\mathbf{j}]$
    (d) $(\sqrt{2}/2)e^{-t}$

2. (a) $\sqrt{9t^2 + 25}$
    (b) $9t/\sqrt{9t^2 + 25},\quad [9(t^2 + 4) - 81t^2/(9t^2 + 25)]^{\frac{1}{2}}$

    (c) $\dfrac{3(\cos t - t\sin t)\mathbf{i} + 3(\sin t + t\cos t)\mathbf{j} + 4\mathbf{k}}{\sqrt{9t^2 + 25}}$

    (d) $\dfrac{[9(t^2 + 4) - 81t^2/(9t^2 + 25)]^{\frac{1}{2}}}{9t^2 + 25}$

3. (a) $\sqrt{3}\,e^t$
    (b) $a_t = \sqrt{3}\,e^t,\ a_n = \sqrt{2}\,e^t$
    (c) $(\sqrt{3}/3)[(\cos t - \sin t)\mathbf{i} + (\sin t + \cos t)\mathbf{j} + \mathbf{k}]$
    (d) $(\sqrt{2}/3)e^{-t}$

4. (a) $10\sqrt{5}$
    (b) $a_t = 0,\ a_n = 80$
    (c) $(\sqrt{5}/5)(2\cos 4t\,\mathbf{i} - 2\sin 4t\,\mathbf{j} + \mathbf{k})$
    (d) $4/25$

5. $\mathbf{F} \times \dfrac{d\mathbf{F}}{dt} \cdot \dfrac{d^3\mathbf{F}}{dt^3}$

6. (a) 1   (b) 0   (c) $a_t = d^2s/dt^2$ (d) 0   (e) ds/dt

7. $\dfrac{2(3t^4 + 2t^3 - 3t^2 - 2t + 2)^{\frac{1}{2}}}{3(2t^4 - 4t^3 + 10t^2 + 1)^{\frac{3}{2}}}$

8. Unit vector perpendicular to the plane of the curve, so that $\mathbf{T}$, $\mathbf{N}$, and $\mathbf{T} \times \mathbf{N}$ form a right-handed system (whenever $\mathbf{N}$ is defined).

Section 2.4 *PAGE 83*

1. $$\left[\frac{d^3r}{dt^3} - 3\frac{dr}{dt}\left(\frac{d\theta}{dt}\right)^2 - 3r\frac{d\theta}{dt}\frac{d^2\theta}{dt^2}\right]\mathbf{u}_r$$
    $$+ \left[3\frac{d^2r}{dt^2}\frac{d\theta}{dt} + 3\frac{dr}{dt}\frac{d^2\theta}{dt^2} + r\frac{d^3\theta}{dt^3} - r\left(\frac{d\theta}{dt}\right)^3\right]\mathbf{u}_\theta$$

2. (a) 0

3. $\mathbf{v} = 4b[(\sin\theta)\mathbf{u}_r + (1 - \cos\theta)\mathbf{u}_\theta]$
    $\mathbf{a} = 16b[(2\cos\theta - 1)\mathbf{u}_r + (2\sin\theta)\mathbf{u}_\theta]$

4. $\mathbf{v} = b[(\cos t)\mathbf{u}_r - e^{-t}(1 + \sin t)\mathbf{u}_\theta]$
    $\mathbf{a} = b([-\sin t - e^{-2t}(1 + \sin t)]\mathbf{u}_r + e^{-t}[1 + \sin t - 2\cos t]\mathbf{u}_\theta)$

5. (a) the second term; (b) the second and third terms; (c) all are nonzero; (d) many possibilities.

6. (a) Yes, except when its velocity is zero; (b) no.

7. (a) $\pi^2 r$ cm/sec^2 (if r is in cm) directed towards the center. Note that 30 rev/min $= \pi$ rad/sec.
    (b) $4\pi\mathbf{u}_\theta$ cm/sec

8. 24π, since $dr/dt = 3$ and $d\theta/dt = 4\pi$.

Section 3.1 *PAGE 92*

1. (a) 0   (b) $-4/3$

2. (a) 10   (b) The maximum rate of increase of r^2 is in the direction of $\mathbf{R}$, whence
    $$\frac{d}{ds}(r^2) = \frac{d}{dr}(r^2) = 2r$$
    which equals 10 at (3,0,4).

3. (a) 5/3   (b) $-2/3$ (c) $-28/3$ (d) $\sqrt{14}/42$

4. $(\cos x + ye^{xy})\mathbf{i} + xe^{xy}\mathbf{j} + \mathbf{k}$

5. yz plane, where $x = 0$.

6. $f(x,y,z) = x^2 + yz + C$

7. $150\sqrt{5}$.   This function equals s^6, where s is the distance to the y axis.   We have $(d/ds)(s^6) = 6s^5 = 150\sqrt{5}$ at this point.

8. any scalar multiple of $4\mathbf{i} + \mathbf{j} + \mathbf{k}$

9. $2x + 4y - z = 21$

10. (a) From your diagram you see that any scalar multiple of $\mathbf{i} + \mathbf{k}$ will do. (b) $4\mathbf{i} + 4\mathbf{k}$.

11. $x + 2y - 8z = -28$

12. $x = y, z = 0$

13. $\pm\dfrac{\sqrt{14}(3\mathbf{i} - \mathbf{j} + 2\mathbf{k})}{14}$

14. $4x + 6y - z = 13$

15. $\pm(\sqrt{2}/2)(\mathbf{i} - \mathbf{j})$. In (c), let $\mathbf{R} = 2\sin t\,\mathbf{i} + 2\cos t\,\mathbf{j} + \sqrt{5}\mathbf{k}$.

16. $\cos^{-1}(31/32)$

17. $\sin^{-1}(2\sqrt{2}/3)$

Section 3.2 PAGE 97

1. See Figure 50.

2. (a) $x(z + a) = -1$, $y(z + b) = -1$
    (b) $x(z - 3) = -1$, $y(z - 3) = -1$

Section 3.3 PAGE 103

1. $1 + 2y - x$

2. $ye^{xy} + x\cos xy - 2x\cos zx \sin zx$

3. 0

4. 3

5. $2x\sin y + 2y\sin yz + y^2z\cos yz + 12xyz^3\cos 3z^4$

6. Infinitely many possibilities, for example $\mathbf{F} = -x\mathbf{i}$.

7. Again there are infinitely many acceptable answers. Two of them are $e^x\mathbf{i}$ and $e^x\mathbf{i} + ye^x\mathbf{j}$.

8. Zero except at the origin, where the field is not defined. The magnitude of this field at any point is $1/r^2$, so this field can be thought of as the electric field intensity due to a charge of suitably chosen magnitude at the origin. A physicist or electrical

engineer might say that the divergence is "infinity" at the origin, since the divergence of an electrostatic field is proportional to the charge density, and the charge density at a point charge is "infinity."

9. Divergence is zero everywhere, since $\partial F_x/\partial x = 0$, $F_y = 0$, and (we assume) $F_z = 0$. Some of my students observe that $\mathbf{F} = Cy\mathbf{i}$ for some constant C, and then compute the answer using the formula for the divergence. This is clever, but not the point of the exercise.

10. Divergence is zero everywhere. For example, consider point P. Along the x axis, $F_x = 0$, so $\partial F_x/\partial x = 0$ at P. As we move through P along the flow line indicated, F_y takes on its maximum value $|\mathbf{F}|$, therefore $\partial F_y/\partial s = 0$ at P, where s is measured along the flow line. But at point P we are moving parallel to the y axis, so $\partial F_y/\partial y = \partial F_y/\partial s$ at P, hence is zero at this point. Another method: Conjecture that $\mathbf{F} = y\mathbf{i} - x\mathbf{j}$ and use the formula.

Section 3.4   *PAGE 110*

1. $x\mathbf{i} - y\mathbf{j} + y(1 - 2x)\mathbf{k}$

2. $-z^2 \sin yz^2\, \mathbf{i} + (y \cos xy - xe^{xy})\mathbf{k}$

3. $-(y^2 + z^2)\mathbf{i} + 2zx\mathbf{j}$

4. The paddle wheel will not tend to rotate.

5. Think of the velocity field of a fluid swirling about the x axis. Assume constant angular velocity $\boldsymbol{\omega}$. Then $\mathbf{v} = \boldsymbol{\omega} \times \mathbf{R}$, and since **curl F** $= 2\boldsymbol{\omega}$ as stated in the text (to be proved later) we have $\boldsymbol{\omega} = \mathbf{i}$ and

$$\mathbf{v} = \mathbf{i} \times \mathbf{R} = \mathbf{i} \times (x\mathbf{i} + y\mathbf{j} + z\mathbf{k}) = y\mathbf{k} - z\mathbf{j}$$

This is one possible answer. Another is $2y\mathbf{k}$, which represents a shearing motion parallel to the xz plane.

6. No. A physicist or engineer would say that in many types of problems arising in practical work it *is* possible.

Review Exercise   *PAGE 110*

The following answers are *barely acceptable* in my opinion. If f is a scalar field, **grad** f at a point is a vector pointing in the direction of maximum rate of increase of f at that point, having magnitude equal to this maximum rate of increase. If **F** is the velocity field of a fluid, div **F** at a point is the time rate of change of volume per unit volume at that point; **curl F** at a point is a vector equal to 2ω, where ω is the angular velocity vector of the fluid at that point.

Section 3.5 *PAGE 114*

1. 16

2. $12\mathbf{i} + 4\mathbf{j} + \mathbf{k}$

3. 64

4. (a) $2xy + 1$ (b) $-2\mathbf{i} + \mathbf{j} - x^2\mathbf{k}$ (c) $2y\mathbf{i} + 2x\mathbf{j}$

5. Scalar field.

6. Vector field.

7. 3, **0**

8. $(x^2 + z^2)e^{xz}$

9. Always **0**.

10. Always 0.

Section 3.6 *PAGE 117*

1. (a) $20x^3yz^3 + 6x^5yz$ (d) 0 except at the origin
   (b) $e^{xyz}(x^2y^2 + y^2z^2 + z^2x^2)$ (e) 0
   (c) $-\sin x - \cos y + e^z$

2. (a) $e^x\mathbf{i} + (x^2 + z^2)e^{xz}\mathbf{j}$ (d) $\mathbf{F}(x,y,z)$
   (b) **0**   (e) $-2yz^2(y^2z^2 + 3x^2z^2 + 6x^2y^2)\mathbf{k}$
   (c) $\mathbf{F}(x,y,z)$

3. (a) vector field (b) scalar field (c) vector field (d) scalar field (e) zero vector field (f) meaningless (g) vector field (h) vector field (i) meaningless (j) vector field

Section 3.7 *PAGE 119*

3. To ensure that the crossed partial derivatives, such as $(\partial^2\phi/\partial x\,\partial y)$ and $(\partial^2\phi/\partial y\,\partial x)$, are equal.

5.   As written, the right side is symmetrical in **F** and **G**, but the left side is not, since $\mathbf{F} \times \mathbf{G} \neq \mathbf{G} \times \mathbf{F}$.

Section 4.1   *PAGE 126*

1.   (a) $(\sqrt{2}/2)(\mathbf{i} + \mathbf{j})$ (b) $\mathbf{i}$ (c) $-\mathbf{j}$

2.   (a) $\sqrt{2}\,dx$ or $\sqrt{2}\,dy$ (b) dx (c) $-dy$

3.   (a) $d\mathbf{R} = dx\,\mathbf{i} + dy\,\mathbf{j} = dx\,\mathbf{i} + dx\,\mathbf{j}$

$$= \left(\frac{\sqrt{2}}{2}\mathbf{i} + \frac{\sqrt{2}}{2}\mathbf{j}\right)\sqrt{2}\,dx = \mathbf{T}\,ds$$

(b) $d\mathbf{R} = dx\,\mathbf{i} + dy\,\mathbf{j} = \mathbf{i}\,dx = \mathbf{T}\,ds$
(c) $d\mathbf{R} = dx\,\mathbf{i} + dy\,\mathbf{j} = dy\,\mathbf{j} = \mathbf{T}\,ds$

4.   (a) Along this path, $\mathbf{F} = \sqrt{1 - x^2}\,\mathbf{i} - x\mathbf{j}$ and

$$d\mathbf{R} = dx\,\mathbf{i} - \frac{x\,dx}{\sqrt{1 - x^2}}\mathbf{j}$$

so

$$\mathbf{F}\cdot d\mathbf{R} = \frac{dx}{\sqrt{1 - x^2}} \quad \text{and} \quad \int \mathbf{F}\cdot d\mathbf{R} = \int_{-1}^{1} \frac{dx}{\sqrt{1 - x^2}} = \pi$$

(b) π

5. $\mathbf{F}\cdot d\mathbf{R} = -d\left(\tan^{-1}\frac{y}{x}\right) = -d\theta$

6.   (a) 8   (b) 8

7.   36 (Caution: $\mathbf{R}\cdot d\mathbf{R} = s\,ds$ in this case because the points are collinear with the origin.)

8. $\pm 8\pi$, depending on direction.

9.   40.   (This can also be done by observing that $\mathbf{F}\cdot d\mathbf{R} = d\phi$ where $\phi = x^2 y + zy$, so that the integral is $\phi(3,4,1) - \phi(1,0,2)$. See Section 4.3 for further discussion of this "trick.")

10.   zero

Section 4.2   *PAGE 131*

1.   Domain, not simply-connected.

2.   Simply-connected domain.

3. Simply-connected domain.

4. Not a domain. (Points on the plane $z = 0$ are not interior.)

5. Simply-connected domain.

6. Domain, not simply-connected.

7. Simply-connected domain.

8. Not a domain (not connected).

Section 4.3 *PAGE 140*

1. The integral over C equals that over C_1 minus that over C_2, so if the first of these is zero the other two are equal.

2, 3. Many possibilities.

4. 2π or -2π, depending on which way the circle is oriented.

5. ϕ is a multiple-valued function, and hence not a scalar field as we have defined it.

6. $\phi = yx + \sin xz + C$

7. $\mathbf{F} = \mathbf{grad}\, \phi$ where $\phi = x^2y + yz$

Section 4.4 *PAGE 149*

1. (a) conservative, $\phi = 6x^2y + xyz + C$
   (b) conservative, $\phi = e^{xz} + C$
   (c) conservative, $\phi = -\cos x + \frac{1}{3}y^3 + e^z + C$
   (d) not conservative
   (e) conservative, $\phi = \ln(x^2 + y^2) + z^2$

2. (e), since the domain of definition is not simply-counnected. You must explicitly construct ϕ.

3. Yes. $\phi + \psi$.

4. $$\phi(x,y,z) = \phi(x_0,y_0,z_0) + \int_{z_0}^z F_3(x_0,y_0,z)\, dz$$
   $$+ \int_{y_0}^y F_2(x_0,y,z)\, dy + \int_{x_0}^x F_1(x,y,z)\, dx$$

5. (b) $\phi = -1/r$ in spherical coordinates. Hence the maximum rate of increase of ϕ is in a direction directly away from the origin, and so $\mathbf{grad}\, \phi = k\mathbf{R}$ for positive k.

$$|\mathbf{grad}\ \phi| = d\phi/dr = 1/r^2$$

so $|k\mathbf{R}| = kr = 1/r^2$ and $k = 1/r^3$.

6. $\phi(1,2,3) = -\sqrt{14}/14$ and $\phi(2,3,5) = -\sqrt{38}/38$; hence the work done is

$$\phi(2,3,5) - \phi(1,2,3) = (\sqrt{14}/14) - (\sqrt{38}/38)$$

7.   No, provided the path avoids the origin.

Note: Conservative fields are sometimes called *potential fields.* The term *irrotational* is also used.   It is not possible for a flow line of such a field to be a closed curve, for the integral of a field about a closed flow line is nonzero, and this would contradict (2).   Therefore the flow lines either have no end-points (i.e., if they "extend to infinity" in both directions) or perhaps they start at a point (called the "source") and perhaps end at another point (called the "sink").   For this reason, such fields are also called *source fields.* A simple example is the electrostatic field due to a positive point charge at the origin.   The origin is the "source" and the flow lines extend radially away from the origin.

Section 4.5   *PAGE 159*

This section makes no pretense to rigor.

2.   (a) $(\sqrt{3}/3)(\mathbf{i} + \mathbf{j} + \mathbf{k})$ (c) $\displaystyle\int_0^1 \int_0^{1-y} \frac{dx\ dy}{|\cos\gamma|}$

(b) $\mathbf{k}\cdot\mathbf{n} = \sqrt{3}/3$ (d) $\sqrt{3}/2$

4. $\sqrt{4x^2 + 4y^2 + 1}\ dx\ dy$

Section 4.6   *PAGE 170*

1. 18π

2.   (a) 8   (b) 16   (c) 24   (d) 0   (e) 0   (f) 0   (g) 0

3. $\displaystyle\int_0^1 \int_0^{2-2x} \frac{7}{2}\cdot\frac{6}{7}\,x\ dy\ dx = 1$

4. $|\mathbf{E}| = \lambda/2\pi\varepsilon_0 r$

6.   (a) $T_r = T_a + \dfrac{1/r - 1/a}{1/b - 1/a}(T_b - T_a)$

(b) no

7.   zero

8. $3\pi a^2$

9. -1

Section 4.7   page 177

3.

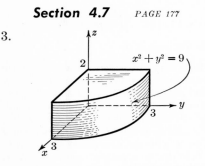

4.   (a) 3   (b) 3   (e) This will be discussed later.

5. $3v$.   Notice that V does not stand for a number but for a domain.   Hence another symbol, v, is used for the *volume* of V, which is a *number*.

6. $\nabla \cdot \mathbf{E} = \rho/\varepsilon_0$ at each point in space.   Here we assume charge to be distributed continuously, i.e., no point charges in the domain.

7. $\pi(1 - e^{-1})$

Section 4.8   page 185

6.   (a) 0   (b) -2 (c) 4   (d) 0   (e) -1

7.   The divergence is identically zero, so the desired integral equals the negative of the integral over the missing top, which in this case is trivial to compute.

8. $\displaystyle \int_{z_0}^{z_1} \int_{y_0}^{y_1} \left[\int_{x_0}^{x_1} \frac{\partial F_1}{\partial x}\, dx \right] dy\, dz$

$$= \int_{z_0}^{z_1} \int_{y_0}^{y_1} [F_1(x_1,y,z) - F_1(x_0,y,z)]\, dy\, dz = \iint \mathbf{F} \cdot \mathbf{n}\, dS$$

where the last integral is over the two faces for which $\mathbf{n} = \mathbf{i}$ and $\mathbf{n} = -\mathbf{i}$ respectively.

Section 4.9   *PAGE 190*

1.   In applying the fundamental theorem of calculus.

2.   To ensure that the volume integral of div **F** over the bounded domain D exists.

5. $\cos \gamma = 0$, so the expression $dx\,dy/|\cos \gamma|$ is meaningless.

6.   Note that $\mathbf{F} \cdot \mathbf{n} = \partial f/\partial n$ and $\nabla \cdot \mathbf{F} = \nabla^2 \phi$.

7.   (b) The lumpiness equals the Laplacian.   Use Exercise 6 to see this.
    (c) The lumpiness is zero.

8.   Second hint: In steady state, rate of heat flow out of a domain equals the rate of heat flow into the domain; otherwise the temperature would be changing.   Hence

$$\iint (\partial\phi/\partial n)\, dS = 0$$

over arbitrary closed surfaces.   Also note that the limit, as $V \to 0$, of

$$\frac{1}{V} \iiint_D \nabla^2 \phi\, dV$$

as the domain D shrinks down to a point, is the value of $\nabla^2 \phi$ at that point, if $\nabla \phi$ is continuous.

9. $c\rho(\partial\phi/\partial t) = k\nabla^2\phi$
    Note: These derivations can be placed on a more rigorous level by making use of the theorem that if f is continuous and

$$\iiint f(x,y,z)\, dV = 0$$

for every domain D, then f is identically zero.   For instance, in Exercise 9 this theorem is used, taking

$$f = c\rho \frac{\partial\phi}{\partial t} - k\nabla^2\phi$$

Section 4.10   *PAGE 196*

6.   zero

7. -36π, since **curl** $\mathbf{F} \cdot \mathbf{k} = -4$ and area enclosed by C is 9π.

8.   (a) 6π (b) 6π

9.   (a) -16 (b) -16 (c) second term

10. 28π

11.   What is the title of Section 1.12?

Section 4.11   *PAGE 203*

1.   The curl of a vector field **F** points in the direction of maximum swirl and its magnitude equals this maximum swirl.

2.   In Chapter Five we return to the paddle wheel.

3.   **curl B** is a scalar multiple of **J**.

4.   Simple-connectedness is needed to ensure that there is a surface whose boundary is related to the two curves.

5.   (a) zero
      (b) zero
      (c) zero.   More rigorously, use the theorem mentioned in the answer to Exercise 9, Section 4.9, to avoid having to speak of "very small" laundry bags.
      (d) identity (7)

Note: The divergence of a vector field at a point is sometimes called the *source density* of the field at that point.   This is because the divergence of the electric intensity of an electrostatic field is equal (within a factor) to the charge density, and electric charge is the "source" or "cause" of the field. The statement "a field has zero divergence in any region that is free of sources" has an intuitive appeal to many students.   The above exercise can be worded: the curl of a vector field is another vector field that is free of sources.

6.   (a) zero   (b) zero   (c) zero

7.   (a) zero   (b) zero   (c) zero vector   (d) identity (6)

Note: The curl of a vector field at a point is sometimes called the *vortex density* of the field at that point.   This is because, in some sense, the curl describes the "eddy" or "whirlpool" nature of the field.   Note that vortex density is a vector quantity.   Just as engineers sometimes think of a point source as a point where the divergence is "infinite," so also do they think of a *vortex filament* as a curve in space along which the magnitude of the curl is "infinite."   The central part of a tornado provides an approximate idea. We leave to the reader the precise formulation of the definition.   The intuitive content of Exercise 7 is that any field that can be derived from a scalar potential must be vortex-free.   It should be noted, however, that if we allow the scalar potential to be a multiple-valued function, it is sometimes possible to find a scalar potential for the velocity field of fluid swirling about a vortex filament. We heartily recommend the chapter on vector analysis in *Mathematics of Circuit Analysis*, by E. A. Guillemin (Wiley, 1949), in which these matters are taken up in greater detail.

Let us now briefly review and extend some of the earlier ideas. We consider only continuously differentiable vector fields.

If a vector field defined in a domain D has any one of the following properties, it has all of them:

(1) Its curl is zero at every point.

(2) Its integral around any closed contour is zero, provided that there is a surface enclosed by the contour entirely within D.

(3) It is the gradient of a scalar function, but this function may possibly be multiple-valued.

If the domain D is simply-connected, we can omit the clauses starting "provided that . . ." and "but this . . ." from these properties. When D is simply-connected, the following terms are used for these fields: conservative field, irrotational field, potential field, source field.

Similarly, any one of the following properties of a continuously differentiable vector field implies the others:

(1) Its divergence is zero at every point in D.

(2) Its integral over every surface is zero, provided that we consider only closed surfaces enclosing points all of which are in D.

(3) It is the curl of another (possibly multiple-valued) vector field.

These statements are not precise and should not be taken very seriously. Terms sometimes used for such fields are: solenoidal field, rotational field, turbulent field, source-free field, vortex field. The terminology is not standardized; in modern usage, the term "turbulent" has an altogether different meaning. In applications, vector fields that are discontinuous along a surface are of considerable importance. We have not discussed such fields because they arise more naturally in courses dealing with applications, where the motivation for studying them is more apparent. The above statements are utterly false for such fields.

Section 4.12   *PAGE 211*

1. $\partial f/\partial n$ in the u_1 direction is $\partial f/h_1\partial u_1$ and its surface integral over $abcd$ is $h_2h_3\,du_2\,du_3$ times this, and so the surface integral over this face and the opposite face is

$$\frac{\partial}{\partial u_1}\frac{h_2h_3}{h_1}\frac{\partial f}{\partial u_1}\,du_1\,du_2\,du_3$$

and similarly for the other pairs of faces. Lumpiness is the overall sum divided by the volume $h_1h_2h_3\,du_1\,du_2\,du_3$.

2.   Spherical coordinates:

$$\nabla f = \mathbf{u}_r \frac{\partial f}{\partial r} + \mathbf{u}_\phi \frac{1}{r} \frac{\partial f}{\partial \phi} + \mathbf{u}_\theta \frac{1}{r \sin \phi} \frac{\partial f}{\partial \theta}$$

$$\nabla \cdot \mathbf{F} = \frac{1}{r^2} \frac{\partial}{\partial r} (r^2 F_r) + \frac{1}{r \sin \phi} \frac{\partial}{\partial \phi} (F_\phi \sin \phi) + \frac{1}{r \sin \phi} \frac{\partial F_\theta}{\partial \theta}$$

$$\nabla \times \mathbf{F} = \frac{1}{r^2 \sin \phi} \begin{vmatrix} \mathbf{u}_r & r\mathbf{u}_\phi & (r \sin \phi)\mathbf{u}_\theta \\ \frac{\partial}{\partial r} & \frac{\partial}{\partial \phi} & \frac{\partial}{\partial \theta} \\ F_r & rF_\phi & (r \sin \phi)F_\theta \end{vmatrix}$$

$$\nabla^2 f = \frac{1}{r^2} \frac{\partial}{\partial r} \left(r^2 \frac{\partial f}{\partial r} \right) + \frac{1}{r^2 \sin \phi} \frac{\partial}{\partial \phi} \left(\sin \phi \frac{\partial f}{\partial \phi} \right) + \frac{1}{r^2 \sin^2 \phi} \frac{\partial^2 f}{\partial \theta^2}$$

3.   Cylindrical coordinates:

$$\nabla f = \mathbf{u}_r \frac{\partial f}{\partial r} + \mathbf{u}_\theta \frac{1}{r} \frac{\partial f}{\partial \theta} + \mathbf{u}_z \frac{\partial f}{\partial z}$$

$$\nabla \cdot \mathbf{F} = \frac{1}{r} \frac{\partial}{\partial r} (rF_r) + \frac{1}{r} \frac{\partial F_\theta}{\partial \theta} + \frac{\partial F_z}{\partial z}$$

$$\nabla \times \mathbf{F} = \frac{1}{r} \begin{vmatrix} \mathbf{u}_r & r\mathbf{u}_\theta & \mathbf{u}_z \\ \frac{\partial}{\partial r} & \frac{\partial}{\partial \theta} & \frac{\partial}{\partial z} \\ F_r & rF_\theta & F_z \end{vmatrix}$$

$$\nabla^2 f = \frac{1}{r} \frac{\partial}{\partial r} \left(r \frac{\partial f}{\partial r} \right) + \frac{1}{r^2} \frac{\partial^2 f}{\partial \theta^2} + \frac{\partial^2 f}{\partial z^2}$$

4.   (a) No.   (b) The element of volume in spherical coordinates is different in shape and position from that in Cartesian coordinates.

5.   (a) $x = (u_1 + u_2)/2, \quad y = (u_1 - u_2)/2, \quad z = u_3/2$
        (b) $h_1 = \sqrt{2}/2, \quad h_2 = \sqrt{2}/2, \quad h_3 = 1/2$

        (c) $\nabla^2 f = 8 \dfrac{\partial^2 f}{\partial u_1{}^2} + 8 \dfrac{\partial^2 f}{\partial u_2{}^2} + 4 \dfrac{\partial^2 f}{\partial u_3{}^2}$

        (d) $\sqrt{2}\mathbf{u}_1 + \sqrt{2}\mathbf{u}_2 + 4\mathbf{u}_3$

6.   (a) $x = (2u_1 + u_2)/3, y = (u_1 - u_2)/3, z = u_3/2$
        (c) This coordinate system is not orthogonal.

7. $(1/u_1)\, du_1\, du_2\, du_3$

8.   This coordinate system is not right-handed, hence the usual formula for curl does not apply.

9. $\mathbf{F} = \mathbf{u}_r/r^3$.   (a) Use the formula given above for divergence in spherical coordinates.   (b) $\mathbf{u}_r \cdot \mathbf{n} = 1$, so the integral is trivial. (c) The divergence theorem applies to fields that are continuously differentiable throughout the given domain, but this field is not defined at the origin.   (d) Zero.

Supplementary Exercises   *PAGE 212*

1.   (a) $8\sqrt{29}/29$ (b) $8\sqrt{77}/77$ (c) any scalar multiple of $6\mathbf{i} + 4\mathbf{j} + 5\mathbf{k}$

3. $90° - \cos^{-1}(\sqrt{35}/7)$

4.   (a) any scalar multiple of $5\mathbf{i} - \mathbf{j} - \mathbf{k}$ (b) $8\sqrt{27}/27$

5.   6

6. $(x - 4)/5 = (y - 2)/(-8) = (z - 1)/(-7)$

7.   (a) $101/6$
     (b) $x - 11y - 14z + 43 = 0$
     (c) $\sqrt{319}/319$

8. $\pm 5(2\mathbf{i} + \mathbf{j} - 2\mathbf{k})/3$

9.   (a) 13   (b) $\mathbf{i} - 3\mathbf{j} - 4\mathbf{k}$ (c) 3   (d) -12

10.   (a) $\sqrt{26}/2$ (b) 2   (c) $\cos^{-1}(4/27)$

11.   (a) $4x\mathbf{i} + \mathbf{j}$ (b) 3   (c) 4   (d) $z\mathbf{i} - 4xz\mathbf{j} + (4xy - x)\mathbf{k}$

12.   (a) $2\mathbf{i}$ (b) $2\mathbf{k}$ (c) -2

13. $40[(z - y)\mathbf{i} + (x - z)\mathbf{j} + (y - x)\mathbf{k}]$

14. $-6\mathbf{i} + 3\mathbf{j} + 2\mathbf{k}$

15. $2\mathbf{A}$

16.   (a) $2\mathbf{R} \cdot \mathbf{A}$ (b) $2\mathbf{R} \times \mathbf{A}$ (c) $2r^2\mathbf{A}$ (d) $4(\mathbf{A} \cdot \mathbf{R})^3\mathbf{A}$ (e) $(\mathbf{A} \cdot \mathbf{R})/r$
      (f) $(\mathbf{A} \cdot \mathbf{R})\mathbf{A}$ (g) 0   (h) $2\mathbf{A}$ (i) 6

17.   (a) any scalar multiple of $6\mathbf{i} + 3\mathbf{j} + 2\mathbf{k}$ (b) 7

18.   (a) $x + y - 4z + 6 = 0$
      (b) $x + 2 = y - 4 = (z - 2)/(-4)$
      (c) $23\sqrt{6}/6$

19. $90° - \cos^{-1} 3\sqrt{122}/305$

20.   Zero vector field except where $r = 0$; not defined where $r = 0$.

21.   div $\mathbf{F} = 0$,   **curl F = 0**

22. $\pm 2\pi$, depending on direction of integration.

23.   (a) no   (b) yes   (c) 4

24.   (a) $2z$ (b) **k**   (c) 4π

25.   (a) 27π (b) 0

26.   (a) 16.8 if volume is proportional to the cube of the minimal diameter   (b) yes

27. $5\varepsilon_0$

28.   30

29. $5v$

30.   yes

31.   (a) An outer sphere with **n** pointing away from the origin and an inner sphere with **n** pointing towards the origin.
      (b) Sum of two integrals.
      (c) They are equal.
      (d) no
      (e) 4π

32.   (a) $1/uv$ (b) $2w/uv$

34.   (a) Use (1), Section 3.7.   (b) 464π

35.   0

36. 8π

37.   (a) $4\pi b^4$ (b) To avoid a triple integral, take $dV = 4\pi r^2 \, dr$, so that the integral is

$$\int_0^b 16\pi r^3 \, dr$$

38.   (a) 108π (b) 1944π. (Exercise 34(a) does not apply in part (b) since this function is not harmonic.)

39.   The term *source* is used rather than *sink* in Exercise 39 be-

cause in electrostatics it is conventional to take the electric field to be the *negative* of the potential.

(a) By Gauss's law and symmetry, $\mathbf{F} = \mathbf{0}$ within the sphere so ϕ is constant within the sphere, and at the center $r = a$ is a constant so $\phi = q/a = 4\pi a^2 \sigma/a$.

(b) By Gauss's law and symmetry, the electric field outside the sphere is the same as that due to a point charge of magnitude $4\pi a^2 \sigma$ located at the center.

40. (a) 8π (Point is within sphere.)
    (b) $16\pi/3$ (Point is outside sphere.)

41. 20π

42. (a) $22\pi/3$ (b) $32\pi/9$

43. $32\sqrt{85}\pi/255$

44. $-4\pi\phi(P)$

45. They are equal

47. $4\pi\phi(0,0,0) = 20\pi$

48. (a) $-4\pi\phi(0,1,0) = -20\pi$
    (b) $-4\pi\phi(2,1,3) = 0$

49. zero

50. (a) div $\mathbf{F}$ (b) **curl F**   (c) **grad** f (d) Laplacian of f

Section 5.2   PAGE 226

(a) 7
(b) 10
(c) $(1)(2) + (5)(5) + (0)(4) + (4)(3) = 39$
(d) $\sum T_j{}^1 x^j = 12$, $\sum T_j{}^2 x^j = 10$, $\sum T_j{}^3 x^j = 14$, $\sum T_j{}^4 x^j = 36$, hence

$$\sum \sum T_k{}^3 T_j{}^k x^j = (1)(12) + (5)(10) + (0)(14) + (4)(36)$$
$$= 206$$

Section 5.3   PAGE 231

1. (a) $v^1 = 5$, $v^2 = -1$ (b) $(5, -1)$
2. (a) $(1,0,0)$, $(0,1,0)$, $(0,0,1)$

(b) (x^1, x^2, x^3)
(c) $(x^2, \frac{1}{2}x^1, x^3 - \frac{1}{2}x^1)$ since
$(x^1, x^2, x^3) = x^2(0,1,0) + \frac{1}{2}x^1(2,0,1) + (x^3 - \frac{1}{2}x^1)(0,0,1)$

3. $(9,7,1)$, since $(3,7,9) = 9\underset{1}{\mathbf{e}} + 7\underset{2}{\mathbf{e}} + \underset{3}{\mathbf{e}}$.

4.   (a) Linearly independent.
(b) Linearly dependent since

$$2(1,1,0,0) - (0,0,1,1) - (2,2,-1,-1) = (0,0,0,0)$$

(c) Linearly dependent since

$$0(1,2,3,4) + 0(2,1,3,4) + 7(0,0,0,0) + 0(3,0,0,0) = (0,0,0,0)$$

(The choice of 7 here was arbitrary.)   A linearly independent set never includes the zero vector.
(d) Linearly independent.
(e) Linearly dependent since

$$(2,4,8,4) - 2(1,2,4,2) = (0,0,0,0)$$

Section 5.4   *PAGE 234*

Note: Matrices should not be confused with determinants.   We are not dealing with determinants in this section.

1. $\begin{pmatrix} 4 & 0 & 0 & -4 \\ 10 & 3 & 4 & -3 \\ 19 & 16 & 13 & 10 \end{pmatrix}$

2.   no

3.   (20)

4. $\begin{pmatrix} 4 & 8 & 12 & 16 \\ 3 & 6 & 9 & 12 \\ 2 & 4 & 6 & 8 \\ 1 & 2 & 3 & 4 \end{pmatrix}$

Half the students taking an examination on this will claim that vw is not defined.

5. $T_4^3 = 3$, $v^2 = 3$, $w_1 = 1$

6. $\begin{pmatrix} 2 \\ 10 \\ 23 \end{pmatrix}$

7.   Not defined.

8.   (16,11,14,9)

9.   (134). Yes.

10. $RP = \begin{pmatrix} 15 & 15 \\ 42 & 42 \end{pmatrix}$, $PR = \begin{pmatrix} 8 & 28 \\ 14 & 49 \end{pmatrix}$. Not equal.

11. Not defined.

12. $\begin{pmatrix} 0 & -2 \\ -7 & 5 \end{pmatrix}$

13. IR and RI both equal R.

Section 5.5   *PAGE 237*

Note: If we were completely consistent in this book, we would have written vectors in R^n as column vectors rather than row vectors from the very beginning. This is, however, typographically inconvenient.

In the exercise, the three matrices are

$$\text{(a)} \begin{pmatrix} 4 & 0 & -6 \\ 0 & 3 & 0 \\ 2 & 0 & 8 \end{pmatrix} \quad \text{(b)} \begin{pmatrix} 4 & -9 & 0 \\ \frac{4}{3} & 8 & 0 \\ 0 & 0 & 3 \end{pmatrix} \quad \text{(c)} \begin{pmatrix} 8 & 6 & 0 \\ -2 & 4 & 0 \\ 0 & 0 & 3 \end{pmatrix}$$

Section 5.6   *PAGE 245*

Note: Some students who are distressed by this section turn out to be having no basic difficulties at all, except perhaps with notation. In earlier chapters we discussed "scalar fields." A linear functional f is a very special and especially simple kind of scalar field. Where we had $i, j,$ and k, now we have $e_1, e_2,$ and e_3. Where we once had $f(x,y,z) = ax + by + cz$, now we have $f(v) = f_1 v^1 + f_2 v^2 + f_3 v^3$. The function $f(x,y,z) = y$ is now written $e_2(v) = v^2$, etc.

No computational exercises are given. The best exercise on linear functionals is to keep on reading the text. You may eventually find out why they are useful.

Section 5.7   *PAGE 249*

2.   Second hint: If $C_1 v_1 + C_2 v_2 + C_3 v_3 = 0$, then

$$0 = v_1 \wedge (C_1 v_1 + C_2 v_2 + C_3 v_3) \wedge v_3 = C_2 (v_1 \wedge v_2 \wedge v_3)$$

3. $v^2 = 2, \quad v^3 = 3$

4.   If every vector can be written in this form, then each of the vectors e_1, e_2, and e_3 can be written this way; thus if we substitute into $e_1 \wedge e_2 \wedge e_3$ and simplify, we obtain a constant times $v_1 \wedge v_2 \wedge v_3$. That is, $1 = e_1 \wedge e_2 \wedge e_3 = C(v_1 \wedge v_2 \wedge v_3)$. Hence $v_1 \wedge v_2 \wedge v_3 \neq 0$.

5.   We finally end up with the fact that v_1, v_2, v_3 is a set whose linear combinations exhaust the space. This, together with their linear independence, shows that the set forms a basis. Note: In any book on modern algebra or vector spaces this is done in great detail, and every library has a dozen such books.

6.   Let $T^{-1}w = v$. That is, $Tv = w$. Hence $T(cv) = cTv = cw$, so by definition $T^{-1}(cw) = cv$.

7.   This hint may help to explain the hint: If $w = Tv$, then

$$T(\sum_i v^i e_i) = \sum_i v^i Te_i = w$$

hence w is a linear combination of, Te_1, Te_2, and Te_3.

Section 5.8   *PAGE 261*

2.   (a) The positive square root of K^2 is $|K|$, not necessarily K. In this case, since A is the average of s and t, the sign of $s - A$ must be opposite to that of $t - A$ (if they are unequal), and so taking positive square roots does not yield $s - A = t - A$.

     This demonstration is more interesting than the usual "proof" that $1 = 2$, since the fallacy does not involve division by zero. I learned this proof when I was a youngster and have been showing it to others for twenty years. About one per cent find the fallacy. I am astonished at how many do not think to substitute some specific values, say $s = 3$ and $t = 5$, to locate the first incorrect equation. I have never found among high-school algebra teachers any who could locate the fallacy in less than a half hour. Like the Pavlovian dogs, their instant response due to conditioning is, "You divided by zero." (Readers of *The New Yorker* will see possibilities in this paragraph.)

     (b) The positive square root of $(|u|\,|v|)^2$ is $|u|\,|v|$, since we know a priori that neither $|u|$ nor $|v|$ is negative.

3.   Yes. Defining $u \cdot v$ to be $u_1v_1 + u_2v_2 + u_3v_3 + 2u_4v_4$, we obtain a scalar product in R^4 satisfying all the properties listed in this section. Therefore the Schwarz inequality is valid. Now let $u_1 = x_1, u_2 = x_2, \ldots, v_1 = x_5, v_2 = x_6$, etc.

4. If v is the zero vector, then $v = 0 \cdot u$. If v is not the zero vector, and if the Schwarz inequality is an equality, then

$$|u - cv|^2 = (|u| - c|v|)^2$$

which must be zero for some scalar c, whence $u = cv$ for some c.

5. The square of $|u|\,|v|\,\sin\theta$.

6. Note that an infinity of distinct planes can be used.

7. $v^1 = 1, v^2 = \frac{4}{5}, v^3 = -\frac{1}{5}$.

8.

$$S = \begin{pmatrix} \frac{1}{14} & \frac{2}{14} & \frac{3}{14} \\ \frac{2}{5} & -\frac{1}{5} & 0 \\ \frac{3}{70} & \frac{6}{70} & -\frac{6}{70} \end{pmatrix}$$

9. No.

10. If p were a covariant vector, $\Sigma\, p_i w^i$ would be independent of basis, since it is the value of a particular linear functional at w. The Grassmann product, however, quite obviously varies with change of basis.

11. Let $w = u \times v$. Then the w's are either

$$w^1 = 6(u^2 v^3 - u^3 v^2)$$

$$w^2 = \tfrac{3}{2}\,(u^3 v^1 - u^1 v^3)$$

$$w^3 = \tfrac{2}{3}\,(u^1 v^2 - u^2 v^1)$$

or the negatives of the respective right-hand quantities. This is easily seen by looking at the base vectors. We must have $e \times e = 6e$, $e \times e = \frac{3}{2}e$, etc., or their negatives, depending on which of the two vector products we choose.

12. $$x \cdot y = x^1 y^1 + \tfrac{1}{16} x^2 y^2 + \tfrac{1}{81} x^3 y^3$$

Section 5.9 *PAGE 274*

1. (a) det $(T_j{}^i) = 11$, det $(S_j{}^i) = 0$

(b) $$\begin{pmatrix} 3 & 7 & 3 \\ 0 & 2 & 0 \\ 10 & 10 & 10 \end{pmatrix}$$

(c) det $(R_j{}^i) = 0$

2.   Twice the first column minus the second column gives three times the third column, so the desired vector is

$$\begin{pmatrix} 2 \\ -1 \\ -3 \end{pmatrix}$$

or any scalar multiple thereof.

3.   no

4.   (a) $-3e_1 + e_2 - 2e_3$

     (b) Note that $f_1 \times f_2 = -f_3$, so that the negative of the usual formula applies. If $w = u \times v$, then $w^1 = u^3v^2 - u^2v^3$, etc.

     (c) $f_1 - 3f_2 - 2f_3$

     (d) The first column represents

$$Tf_1 = Te_2 = 2e_1 - 3e_3 = 2f_2 - 3f_3$$

Similarly,

$$Tf_2 = Te_1 = -2e_2 - e_3 = -2f_1 - f_3$$

and

$$Tf_3 = Te_3 = e_1 + 3e_2 = 3f_1 + f_2$$

Hence the desired matrix is

$$\begin{pmatrix} 0 & -2 & 3 \\ 2 & 0 & 1 \\ -3 & -1 & 0 \end{pmatrix}$$

     (e) If $w = A \times v$, then $w^1 = A^3v^2 - A^2v^3 = -2v^2 + 3v^3$, etc. Compare with $w = Tv$ using the matrix in part (d).

5.   The sum $\sum \sum \sum \varepsilon_{ijk}S_m{}^iS_p{}^jS_r{}^k$ is the determinant of a matrix whose first, second, and third columns are the mth, pth, and rth columns of S, respectively. Using the facts that the interchange of two columns of a matrix changes the sign of the determinant, and that if two columns are equal the determinant is zero, we see that

$$\sum \sum \sum \varepsilon_{ijk}S_m{}^iS_p{}^jS_r{}^k = \sum \sum \sum \varepsilon_{mpr}\varepsilon_{ijk}S_1{}^iS_2{}^jS_3{}^k$$

This is the crucial step.

Section 5.10   *PAGE 280*

1. Their product is the identity matrix.

2. Use (5):

$$\underset{1}{e} + 3\underset{2}{e} - 2\underset{3}{e} = \tfrac{1}{2}\,(\underset{1'}{e} + \underset{2'}{e}) + \tfrac{3}{2}\,(\underset{1'}{e} - \underset{2'}{e}) - 4\underset{3'}{e}$$

$$= 2\underset{1'}{e} - \underset{2'}{e} - 4\underset{3'}{e}$$

so that the new components are $x^{1'} = 2$, $x^{2'} = -1$, $x^{3'} = -4$. Or form the matrix product $(A_j^{i'})(x^i)$ using the matrix (6).

3. $(1, -1, -\tfrac{1}{2})$. Calculate the product $(f_i)(A_{j'}{}^i)$.

4. $$\begin{pmatrix} 6 & -1 & 1 \\ -3 & 0 & \tfrac{1}{2} \\ -2 & -2 & 2 \end{pmatrix}$$

5. (a) orthonormal bases; (b) ratio of volume of parallelepiped to volume of parallelepiped determined by the base vectors; (c) relative volume; (d) oriented volume of the parallelepiped determined by $T\underset{1}{e}$, $T\underset{2}{e}$, and $T\underset{3}{e}$, in that order; (e) if $\underset{1}{e}$, $\underset{2}{e}$, and $\underset{3}{e}$ comprise a right-handed system, then $\underset{1}{v}$, $\underset{2}{v}$, and $\underset{3}{v}$ comprise a left-handed system.

6. (a) true (b) false (c) false (d) false (e) true (f) true (g) true (h) true. It will be noted that the trace is a linear functional on the vector space of all linear transformations of V. *Note:* Where we said "false" above we meant "not true in general." These statements are true in some special cases, as for example if T and S are both the zero transformation.

7. $A_j^{i'} = \partial x^{i'}/\partial x^j$

Section 5.11   *PAGE 286*

1. $(A_{j'}{}^i) = \begin{pmatrix} 1 & -1 & 0 \\ 1 & 1 & 0 \\ 0 & 0 & 2 \end{pmatrix}$, $(A_j^{i'}) = \begin{pmatrix} \tfrac{1}{2} & \tfrac{1}{2} & 0 \\ -\tfrac{1}{2} & \tfrac{1}{2} & 0 \\ 0 & 0 & \tfrac{1}{2} \end{pmatrix}$

2. $\begin{pmatrix} 3 \\ 2 \\ 2 \end{pmatrix}$

3. $(6, 4, 8)$

4. $$\begin{pmatrix} \frac{7}{2} & \frac{1}{2} & 2 \\ -\frac{3}{2} & -\frac{1}{2} & 0 \\ \frac{3}{2} & -\frac{3}{2} & 4 \end{pmatrix}$$

5. Orthogonal but not orthonormal.

6. $$\begin{pmatrix} 2 & 0 & 0 \\ 0 & 2 & 0 \\ 0 & 0 & 4 \end{pmatrix}$$

    [For example, $g_{1'1'} = \underset{1'}{e} \cdot \underset{1'}{e} = (\underset{1}{e} + \underset{2}{e}) \cdot (\underset{1}{e} + \underset{2}{e}) = 2.$]

7. $u \cdot v = -2,\quad u = -2\underset{1}{e} + 2\underset{3}{e},\quad v = -\underset{1}{e} + 5\underset{2}{e} - 2\underset{3}{e}$

8. $$\begin{pmatrix} \frac{7}{4} & \frac{1}{4} & \frac{1}{2} \\ -\frac{3}{4} & -\frac{1}{4} & 0 \\ \frac{3}{4} & -\frac{3}{4} & 1 \end{pmatrix}$$

9. $(1,5,4),\ (6,4,8)$

10. (a) iii (b) ii (c) i (d) iv

11. (a) $\displaystyle \sum f_i x^i = \sum \left(\sum A_i{}^{j'} f_{j'}\right)\left(\sum A_{k'}{}^i x^{k'}\right)$

    $\displaystyle \qquad = \sum\sum \left(\sum A_i{}^{j'} A_{k'}{}^i\right) f_{j'} x^{k'} = \sum\sum \delta_{k'}{}^{j'} f_{j'} x^{k'}$

    $\displaystyle \qquad = \sum f_{j'} x^{j'} = \sum f_{i'} x^{i'}$

    where $(\delta_{k'}{}^{j'})$ denotes the identity matrix.
    (b) No, not in general (it can happen in special cases).

The line segment in Figure 100 is said to have *outer orientation*, whereas an arrow has *inner orientation*. See J. A. Schouten, *Tensor Analysis for Physicists* (Oxford, 1951), page 7.

Section 5.12 *PAGE 291*

1. $\underset{i}{e} \cdot T\underset{j}{e} = T_j{}^i = T_i{}^j = \underset{j}{e} \cdot T\underset{i}{e} = T\underset{i}{e} \cdot \underset{j}{e}$ for all i,j.   Hence

    $\displaystyle x \cdot Ty = \left(\sum_i x^i \underset{i}{e}\right) \cdot T\left(\sum_j y^j \underset{j}{e}\right) = \sum_i \sum_j x^i y^j \underset{i}{e} \cdot T\underset{j}{e} = \sum_i \sum_j x^i y^j T\underset{i}{e} \cdot \underset{j}{e}$

    $\displaystyle \qquad = T\left(\sum_i x^i \underset{i}{e}\right) \cdot \left(\sum_j y^j \underset{j}{e}\right) = Tx \cdot y$

    The colloquial expression for this is: $x \cdot Ty = Tx \cdot y$ when x and y are base vectors, and hence by linearity we can extend the equality to all pairs x and y.

2. By the hint, if $w \cdot v = 0$, then $Tw \cdot v = 0$.

3. If $\det S = 0$, then there is a nonzero v such that Sv is the zero vector. If $(T - c_1 I)v$ is the zero vector, then $Tv = c_1 v$.

4. Every cubic polynomial has at least one real root. Use Exercise 3.

5. $T\underset{1}{e} = C_1 \underset{1}{e}$. By Exercise 2, if $\underset{2}{e}$ and $\underset{3}{e}$ are orthogonal to $\underset{1}{e}$, then so also are $T\underset{2}{e}$ and $T\underset{3}{e}$, and so $T_j{}^1 = \underset{1}{e} \cdot T\underset{j}{e} = 0$ when $j = 2$ or 3. Since $T_1{}^j = T_j{}^1$, the matrix has at least four zeros, as shown. At this point in the proof, we know that the transformation stretches or contracts vectors along $\underset{1}{e}$, and that it transforms every vector in the plane determined by $\underset{2}{e}$ and $\underset{3}{e}$ into a vector also in this plane.

6. Use the hint. We are now restricting attention to what happens in the plane mentioned above.

7. By Exercise 6, there is an eigenvector in the plane perpendicular to $\underset{1}{e}$. Let $\underset{2}{e}$ denote a unit vector parallel to this eigenvector. Then $\underset{2}{e}$ is also an eigenvector. Let $\underset{3}{e}$ be a unit vector orthogonal to $\underset{1}{e}$ and $\underset{2}{e}$. Then (Exercise 2) $T\underset{3}{e}$ is also orthogonal to $\underset{1}{e}$ and $\underset{2}{e}$, and hence is a scalar multiple of $\underset{3}{e}$. This is the geometrical idea, but you should write out the necessary algebra in detail.

8. $\operatorname{tr} T = \operatorname{tr} (\overset{+}{T} + \overset{-}{T}) = \operatorname{tr} \overset{+}{T} + \operatorname{tr} \overset{-}{T} = \operatorname{tr} \overset{+}{T}$

    since $\operatorname{tr} \overset{-}{T} = 0$.

9. Look at the matrix given in Exercise 7.

10. (a) See Theorem 2, Section 5.8.

    (b) $\overset{*}{T}x \cdot y = \sum g_{ik}(\sum \overset{*}{T}_j{}^i x^j) y^k$. Substitute for $\overset{*}{T}_j{}^i$ and calculate like crazy, man.

    (c) $\overset{+}{T} = \frac{1}{2}(T + \overset{*}{T}), \quad \overset{-}{T} = \frac{1}{2}(T - \overset{*}{T})$

    (d) The hint should be sufficient. Don't forget to prove the uniqueness of u. That is, if $u \cdot y = u' \cdot y$ for all y, then $u = u'$.

Section 5.13   *PAGE 299*

Note that (4) is used in the next to last step, and the continuous differentiability of f is used when we let h tend to zero.

Section 5.14   *PAGE 308*

1. R does not satisfy (12). The argument given here can be made rigorous: see Nickerson, Spencer, and Steenrod, referred to in this section.

2. $2, \frac{1}{2}$

3. Hint: Use the change of variables suggested in the preceding exercise. The answer is $(e - e^{-1})/4$.

INDEX